CONTENTS

SECTION 2   Activities

Section 3   Objective Questions

INTRODUCTION

This Third Edition of the *Laboratory Manual and Study Guide* has been planned as a companion to the Fourth Edition of *Chemistry in Context*. It is, however, self-contained and can be used quite independently of the main text.

The book has three major sections:

Section 1	Laboratory Work
Section 2	Activities
Section 3	Objective Questions

Section 1　Laboratory Work

Part 1a Practicals

Each practical is self-contained and designed to introduce or develop a major area of chemistry. The practicals include detailed instructions and, in general, take one double period (about 80 minutes) to complete. An approximate time allocation is indicated after the list of Requirements. The practicals include questions designed to encourage students to think about what they are doing, rather than performing operations mechanically.

Part 1b Investigations

This part provides starting points for students to carry out their own open-ended investigations. They contain no detailed instructions, the intention being for students to plan their own experimental procedures. Students will, of course, need to discuss their plans with the teacher before starting work and the teacher will need to check safety in particular. Further guidance on the use of these Investigations is given in the separate booklet of *Teachers' Notes* which accompanies this book, available from the publishers.

Section 2　Activities

The activities in this section are designed to develop important skills and to extend the contexts in which understanding and application of chemical ideas are relevant.

The skills developed include those involved in data analysis, data interpretation, comprehension, prediction, problem solving, modified role play, modelling and equation writing.

Each of the activities consists of a passage concerning some area of chemistry or its applications, followed by questions which develop the skills listed above.

The passages which have been chosen cover material in the new syllabuses and illustrate the wider contexts of chemistry in everyday life, in the home and in industry.

The *Teacher's Notes* for Section 2 show the skills developed in each activity and provide references to *Chemistry in Context*.

Section 3 Objective Questions

Each of the thirty-five objective tests is based on a chapter in *Chemistry in Context*, Fourth Edition. Thus, Test 1, entitled 'Atoms, Atomic Masses and Moles' relates to the ideas and information presented in Chapter 1 of *Chemistry in Context*.

Each test contains between fourteen and twenty-five questions. These are mainly multiple choice items together with a few of the multiple completion type. The answers to the objective questions are included in the separate *Teacher's Notes*.

Nomenclature, units and abbreviations

Throughout the text, we have used the International System of Units (SI) and nomenclature, following recommendations in the third edition of *Chemical Nomenclature, Symbols and Terminology* published by the Association for Science Education.

Safety

In planning and writing the laboratory work for Section 1, safety considerations have been given the highest priority. We are particularly grateful for the helpful and experienced guidance of Peter Borrows of the Safeguards in Science Committee of the Association for Science Education.

In **Part 1a (Practicals)**, hazardous substances and operations are identified and indicated by standard symbols, and appropriate precautions are recommended. Nevertheless, teachers should be aware of their obligations under the Health and Safety at Work, etc. Act and the Control of Substances Hazardous to Health (COSHH) Regulations. In this respect, they should follow the requirements of their employers at all times.

In **Part 1b (Investigations)**, it will be necessary to make individual Risk Assessments according to the practical procedures students plan to use. (See 'Some general guidance on investigations' on pages 113–115 of this book, and the separate *Teachers' Notes* giving guidance on Investigations.)

Concentration of solutions

In general, the recommended concentrations of solutions are given in the lists of Requirements for the practical concerned. However, where the common dilute acid and alkalis are involved, we have made the following assumptions:

dilute hydrochloric, nitric and acetic (ethanoic) acids	$2\,mol\,dm^{-3}$
dilute sulphuric acid	$1\,mol\,dm^{-3}$
dilute sodium hydroxide, potassium hydroxide and ammonia solutions	$2\,mol\,dm^{-3}$

Once again we are greatly indebted to our publishers for their competent and helpful handling of the manuscript. We would also like to thank Derek Denby of John Leggott College, Scunthorpe, for his valuable help with the Investigations in Part 1b. Finally, we thank our wives, Elizabeth and Wendy, for their continued support and encouragement.

Graham Hill
John Holman
May 1994

TO THE STUDENT

Safety in the chemistry laboratory

Figure 1
Flammable liquids should be heated in a beaker of hot water with no naked flames nearby.

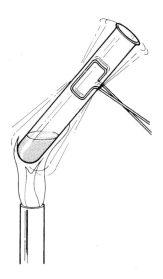

Figure 2
Non-flammable liquids should be heated in a boiling tube not more than one-fifth full, with gentle shaking.

It is your duty (in law) to take reasonable care for your own health and safety, and that of others working in the laboratory. Safety is largely a matter of common sense, provided you know the hazards associated with the chemicals and procedures you are using.

To alert you to the more hazardous materials and operations, we have printed safety warnings in the text in bold type.
It is sensible, however, to regard **all** chemicals as potentially hazardous.

Some important points to remember

Always wear eye or face protection when carrying out practical work. Eye protection should be worn by *everyone* when anyone in the laboratory is doing something that might be hazardous to eyes.

Always handle flammable liquids, such as ethanol and propanone, with great care and keep them away from naked flames. Heat test tubes of flammable liquids by immersing them in a beaker of hot water, taken from a hot tap or electric kettle, as shown in figure 1.

Always use a boiling tube when heating a non-flammable liquid over a bunsen flame and shake very gently during heating as shown in figure 2. Do not fill the tube more than one-fifth full.

Never point a test tube containing chemicals which you are heating towards yourself or anyone else. Do not fill tubes more than one-fifth full of the substance you are heating, as shown in figure 3.

Always report accidents, spills and breakages, however small, to your teacher.

Always make sure chemicals are labelled, and check the name on the bottle is *exactly* that of the chemical you require. Label clearly any chemicals you are keeping for future use.

Always work steadily and without undue haste.

Always pipette liquids with a safety filler.

Always wear a laboratory coat whenever possible. Make sure it is fastened, not flapping open. Do not allow ties or scarves to hang loosely.

Always wash your hands after practical work.

Never put your head or clothes near a bunsen flame. Long hair should be tied back. Some hair preparations (e.g. wet-look gels) make the hair more flammable than usual and should be avoided. Adjust the bunsen to give a luminous flame when you are not using it.

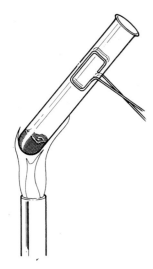

Figure 3
Solids should be heated in a tube not more than one-fifth full, and not pointing at anyone.

Never wear open-toed sandals in the laboratory. Your footwear should give some protection to your feet.

Never smell gases directly—only very cautiously, and with your lungs already filled with air. Waft the fumes of gas gently towards your nose as shown in figure 4. If you are asthmatic, make sure your teacher is aware of this.

Never put your thumb or finger over the end of a test tube when shaking. Stopper the tube with a cork or bung.

Never try to force glass tubing when putting it into, or removing it from, corks or bungs. Always hold glass tubing in a cloth when performing these operations.

Never hold bottles by the neck. If a stopper is tight, get help. Do not try to force it off.

Never remove chemicals or equipment from the laboratory.

Never do practical work alone. If you are allowed by your teacher to do practical work outside school hours, make sure somebody is within ear-shot.

Never perform unauthorised experiments. If you are asked to design or plan an investigation, always get it approved by your teacher before carrying it out.

Never taste anything unless instructed to do so.

Never eat, drink or apply cosmetics in the laboratory.

Figure 4
Smelling a gas safely. Cautiously waft the smell towards your nose, with your lungs full of air.

SECTION ONE
LABORATORY WORK

This section is in two parts.

1a   Practicals

These include detailed instructions and, in general, only take one or two laboratory sessions to complete.

1b   Investigations

These are more open-ended and require detailed planning. They need several laboratory sessions.

1a PRACTICALS

Practical 1

An analysis of aspirin tablets

REQUIREMENTS

Each pair of students will need:

- Eye protection
- Aspirin tablets (about 5)
- Pipette ($25\,cm^3$) and safety filler
- Burette and stand
- Small beaker
- 2 standard flasks ($250\,cm^3$) (one for each partner)
- Conical flask ($250\,cm^3$)
- Small funnel
- Bunsen burner
- Tripod and gauze

Approximately $1.0\,mol\,dm^{-3}$ NaOH ($30\,cm^3$), $0.10\,mol\,dm^{-3}$ hydrochloric acid ($150\,cm^3$), phenol red (or phenolphthalein) indicator (**flammable solution**)

Time required 1 double period

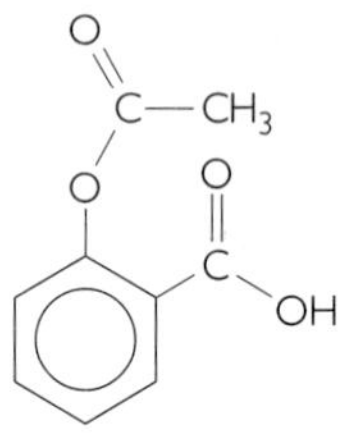

Figure 1
2-Ethanoylhydroxybenzoic acid (acetylsalicylic acid).

Introduction

Aspirin is an analgesic and antipyretic drug. Analgesics are drugs which relieve pain. Antipyretics are drugs which lower body temperature.

The main constituent of aspirin tablets is 2-ethanoylhydroxybenzoic acid (acetylsalicylic acid, $CH_3COOC_6H_4COOH$, figure 1). Aspirin passes unchanged through the acidic conditions in the stomach but is hydrolysed to ethanoate (acetate) ions and 2-hydroxybenzoate (salicylate) ions by the alkaline juices in the intestines.

$$CH_3COOC_6H_4COOH + 2OH^- \longrightarrow CH_3COO^- + HOC_6H_4COO^- + H_2O$$

Salicylates lower body temperature rapidly and effectively in feverish patients (antipyretic action), but have little effect if the temperature is normal. They are also mild analgesics, relieving certain types of pain such as headaches and rheumatism.

Although the toxic dose from salicylates is relatively large, their uncontrolled use could be dangerous. Single doses of 5 to 10 g of salicylate have caused death in adults, and 12 g taken over a period of twenty-four hours produces symptoms of poisoning.

Principle

The object of this experiment is to determine the percentage of 2-ethanoylhydroxybenzoic acid (acetylsalicylic acid) in aspirin tablets. A known amount of standard sodium hydroxide solution is used in excess to hydrolyse a known mass of aspirin tablets.

$$CH_3COOC_6H_4COOH + 2NaOH \longrightarrow CH_3COONa + HOC_6H_4COONa + H_2O$$

The unused sodium hydroxide which remains is then titrated with standard acid. The amount of alkali required for the hydrolysis can now be calculated and from the above equation, the amount in moles of acetylsalicylic acid which has been hydrolysed can be found.

Procedure

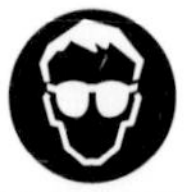

EYE PROTECTION MUST BE WORN

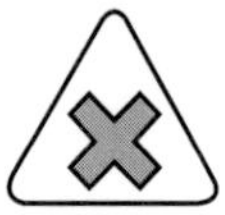

IRRITANT Sodium hydroxide

CARE Eye protection must be worn.

Work in pairs.

Partner No. 1 should standardise the approximately $1.0\,mol\,dm^{-3}$ NaOH used for the hydrolysis as follows.

Using a safety filler, pipette exactly $25\,cm^3$ of the approximately $1.0\,mol\,dm^{-3}$ NaOH solution into a $250\,cm^3$ standard flask and make up to the mark. Now titrate $25\,cm^3$ of this solution against $0.10\,mol\,dm^{-3}$ hydrochloric acid using phenol red (or phenolphthalein) indicator.

Carry out one rough and two accurate titrations.

1 Record your results in a table similar to the one below.

Titration number	Rough	Accurate 1	Accurate 2
Final burette reading/cm³ Initial burette reading/cm³			
Volume of 0.1 mol dm⁻³ HCl added/cm³			

2 Calculate the accurate concentration, in $mol\,dm^{-3}$, of the approximately $1.0\,mol\,dm^{-3}$ NaOH.

HARMFUL
Aspirin

Partner No. 2 should hydrolyse the aspirin as follows.
Weigh accurately between 1.3 g and 1.7 g of the aspirin tablets into a clean conical flask. (This will be about 5 tablets.) **Using a safety filler**, pipette $25\,cm^3$ of the approximately $1.0\,mol\,dm^{-3}$ NaOH on to the tablets, followed by about the same volume of distilled water. Simmer the mixture gently for ten minutes to hydrolyse the acetylsalicylic acid.

Now, cool the mixture and transfer with washings to a $250\,cm^3$ standard flask and make up to the mark with distilled water.

3 Record the mass of aspirin tablets taken.

4 Why is the mixture simmered gently and carefully during hydrolysis? Why is it unwise to boil it vigorously?

5 Why should the washings be transferred carefully to the $250\,cm^3$ standard flask?

Both partners should now estimate the quantity of unused NaOH after the hydrolysis as follows.
Pipette $25\,cm^3$ of the hydrolysed solution into a conical flask. Titrate this against $0.10\,mol\,dm^{-3}$ hydrochloric acid using phenol red (or phenolphthalein) indicator.

6 Record your titration results in a table similar to that in question 1.

7 How many moles of NaOH

    a are added to the flask before hydrolysis of the aspirin?

    b remain after hydrolysis of the aspirin?

    c are used in the hydrolysis of the aspirin?

8 How many moles of acetylsalicylic acid have been hydrolysed?

9 What percentage of the aspirin tablets is acetylsalicylic acid?

10 What might the remainder of the tablets be made of?

Practical 2
An analysis of iron tablets

REQUIREMENTS

Each pair of students will need:
- Eye protection
- Iron tablets (5), sold by chemists as ferrous sulphate tablets
- 1.0 mol dm^{-3} sulphuric acid (200 cm^3)
- 0.01 mol dm^{-3} potassium manganate(VII) (75 cm^3). Dissolve 1.58 g in distilled water and make up to 1 dm^3 (**solid is oxidising and harmful**)
- 2 conical flasks (250 cm^3)
- Standard flask (250 cm^3)
- Burette and stand
- Pipette (25 cm^3) and safety filler
- Filter funnel
- Filter paper
- Wash bottle and distilled water

Time required 1 double period

IRRITANT
Dilute sulphuric acid

EYE PROTECTION
MUST BE WORN

Introduction

Iron is essential to the human body. Its principal role is as a constituent of haemoglobin, the oxygen-carrying agent in the blood. Iron is also present in a number of enzymes and co-enzymes involved in redox processes in the body.

Healthy adult males need little iron in their diet, but some groups in the population need substantial amounts in order to produce extra haemoglobin. Such people include growing children, pregnant and menstruating women, and individuals who have for various reasons lost considerable amounts of blood. A satisfactory intake of iron can normally be ensured by eating a suitable diet, because certain foods—liver, kidney, egg yolk and spinach for example—are rich in iron. Nevertheless, it is sometimes necessary to supplement the iron taken in the natural diet with 'iron tablets'.

Iron tablets bought at the chemist usually contain iron(II) sulphate (ferrous sulphate), a cheap, soluble form of iron. In this practical you will attempt to find the actual percentage of iron(II) sulphate in the tablets and then compare this result with the quantity stated on the bottle.

Assuming all the iron in the tablets is in the form of Fe^{2+}, it is possible to estimate the iron content by titration against potassium manganate(VII), KMnO$_4$.

1 Write an ionic equation for the reaction of Fe^{2+} with MnO$_4^-$ in acid solution.

Procedure

Making a solution of the tablets

Weigh accurately five of the iron tablets, then dissolve them in about 100 cm^3 of 1.0 mol dm^{-3} sulphuric acid in a conical flask. This will probably require heating, but do not heat more than necessary to dissolve the tablets.

2 Why should the tablets not be heated more than necessary?

3 Why are the tablets dissolved in sulphuric acid instead of water?

The outer coating of the tablets will probably not dissolve, so the solution will need filtering.

4 What do you think the outer coating might be?

Filter the mixture into a beaker, making sure you do not lose any of the solution, then wash out the conical flask with water and pour the washings through the filter. Finally pour distilled water over the residue and collect these washings as well. Pour the filtrate into a 250 cm^3 standard flask, washing out the beaker and adding the washings to the standard flask. Make up to the mark with distilled water.

Titration with potassium manganate(VII)

Using a safety filler, pipette 25 cm^3 of the iron(II) solution into a conical flask. Add about 25 cm^3 of 1.0 mol dm^{-3} sulphuric acid and titrate with 0.01 mol dm^{-3} potassium manganate(VII) solution. Repeat until two consistent results are obtained.

5 How many moles of MnO_4^- were needed to react with $25\,cm^3$ of your Fe^{2+} solution?

6 How many moles of Fe^{2+} were there in $25\,cm^3$ of the solution?

7 How many moles of Fe^{2+} were there in all the tablets?

8 What mass of **a** iron **b** $FeSO_4$ **c** $FeSO_4.7H_2O$ is there in one tablet?

9 What mass of iron(II) sulphate is stated by the makers to be present in each tablet?

10 Compare your answer with the mass stated by the makers, and comment.

INVESTIGATION

See Investigation 1

Practical 3

The principles of titrations involving iodine/thiosulphate.
Determination of the percentage of copper in brass

EYE PROTECTION
MUST BE WORN

REQUIREMENTS

Each student, or pair of students, will need:

- Eye protection
- Burette and stand
- Pipette (25 cm³) and safety filler
- Conical titration flask (250 cm³)
- Measuring cylinder (25 or 50 cm³)
- Small beaker
- Beaker (250 cm³)
- Standard flask (250 cm³)
- 2 test tubes
- Concentrated nitric acid
- Hydrogen peroxide solution (6%, or '20 volume')
- Dilute sulphuric acid
- Distilled water
- Sodium carbonate solution (1.0 mol dm⁻³)
- Dilute acetic acid
- Approx. 1 mol dm⁻³ KI (30 cm³) (166 g KI in 1 dm³ of solution)
- 0.1 mol dm⁻³ Na₂S₂O₃ (100 cm³) (24.8 g Na₂S₂O₃.5H₂O in 1 dm³ of solution)
- Starch solution (6 cm³). (Make 2 g of soluble starch and 0.01 g of HgCl₂ (**toxic solid**) into a thin paste with water. Add slowly to 1 dm³ of boiling water with stirring. Boil for a few minutes and cool.)
- Brass (about 3 g) (brass screws are ideal)
- Access to balance

Time required 1 double period

IRRITANT
Dilute
sulphuric acid

CARE Eye protection must be worn for both experiment 1 and experiment 2.

Experiment 1: The principles of titrations involving iodine/thiosulphate

Iodine/thiosulphate titrations are often used to determine the concentration of solutions of oxidising agents.

A known volume of the oxidising agent is first added to an excess of acidified potassium iodide solution, thus liberating iodine. The liberated iodine is then estimated by titration against standard sodium thiosulphate solution.

> **A** Add a few drops of hydrogen peroxide solution (an oxidising agent) to a mixture of 3 cm³ KI(aq) and 3 cm³ of dilute H₂SO₄. Keep the final solution for part **B**.

1 Describe and explain what happens.

2 H₂O₂ acts according to the half-equation,

$$H_2O_2 + 2H^+ + 2e^- \longrightarrow 2H_2O.$$

Write a half-equation for the oxidation of iodide ions to iodine.

> **B** Add sodium thiosulphate solution to the final mixture from part **A** until no further changes occur.

3 Describe and explain what happens.

4 Thiosulphate ions, $S_2O_3^{2-}$, are oxidised by iodine according to the half-equation,

$$2S_2O_3^{2-} \longrightarrow S_4O_6^{2-} + 2e^-.$$

Write an equation for the reduction of iodine by $S_2O_3^{2-}$.

5 How many moles of $S_2O_3^{2-}$ react with one mole of I_2?

In iodine/thiosulphate titrations, a standard solution of sodium thiosulphate is added to the iodine solution from a burette. In these circumstances, the colour would change from a pale yellow solution of I_2 to a clear solution of I^- ions at the end-point. Generally, however, starch is added to improve the detection of the end-point. With iodine, starch forms a deep blue colour which disappears at the end-point. The starch should not be added until the iodine has been reduced to a pale yellow colour, otherwise iodine becomes strongly adsorbed on to the starch and the titration is less accurate.

Experiment 2: Determination of the percentage of copper in brass

In the following experiment, a weighed sample of brass is first dissolved in nitric acid, forming a solution of copper(II) ions. When this solution is treated with aqueous potassium iodide, copper(I) iodide is precipitated as a white solid, and iodine is produced.

$$2Cu^{2+}(aq) + 4I^-(aq) \longrightarrow 2CuI(s) + I_2(aq)$$

The liberated iodine can be estimated using standard sodium thiosulphate solution. Knowing the amount of iodine formed, the mass of copper present in the original sample of brass can be determined.

USE A FUME CUPBOARD

CORROSIVE Concentrated nitric acid

TOXIC Nitrogen dioxide

IRRITANT Dilute acetic acid

CARE Eye protection must be worn when working with concentrated nitric acid. Any splashes on the skin must be washed off at once.
CARE Toxic nitrogen dioxide is evolved. This reaction must be carried out in a fume cupboard.

Weigh accurately somewhere between 2.5 g and 3.0 g of brass. Dissolve this in the minimum quantity necessary of concentrated nitric acid in a 250 cm^3 beaker. About 20 cm^3 of concentrated nitric acid should be sufficient.

Transfer the solution, with washings from the beaker, to a 250 cm^3 standard flask. Make up the solution to the mark and mix well.

Using a safety filler, pipette 25 cm^3 of the brass solution into a conical flask and add sodium carbonate solution until a slight permanent precipitate is obtained. This neutralises excess nitric acid in the solution. Dissolve the precipitate in the minimum volume of dilute acetic acid and then add 10 cm^3 of approximately 1 mol dm^{-3} KI.

Finally titrate the liberated iodine against standard 0.1 mol dm^{-3} sodium thiosulphate solution, adding about 2 cm^3 of starch indicator when the iodine colour is pale yellow.

Repeat the experiment until two consistent results are obtained.

6 Describe what happens when

a brass is treated with concentrated HNO$_3$.

b Cu^{2+}(aq) is treated with KI(aq).

7 Record your results in a table similar to the one below.

Titration number	Rough	Accurate I	Accurate 2
Final burette reading/cm^3			
Initial burette reading/cm^3			
Vol. of 0.I mol dm^{-3} Na$_2$S$_2$O$_3$ added/cm^3			

Average accurate titration =   cm^3

8 Why is it necessary to neutralise the excess nitric acid used to dissolve the brass? (Hint: nitric acid is an oxidising agent.)

9 Write an equation for

a the reaction of copper in brass with concentrated nitric acid.

b the neutralisation of excess nitric acid with sodium carbonate solution.

10 How many moles of S$_2$O$_3^{2-}$ react during titration?

11 How many moles of I$_2$ react with this amount of S$_2$O$_3^{2-}$?

12 How many moles of Cu^{2+} ions liberate this amount of I$_2$?

13 How many moles of Cu^{2+} ions are there in the 250 cm^3 of 'brass solution'?

14 How many grams of copper are there in 250 cm^3 of 'brass solution'?

15 What is the percentage by mass of copper in the brass? (Cu = 63.5)

Practical 4

Determination of the concentration of chloride ions in sea water

REQUIREMENTS

Each student, or pair of students, will need:

- Eye protection
- Burette and burette stand
- Small funnel
- Pipette ($10\,cm^3$) and safety filler
- 2 beakers ($100\,cm^3$)
- 3 conical flasks ($100\,cm^3$ or $250\,cm^3$)
- Graduated flask ($100\,cm^3$)
- White tile
- Sea water ($10\,cm^3$)
  (If none is available, a suitable substitute can be made by weighing out the following salts and dissolving in water to give $1\,dm^3$ of solution:

NaCl	27 g
$MgCl_2.6H_2O$	11 g
$MgSO_4.7H_2O$	13 g
KCl	0.75 g
KBr	0.10 g
$CaSO_4.2H_2O$	2 g
$NaHCO_3$	0.1 g)

- Potassium chromate(VI) solution (about $0.1\,mol\,dm^{-3}$)
- $0.05\,mol\,dm^{-3}$ silver nitrate solution ($50\,cm^3$). Dissolve 8.49 g of solid silver nitrate (**corrosive**) in distilled water and make up to $1\,dm^3$.

Time required 1 double period

Table 1
Some of the more abundant ions present in sea water

Na^+	Cl^-
Mg^{2+}	SO_4^{2-}
Ca^{2+}	Br^-
K^+	HCO_3^-

Introduction

Every cubic decimetre (litre) of sea water contains about 35 g of dissolved salts, though the mass varies according to locality.

Many different ions are present in sea water, including gold ions. Table 1 shows some of the more abundant ions present. The commonest cation is Na^+ and the commonest anion is Cl^-. The object of this practical is to determine the concentration of chloride ions, Cl^-, in sea water.

The method used is the standard one for determining the concentration of chloride ions—titration with silver nitrate solution of known concentration. Silver ions form insoluble silver chloride when added to a solution containing chloride ions:

$$Ag^+(aq) + Cl^-(aq) \longrightarrow AgCl(s)$$

By adding silver ions until silver chloride is no longer precipitated, the amount of chloride in a solution can be found.

Potassium chromate(VI) can be used to indicate the end-point of the titration—the point at which all chloride ions have been precipitated. Silver ions combine with chromate(VI) ions to form a red precipitate of silver chromate(VI):

$$2Ag^+(aq) + CrO_4^{2-}(aq) \longrightarrow Ag_2CrO_4(s)$$

When both chloride ions and chromate(VI) ions are present, however, no silver chromate(VI) is precipitated until all the chloride ions have been removed. The sudden appearance of red silver chromate(VI) therefore indicates the end-point of the titration.

Procedure

Note It is particularly important in this practical to rinse all the glassware with distilled water before use.

Silver nitrate is expensive, and is normally used in fairly low concentration. In this titration you will use $0.05\,mol\,dm^{-3}$ $AgNO_3(aq)$. To obtain sensible results, it is therefore first necessary to dilute the sea water ten-fold in order to give a concentration of chloride ions comparable to that of the silver nitrate.

Pipette $10\,cm^3$ of sea water into a $100\,cm^3$ graduated flask. Make up to the mark with distilled water, stopper the flask and mix thoroughly.

Pipette $10\,cm^3$ of the diluted sea water into a conical flask and add about 10 drops of potassium chromate(VI) indicator. Rinse a burette with a silver nitrate solution, then fill it with the solution. Titrate the sea water in the conical flask against the silver nitrate solution from the burette until a reddish tinge just begins to appear. You may find the end-point a little difficult to detect, so it is best to carry out a rough titration first and keep the result to remind you of the end-point colour when carrying out later, accurate titrations.

Repeat the titration until two consistent results are obtained.

1 What volume of $0.05\,mol\,dm^{-3}$ silver nitrate was needed to react exactly with $10\,cm^3$ of the diluted sea water?

2 How many moles of silver ions are there in this volume of $0.05\,mol\,dm^{-3}$ solution?

3 How many moles of chloride ions must there have been in the $10 \, cm^3$ of solution?

4 How many moles of chloride ions must have been in $1 \, dm^3$ of the original, undiluted sea water?

5 What is the concentration, in $g \, dm^{-3}$, of chloride ions in this sample of sea water?

6 What are the major sources of error in this experiment?

7 Sea water contains fluoride, bromide and iodide ions as well as chloride, although their concentrations are much lower. (Chloride is about 300 times more concentrated than bromide, the next commonest halide ion in sea water.) Do you think the presence of these other halides will have affected the accuracy of your results? Explain.

8 It is essential in this experiment that glassware is washed with distilled water, not tap water. Why is this?

9 How did chloride ions get into the oceans? Why do oceans contain high concentrations of dissolved salts, while inland lakes do not?

INVESTIGATION

See Investigation 2

Practical 5
A test-tube study of redox reactions

Introduction

Redox reactions involve electron transfer. When a substance is oxidised it loses electrons, and the substance which receives the electrons is reduced. If a substance has a strong tendency to lose electrons it behaves as a **strong reducing agent** because it will tend to reduce other substances by giving them electrons. If a substance has a strong tendency to gain electrons it behaves as a **strong oxidising agent** because of its readiness to gain electrons from other substances and oxidise them. The intention of this practical is to investigate reactions between pairs of substances which can behave as oxidising and reducing agents, and try to place these substances in order of strength as oxidisers or reducers.

Consider the reaction between chlorine water and a solution containing iodide ions. The mixture turns brown rapidly as iodide ions are oxidised to iodine molecules. At the same time chlorine molecules are reduced to chloride ions:

$$2I^-(aq) + Cl_2(aq) \longrightarrow I_2(aq) + 2Cl^-(aq)$$

Chlorine molecules and chloride ions can be regarded as a **redox pair** and this is summarised in the following half-equation:

$$Cl_2 + 2e^- \rightleftharpoons 2Cl^-$$

When chlorine acts as an oxidiser, it accepts electrons and the half-equation moves from left to right. When chloride ions act as a reducer they lose electrons and the half-equation moves from right to left. We can think of the I_2/I^- pair acting in the same way:

$$I_2 + 2e^- \rightleftharpoons 2I^-$$

In the reaction between chlorine and iodide, it is impossible for both the half-equations $Cl_2 + 2e^- \rightleftharpoons 2Cl^-$ and $I_2 + 2e^- \rightleftharpoons 2I^-$ to move in the same direction, because there would be nothing to provide the electrons needed by both half-equations. One of the half-equations must move from right to left instead of left to right.

The results of the reaction tells us that it is the iodine/iodide equation that moves from right to left. This is because chlorine molecules have a greater tendency to accept electrons than iodine molecules. In other words, chlorine is a stronger oxidiser than iodine. Of course, at the start of the reaction there were neither iodine nor chloride ions present, so the reaction could not have proceeded in the other direction in any case. In fact, though, if the reaction is carried out with chlorine, chloride ions, iodine and iodide ions all present, the result is still the same—chlorine oxidises iodide to iodine. We can therefore place the two half-equations in order of the tendency to proceed to the right and this shows the order of strength of the oxidising agents.

$$\text{increasing oxidising strength} \left\uparrow \begin{array}{l} Cl_2 + 2e^- \rightleftharpoons 2Cl^- \\ I_2 + 2e^- \rightleftharpoons 2I^- \end{array}\right.$$

In this practical you will attempt to place a number of redox pairs in order of oxidising strength by carrying out suitable experiments. The redox pairs

REQUIREMENTS

Each student, or pair of students, will need:
- Eye protection
- 6 test tubes
- Universal indicator paper
- Splints
- Dilute sulphuric acid
- Sodium chlorate(I) (hypochlorite) solution
- Iodine in potassium iodide solution
- Starch solution
- Hydrogen peroxide ('20 volume')
- Sulphurous acid (a solution of sulphur dioxide in water)
- Chlorine water
- Solutions of the following at concentrations of about $1 \, mol \, dm^{-3}$:
  iron(III) chloride
  potassium iodide
  iron(II) sulphate
  potassium bromide
  or sodium bromide

Time required | double period

concerned are:

$$\text{A} \qquad I_2 + 2e^- \rightleftharpoons 2I^-$$

$$\text{B} \qquad SO_4^{2-} + H^+ + e^- \rightleftharpoons H_2SO_3 + H_2O$$

$$\text{C} \qquad ClO^- + H_2O + e^- \rightleftharpoons Cl^- + OH^-$$

$$\text{D} \qquad Cl_2 + 2e^- \rightleftharpoons 2Cl^-$$

$$\text{E} \qquad Br_2 + 2e^- \rightleftharpoons 2Br^-$$

$$\text{F} \qquad Fe^{3+} + e^- \rightleftharpoons Fe^{2+}.$$

ClO^- is called chlorate(I) (hypochlorite) ion, and H_2SO_3 is sulphurous acid.

1 Half-equations **B** and **C** are not balanced. Answer these questions with reference to each of **B** and **C**.

    a Which element is undergoing redox?

    b Work out the oxidation number of this element in both its oxidised and reduced forms.

    c Balance the half-equation.

Procedure

EYE PROTECTION
MUST BE WORN

CARE Eye protection must be worn for all these experiments.

Experiments 1–6: Placing the half-equations in order of oxidising strength

Experiment 1

Add a little of a solution of iron(III) ions to a solution of iodide ions. Describe what happens and test to see if iodine has been formed.

    The half-equations involved are:

$$\text{A} \qquad I_2 + 2e^- \rightleftharpoons 2I^-$$

$$\text{F} \qquad Fe^{3+} + e^- \rightleftharpoons Fe^{2+}$$

2 Use these half-equations to write a balanced ionic equation for the reaction that has occurred.

3 In this reaction, which of the half-equations moved from right to left instead of left to right?

4 Place **A** and **F** in order of oxidising strength.

CORROSIVE
Sodium chlorate(I)
solution

Experiment 2

Add a little sodium chlorate(I) solution to a solution containing iron(II) ions. Decide whether or not Fe^{2+} ions have been oxidised. (**Note** when chlorate(I) acts as an oxidising agent, hydroxide ions are produced. What effect will this have on iron(II) or iron(III) ions?)

5 Place half-equation **C** in its correct position relative to **A** and **F**.

6 Write a balanced ionic equation for the reaction.

Experiment 3

Add a little sodium chlorate(I) solution to a solution containing bromide ions. Decide whether or not bromide ions have been oxidised to bromine.

7 Can chlorate(I) ions oxidise bromide to bromine?

8 Place half-equation **E** in its correct position in the list.

9 Write a balanced ionic equation for the reaction.

HARMFUL
Sulphurous acid

IRRITANT
Iodine solution

TOXIC
Chlorine gas released
from chlorine water

Experiment 4

Add a little sulphurous acid to a solution containing iodine, I_2, and note the result.

10 Place half-equation **B** in its correct position in the list.

11 Write a balanced ionic equation for the reaction.

Experiment 5

Finally, decide the position of half-equation **D** by adding chlorine water to a solution containing bromide ions.

12 Place half-equation **D** in its correct position.

13 Write a balanced ionic equation for the reaction.

14 Use your final order of oxidising power to predict whether chlorate(I) ions will oxidise iodide ions to iodine.

Experiment 6

Test your prediction experimentally.

Experiments 7 and 8: Redox reactions of hydrogen peroxide

Hydrogen peroxide, H_2O_2, can behave as both an oxidiser and a reducer depending on the conditions. Half-equation **G** shows hydrogen peroxide behaving as an oxidising agent.

$$\textbf{G} \quad H_2O_2 + 2H^+ + 2e^- \rightleftharpoons 2H_2O$$

Half-equation **H** shows hydrogen peroxide behaving as a reducing agent.

$$\textbf{H} \quad O_2 + 2H^+ + 2e^- \rightleftharpoons H_2O_2$$

When hydrogen peroxide acts as a reducing agent half-equation **H** will, of course, proceed in the **reverse** direction.

Experiment 7

Add a little hydrogen peroxide solution to a solution of sodium chlorate(I) and note what happens. Decide whether the hydrogen peroxide is behaving as an oxidiser or as a reducer.

15 Which half-equation, **G** or **H**, describes the behaviour of hydrogen peroxide in this experiment?

16 Decide whether this half-equation should be placed above or below half-equation **C**. (**Note** It will be impossible to determine the exact position of the half-equation.)

17 Write a balanced ionic equation for the reaction of hydrogen peroxide with chlorate(I) ions.

Experiment 8

Acidify a little potassium iodide solution with dilute sulphuric acid. Add a little hydrogen peroxide solution. Describe what occurs.

IRRITANT
Dilute sulphuric acid

18 Is hydrogen peroxide behaving as an oxidiser or as a reducer?

19 Which half-equation describes the behaviour of hydrogen peroxide in this reaction?

20 Decide whether this half-equation should be placed above or below half-equation **A**.

21 Write a balanced ionic equation for the reaction of hydrogen peroxide with iodide ions in acid solution.

When hydrogen peroxide is left for some time, it slowly decomposes into water and oxygen. This decomposition is speeded up by various catalysts, such as manganese(IV) oxide. The equation for the reaction is:

$$2H_2O_2 \longrightarrow 2H_2O + O_2$$

22 Work out the oxidation number of oxygen in H_2O_2, H_2O and O_2.

23 Does the conversion of hydrogen peroxide to **oxygen** involve oxidation or reduction? What substance is acting as the oxidiser or reducer?

24 Does the conversion of hydrogen peroxide to **water** involve oxidation or reduction? What substance is acting as the oxidiser or reducer?

25 Show how the equation for the decomposition of hydrogen peroxide can be derived from half-equations **G** and **H**.

26 Explain what is meant by the term **disproportionation**.

Further work

If you have time, devise tests to establish more precisely the positions of **G** and **H** in the table.

Practical 6
Structure, bonding and properties

REQUIREMENTS

Each student, or pair of students, will need:
- Eye protection
- Polythene rod and fur for charging
- Burette
- 3 beakers (100 cm³)
- Rack with 6 test tubes
- Pair of carbon electrodes*
- 100 mA ammeter*
- 6 V battery or power pack*
- Leads and crocodile clips*
- Iodine
- Calcium chloride (solid)
- Powdered graphite
- Ethanol
- Hexane
- Distilled water
- Silver nitrate solution (about 0.1 mol dm⁻³)
- Ethyl ethanoate (ethyl acetate)
- 1,1,1-trichloroethane

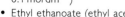

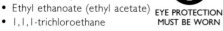

EYE PROTECTION MUST BE WORN

One set of these items could be shared by three or four pupils

Time required 2 double periods

HIGHLY FLAMMABLE
Hexane
Ethanol

HARMFUL
Ethanol

Introduction

Most of the physical and chemical properties of a substance can be related to the type of bonding present in that substance. In this practical you will investigate properties such as volatility and conductivity and try to explain these properties in terms of the bonding in the substance involved.

Substances that are ionically bonded contain positive and negative ions. Substances that are covalently bonded contain molecules; if these molecules contain atoms of different sorts, they may be polar due to the unequal sharing of electrons between the different atoms. The degree of polarity in a molecule, determined by the shape of the molecule and the relative electronegativities of the atoms in it, has a great effect on the properties of the substance.

Procedure

CARE Wear eye protection for all these experiments.

Experiment 1: The effect of a charged rod on liquid jets

Charge a polythene rod by rubbing it on a piece of fur. Hold the rod about 1 cm from a jet of water issuing from a burette and note what happens.

1 What sort of particles does water contain?

2 Are these particles polar?

3 Explain the effect of the charged rod on the jet of water.

4 What do you think would happen with a rod of opposite charge? Explain your answer.

Repeat the experiment using hexane, and then ethanol, instead of water.

CARE Highly flammable liquids. No flames.

5 Relate the behaviour of jets of these liquids towards a charged rod to the nature of the particles they contain.

6 Look up the boiling points and relative molecular masses of water, ethanol and hexane. Try to explain qualitatively the relative magnitudes of their boiling points in terms of polarity.

Experiment 2: Miscibility of liquids

Test the miscibility of **a** water and ethanol, **b** water and hexane, **c** hexane and ethanol.

7 Try to explain the results of experiment 2 in terms of the polarities of the molecules in the different liquids.

CORROSIVE
Iodine

HARMFUL
Iodine

Experiment 3: Solubility of iodine in different liquids

Keep the solutions from this experiment and from experiments **4** and **5** for use in experiment **7**.

Put a very small crystal of iodine in a test tube. Add $5\,cm^3$ distilled water, put a stopper in the tube and shake. Try to decide roughly how soluble iodine is in water. Repeat the experiment using ethanol as the solvent instead of water, and finally using hexane as the solvent.

8 What sort of particles does iodine contain?

9 What forces hold these particles together?

10 Explain the relative solubility of iodine in the three solvents.

11 Suggest a reason for the differing colours of solutions of iodine in different solvents. (If you have time, you could explore this question further in experiment **8**.)

Experiment 4: Solubility of graphite in liquids

Repeat experiment **3**, using powdered graphite instead of iodine. Answer questions **7** to **9** with reference to graphite instead of iodine.

Experiment 5: Solubility of calcium chloride in liquids

IRRITANT
Calcium chloride

Repeat experiment **3**, using calcium chloride instead of iodine. As solutions of calcium chloride are colourless, use the following procedure to decide how much has dissolved.

After shaking the crystal with the solvent, decant the liquid into a test tube, leaving the excess crystal behind. Add $2\,cm^3$ of silver nitrate solution to the decanted liquid and shake. From the amount of silver chloride precipitated, judge the relative solubility of calcium chloride in the three solvents.

Answer questions **7** to **9** with reference to calcium chloride instead of iodine.

Experiment 6: Volatility of iodine, graphite and calcium chloride

CORROSIVE
Iodine

HARMFUL
Iodine

CARE Iodine vapour is corrosive and toxic. Use only a very small crystal of iodine and work in a fume cupboard.

Heat a crystal of each of the solids in turn in a hard-glass test tube and judge their relative volatilities.

12 Try to explain the relative volatility of these three solids in terms of the particles they contain and the forces between them.

Experiment 7: Conductivity

Collect each of the solutions produced in experiments **3**, **4** and **5**. Test the conductivity of each solution by the following procedure.

Connect a pair of carbon electrodes in series with a 6V battery and a 100 mA ammeter. Dip the electrodes in the solution and note the meter reading in each case. Test the same depth of solution each time. (If the solid showed no sign of dissolving at all, do not bother to perform the test in that particular case.) You should also test the conductivity of each of the pure solvents.

Note Keep the electrodes clean and make sure they are not contaminated with liquid from a previous test.

13 Try to give a qualitative explanation of the relative conductivities of the different solutions.

Experiment 8: The colour of iodine in solution

If you have time, try the following tests, then see if you can suggest an explanation for the different colours of iodine in different solvents.

A Find the colour of iodine in solution in the following solvents: hexane, ethanol, ethyl ethanoate, 1,1,1-trichloroethane.

CARE Flammable liquids. No flames.

B Add one drop of ethanol to a solution of iodine in hexane.

C Add one drop of hexane to a solution of iodine in ethanol.

14 What is the colour of iodine vapour?

15 Try to suggest a theory to explain the variation of colour of iodine in different solvents.

INVESTIGATION

See Investigation 3

Practical 7
Enthalpy changes of neutralisation

REQUIREMENTS

Each student, or pair of students, will need:
- Eye protection
- Plastic beaker (the sort used in drink dispensing machines is ideal)
- 0–100°C thermometer
- Measuring cylinder (50 cm^3)
- The following solutions.

CARE Take care making up the solutions. Concentrated acids and solid alkalis are corrosive. Eye protection is essential.

- 2.0 mol dm^{-3} nitric acid (25 cm^3) (Make 128 cm^3 of concentrated acid up to 1 dm^3)
- 2.0 mol dm^{-3} hydrochloric acid (100 cm^3) (Make 172 cm^3 of concentrated acid up to 1 dm^3)
- 2.0 mol dm^{-3} sulphuric acid (50 cm^3) (Make 107 cm^3 of concentrated acid up to 1 dm^3)
- 2.0 mol dm^{-3} sodium hydroxide (75 cm^3) (Dissolve 80 g of pellets or flakes in distilled water and make up to 1 dm^3)
- 4.0 mol dm^{-3} sodium hydroxide (25 cm^3) (Dissolve 160 g of pellets or flakes in distilled water and make up to 1 dm^3)
- 2.0 mol dm^{-3} potassium hydroxide (25 cm^3) (Dissolve 112 g of pellets in distilled water and make up to 1 dm^3)

Time required 1 double period

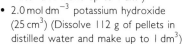

EYE PROTECTION MUST BE WORN

CORROSIVE
Sodium hydroxide solution
Potassium hydroxide solution

IRRITANT
Hydrochloric acid

Introduction

When an alkali neutralises an acid, a salt and water are formed. Aqueous hydrogen ions ($H^+(aq)$) from the acid react with the hydroxide ions ($OH^-(aq)$) from the alkali, forming water. The identity of the salt will of course depend on the nature of the acid and alkali used. For hydrochloric acid and sodium hydroxide:

$$\underbrace{H^+(aq) + Cl^-(aq)}_{\text{hydrochloric acid}} + \underbrace{Na^+(aq) + OH^-(aq)}_{\text{sodium hydroxide}} \longrightarrow \underbrace{Na^+(aq) + Cl^-(aq)}_{\text{sodium chloride}} + H_2O(l)$$

Notice in this equation that the Na^+ and Cl^- ions are unchanged. The only chemical reaction occurring is between H^+ and OH^- ions:

$$H^+(aq) + OH^-(aq) \longrightarrow H_2O(l)$$

The combination of H^+ and OH^- ions in this way releases energy. In this practical, the enthalpy changes accompanying different neutralisation reactions will be measured. Because the number of moles of water formed varies according to the acid and alkali used, it is the convention to measure enthalpies of neutralisation in kilojoules per mole of water formed.

Procedure

CARE Wear eye protection for all these experiments.

Experiment 1: The reaction between hydrochloric acid and sodium hydroxide

Measure 25 cm^3 of 2.0 mol dm^{-3} hydrochloric acid into a plastic beaker. Record its temperature. Put 25 cm^3 of 2.0 mol dm^{-3} sodium hydroxide solution in a measuring cylinder and take its temperature. Now pour this into the acid, stir and take the final temperature.

1 What was the temperature rise? (If the acid and alkali were not at the same temperature initially, use the mean of their initial temperatures as the starting temperature.)

2 How much energy was delivered to the 50 cm^3 of final solution during the reaction? (Assume the specific heating capacity of the plastic cup is negligible, and that the specific heating capacity of the solution is $4.2 \, J \, K^{-1} \, g^{-1}$.)

3 How many moles of water were formed by the reaction you have just carried out?

4 Work out the enthalpy change of neutralisation for this reaction in kilojoules per mole of water formed.

Experiment 2: The reaction between hydrochloric acid and potassium hydroxide

Repeat experiment 1 using $2.0\,mol\,dm^{-3}$ potassium hydroxide solution instead of the sodium hydroxide.

5 Write an ionic equation like the one in the introduction to represent the reaction that has occurred.

6 Using the method outlined in questions **1** to **4** above, work out the enthalpy change of neutralisation for this reaction.

Experiment 3: The reaction between nitric acid and sodium hydroxide

IRRITANT
Nitric acid

Repeat experiment 1 using $2.0\,mol\,dm^{-3}$ nitric acid instead of the hydrochloric acid.

7 Write an ionic equation to represent the reaction which has occurred.

8 Work out the enthalpy change of neutralisation for this reaction.

9 Compare the values you have obtained for the enthalpy changes of neutralisation of the three reactions and explain the way the values compare.

Accepted values for the enthalpy changes of neutralisation of some acids and alkalis are shown in table 1.

Table I

Reaction			Enthalpy change of neutralisation /kJ mol^{-1}
$HCl(aq)$ hydrochloric acid	$+$ $NaOH(aq)$ sodium hydroxide	$\longrightarrow$ $NaCl(aq) + H_2O(l)$	-57.9
$HNO_3(aq)$ nitric acid	$+$ $NaOH(aq)$ sodium hydroxide	$\longrightarrow$ $NaNO_3(aq) + H_2O(l)$	-57.6
$HBr(aq)$ hydrobromic acid	$+$ $NaOH(aq)$ sodium hydroxide	$\longrightarrow$ $NaBr(aq) + H_2O(l)$	-57.6
$CH_3COOH(aq)$ ethanoic acid	$+$ $NaOH(aq)$ sodium hydroxide	$\longrightarrow$ $CH_3COONa(aq) + H_2O(l)$	-56.1
$H_2S(aq)$ hydrogen sulphide	$+$ $NaOH(aq)$ sodium hydroxide	$\longrightarrow$ $NaHS(aq) + H_2O(l)$	-32.2

10 How do the values for the first two reactions in this table compare with your own experimental results for the same reactions? Account for any errors in your results.

11 Do the values for the first three reactions in the table agree with the explanation you have given in question **9**?

12 Suggest why the enthalpy change of neutralisation for the reaction involving ethanoic acid is slightly lower than the values for the first three reactions, and why the enthalpy change of neutralisation for the reaction involving hydrogen sulphide is substantially lower. (The dissociation constants, K_a, for hydrochloric acid, hydrobromic acid and nitric acid are very large; that of ethanoic acid is $1.7 \times 10^{-5}\,mol\,dm^{-3}$ and that of hydrogen sulphide is $8.9 \times 10^{-8}\,mol\,dm^{-3}$.)

You should now have some idea of how the relative magnitudes of enthalpy changes of neutralisation can be explained. You can use these ideas in the following experiment.

Experiment 4: The reaction between sulphuric acid and sodium hydroxide

CORROSIVE
Sulphuric acid

Repeat experiment 1 using $25\,cm^3$ of $2.0\,mol\,dm^{-3}$ sulphuric acid and $25\,cm^3$ of $2.0\,mol\,dm^{-3}$ sodium hydroxide. Record the temperature rise on mixing as before.

Now repeat the experiment you have just done using $25\,cm^3$ of $4.0\,mol\,dm^{-3}$ sodium hydroxide instead of $2.0\,mol\,dm^{-3}$.

13 Compare the temperature rises for the two experiments and explain their relative values.

Repeat the experiment using $25\,cm^3$ of $2.0\,mol\,dm^{-3}$ hydrochloric acid and $25\,cm^3$ of $4.0\,mol\,dm^{-3}$ sodium hydroxide.

INVESTIGATION

See Investigation 4

14 Compare the temperature rise when $25\,cm^3$ of $2.0\,mol\,dm^{-3}$ hydrochloric acid neutralises $25\,cm^3$ $2.0\,mol\,dm^{-3}$ sodium hydroxide with the rise when $4.0\,mol\,dm^{-3}$ sodium hydroxide is used instead. Explain their relative values. Compare your answer here with your answer to question **13.**

Practical 8

Determination of the enthalpy change for the thermal decomposition of potassium hydrogencarbonate

Principle

When potassium hydrogencarbonate, $KHCO_3$, is heated, it decomposes to form potassium carbonate, K_2CO_3. The object of this experiment is to determine the enthalpy change during this reaction. This enthalpy change is difficult to measure directly, so an indirect method is used.

1 Explain the following terms:

   a enthalpy

   b enthalpy change

2 Write an equation including state symbols for the thermal decomposition of potassium hydrogencarbonate to potassium carbonate, showing the products in their usual states under standard conditions.

3 What are the standard conditions for thermochemistry?

4 Why is it difficult to determine this enthalpy change directly?

You are provided with $2 \, mol \, dm^{-3}$ hydrochloric acid, solid potassium carbonate and solid potassium hydrogencarbonate. By determining the enthalpy change of reaction between potassium carbonate and hydrochloric acid and that between potassium hydrogencarbonate and hydrochloric acid, it is possible to obtain indirectly the enthalpy change for the decomposition of potassium hydrogencarbonate.

Procedure

EYE PROTECTION
MUST BE WORN

IRRITANT
Hydrochloric acid
Anhydrous potassium carbonate

CARE Eye protection must be worn for both experiment 1 and experiment 2.

Experiment 1: The reaction of potassium carbonate with hydrochloric acid

Using a burette, measure $30 \, cm^3$ of approximately $2 \, mol \, dm^{-3}$ hydrochloric acid into a plastic beaker. Take the temperature of the acid and record this in a table similar to table 1 (see next page).

Accurately weigh a test tube containing between 2.5 g and 3.0 g of anhydrous potassium carbonate (K_2CO_3). Record the mass in a table similar to table 1.

Now add the weighed portion of K_2CO_3 to the acid and stir the mixture carefully with the thermometer until all the solid has reacted. Rapid effervescence will occur. Be careful not to lose any of the reaction mixture by spilling. Record the maximum temperature of the solution after mixing and then re-weigh the empty test tube.

5 Write an equation, including state symbols, for the reaction between potassium carbonate and hydrochloric acid.

6 From your results in table 1, calculate the energy released or absorbed during the reaction between the potassium carbonate and the acid.

(Assume that the specific heating capacities of all the solutions are the same as that of water (i.e. $4.2\,J\,g^{-1}\,K^{-1}$), and that the solutions have a density of $1.0\,g\,cm^{-3}$. Assume that the specific heating capacity of the plastic beaker is negligible.)

Table 1

Mass of test tube + potassium carbonate	g
Mass of empty test tube	g
Mass of potassium carbonate used	g
Temperature of acid initially	°C
Temperature of solution after mixing	°C
Temperature change during reaction	°C

7 Calculate the enthalpy change for one mole of potassium carbonate.

8 Why is the exact concentration of the acid unimportant?

9 Why is it better to re-weigh the test tube after emptying out the solid than to record the mass of the clean test tube?

Experiment 2: The reaction of potassium hydrogencarbonate with hydrochloric acid

EYE PROTECTION
MUST BE WORN

Repeat experiment **1** using an accurately weighed sample of potassium hydrogencarbonate between 3.25 g and 3.75 g in place of the potassium carbonate. Record all masses and temperatures in a table similar to table 2.

Table 2

Mass of test tube + potassium hydrogencarbonate	g
Mass of empty test tube	g
Mass of potassium hydrogencarbonate used	g
Temperature of acid initially	°C
Temperature of solution after mixing	°C
Temperature change during reaction	°C

10 Write an equation, including state symbols, for the reaction between potassium hydrogencarbonate and hydrochloric acid.

11 From your results in table 2, calculate the energy released or absorbed during the reaction between the potassium hydrogencarbonate and the acid. (You should make the same assumptions as in question **6**.)

12 Calculate the enthalpy change for one mole of potassium hydrogencarbonate.

13 Mention three major sources of error in your experiments.

14 Draw an enthalpy diagram linking the reaction of $K_2CO_3(s)$ with $HCl(aq)$, the reaction of $KHCO_3(s)$ with $HCl(aq)$ and the decomposition of $KHCO_3(s)$.

15 What is the enthalpy change for the decomposition of potassium hydrogencarbonate?

16 What law have you used in answering question **15** and on what thermodynamic principle does this law depend?

Practical 9
Enthalpy changes of solution

REQUIREMENTS

Each student, or pair of students, will need:
- Eye protection
- Sodium chloride
- Ammonium nitrate
- Sodium hydroxide (flakes or pellets)
- Sodium thiosulphate-5-water, $Na_2S_2O_3.5H_2O$
- Measuring cylinder ($100\,cm^3$)
- Thermometer ($0-50°C$)
- Plastic beaker (the sort used in drink dispensing machines does very well)
- Pestle and mortar
- Weighing bottle
- Access to a balance

EYE PROTECTION MUST BE WORN   WEAR PROTECTIVE GLOVES

Time required I double period

CORROSIVE   OXIDISING
Sodium hydroxide Ammonium nitrate

Introduction

When an ionic solid dissolves in water to form an aqueous solution, a temperature change is always observed. In the first part of this practical we shall look in a simple, qualitative way at the magnitude of the temperature changes involved. In the second part, we will attempt to obtain an accurate value for the enthalpy change of solution of an ionic solid.

Procedure

Experiment 1: Temperature changes on dissolving different ionic solids in water

The following procedure should be carried out separately for each of the three solutes: sodium chloride, sodium hydroxide and ammonium nitrate.

CARE Sodium hydroxide is very corrosive: avoid all contact with the skin and eyes. Eye protection and protective gloves must be worn. If any sodium hydroxide comes into contact with the skin, wash it immediately with plenty of cold water.

Weigh out 0.1 mol of the solid. In the case of sodium hydroxide the pellets or flakes should be weighed in a sealed weighing bottle.

Measure $100\,cm^3$ distilled water into a plastic beaker and measure its temperature. Quickly dissolve the 0.1 mol of solid in the water, stirring briskly with the thermometer, and record the final temperature.

Tabulate your results, showing the temperature rise for each solute.

1 Why, apart from the danger of skin contact, is it particularly important to weigh the sodium hydroxide in a sealed bottle?

2 Which solute, or solutes, gave out energy as they dissolved? Which absorbed energy?

When an ionic solid dissolves in water, two processes occur. First, the ions in the solid lattice must be separated from one another. As the ions carry opposite charges and attract one another, this process of bond-breaking requires the *input* of energy. The second process involves the interaction of the ions of the solute with polar water molecules—positive ions attract the negative ends of H_2O dipoles, and negative ions attract the positive ends. This process of bond-making *releases* energy. The sign and magnitude of the overall energy change depends on the relative sizes of the energy changes ocurring in these two processes.

(See *Chemistry in Context*, Fourth Edition, section 12.14, for a more detailed consideration of the processes that occur when an ionic solid dissolves.)

3 Explain, in terms of the two energy changes referred to above, the signs and relative magnitudes of the temperature changes that occurred when each of the three solutes dissolved.
Note With some solutes, including sodium hydroxide, the situation is complicated by the formation of hydrates when the anhydrous solute dissolves. Leave this consideration aside when answering this question.

4 If you had used excess solute in your experiment, a saturated solution would have been formed, with undissolved solute in equilibrium with its aqueous solution, for example:

$$NH_4^+ NO_3^- (s) + aq \rightleftharpoons NH_4^+ (aq) + NO_3^- (aq)$$

By applying Le Chatelier's principle to this equilibrium, decide whether the solubility of ammonium nitrate will increase or decrease when the temperature is raised. How will the solubility of sodium chloride change when the temperature is raised?

Experiment 2: Measurement of the enthalpy change of solution of sodium thiosulphate

The enthalpy change of solution, ΔH_{soln}, of a solute is the enthalpy change that occurs when one mole of the solute dissolves to form an infinitely dilute solution. In this part of the practical you are to devise and carry out a simple experiment to obtain as accurate a value as possible for ΔH_{soln} for hydrated sodium thiosulphate, $Na_2S_2O_3.5H_2O$. In principle this can be done by measuring the temperature change of the water in which the sodium thiosulphate dissolves, but you should bear the following points in mind when designing your experiment.

A Heat losses must be minimised. In particular, you will need good insulation and the sodium thiosulphate should be dissolved as quickly as possible. You may be able to think of other ways of reducing heat losses.

B It will not, of course, be possible to produce an infinitely dilute solution, and your solution will need to be concentrated enough to produce an accurately measurable temperature rise. You should think carefully about the best concentration to use.

C You can assume that the specific heating capacity of sodium thiosulphate solution is the same as that of water, i.e. $4.2\,J\,g^{-1}\,K^{-1}$.

D You will need to bear in mind the apparatus available to you.

5 Write a brief description of your experiment and tabulate the results.

6 Work out a value for the enthalpy change of solution of sodium thiosulphate as follows.

a Use the temperature change of the solution to calculate the enthalpy change that occurred in the solution.

b Knowing the amount of sodium thiosulphate used, calculate the enthalpy change that would have occurred if one mole of sodium thiosulphate had been used.

7 What do you consider to be the major sources of error in your experiment?

8 How might these errors have been reduced if more sophisticated apparatus had been available?

9 How would you expect the value for ΔH_{soln} to change if you used *anhydrous* sodium thiosulphate instead of $Na_2S_2O_3.5H_2O$?

10 Strictly speaking, ΔH_{soln} applies to the formation of *infinitely dilute* solutions. What simple experiment could you perform with the solution you obtained to decide whether a significant error was introduced by not making it infinitely dilute?

INVESTIGATION

See Investigation 5

Practical 10
Acids, bases and indicators

Introduction

If we define acids as proton donors and bases as proton acceptors, it is clear that every acid must have a corresponding base. This is formed when the acid loses a proton:

$$HA \rightleftharpoons H^+ + A^-$$

$$\text{acid} \qquad\qquad \text{base}$$

A^- is said to be the **conjugate base** of the acid HA, and vice-versa.

Acids differ markedly in their tendency to lose a proton. Acids which donate protons readily are said to be **strong acids**. Strong acids have weak conjugate bases, because the conjugate base will have little tendency to accept the proton back. Weak acids, on the other hand, have strong conjugate bases. For example, hydrochloric acid, HCl, is a strong acid whereas ethanoic acid, CH_3COOH, is weak. From this, it follows that the chloride ion, Cl^-, is a weak base whereas the ethanoate ion, CH_3COO^-, is a stronger base. We can therefore arrange these two acid–base pairs in order of strength as acids and bases.

	Acid		**Base**	
increasing acid strength ↑	HCl	$\rightleftharpoons$ $H^+ + Cl^-$		increasing base strength ↓
	CH_3COOH	$\rightleftharpoons$ $H^+ + CH_3COO^-$		

This idea has been extended in table 1 to show a number of well-known acids and their conjugate bases in order of strength. Table 1 includes several of the acids you will meet in this practical. Note that ethanol and water appear as acids in table 1, even though both are so weak that they are not normally regarded as acids.

Table 1
Conjugate acid–base pairs arranged in order of decreasing acid strength

Name of acid	Acid		Base	Name of base
chloric(VII) acid	$HClO_4$	$\rightleftharpoons$	$H^+ + ClO_4^-$	chlorate(VII) ion
hydrochloric acid	HCl	$\rightleftharpoons$	$H^+ + Cl^-$	chloride ion
oxonium ion	H_3O^+	$\rightleftharpoons$	$H^+ + H_2O$	water
methanoic acid	HCOOH	$\rightleftharpoons$	$H^+ + HCOO^-$	methanoate ion
ethanoic acid	CH_3COOH	$\rightleftharpoons$	$H^+ + CH_3COO^-$	ethanoate ion
ammonium ion	NH_4^+	$\rightleftharpoons$	$H^+ + NH_3$	ammonia
phenol	C_6H_5OH	$\rightleftharpoons$	$H^+ + C_6H_5O^-$	phenoxide ion
water	H_2O	$\rightleftharpoons$	$H^+ + OH^-$	hydroxide ion
ethanol	CH_3CH_2OH	$\rightleftharpoons$	$H^+ + CH_3CH_2O^-$	ethoxide ion

Procedure

EYE PROTECTION
MUST BE WORN

CARE Eye protection must be worn in all these experiments.

Experiment 1: Proton-transfer reactions between acids and bases

CARE When smelling substances, do so very cautiously. Fill your lungs with air, hold the tube at a distance and waft the gas towards your nose.

1 Do **a** hydrochloric acid, **b** ethanoic acid, **c** ethanoate ions have characteristic smells?

   A Add a little dilute hydrochloric acid to a little solid sodium ethanoate, and warm. Smell the reaction mixture cautiously.

2 Has a proton-transfer reaction occurred? If so, what substance has behaved as an acid, and what has behaved as a base?

   B Add a little dilute ethanoic acid to a little solid sodium chloride and warm.

3 Is there any evidence that a proton-transfer reaction has occurred?

IRRITANT
Dilute ethanoic acid

   C Your observations in this experiment illustrate a simple rule: if an acid, HA_1, is added to the conjugate base, A_2^-, of a weaker acid, HA_2, a proton-transfer reaction occurs, forming A_1^- and HA_2.

$$HA_1 + A_2^- \rightleftharpoons HA_2 + A_1^-$$

   stronger   weaker
   acid   acid

This is because HA_1 has a greater tendency to donate protons than HA_2. This rule can be illustrated further using phenol.

WEAR PROTECTIVE   CORROSIVE   TOXIC
GLOVES   Phenol   Phenol

CORROSIVE
Sodium hydroxide solution

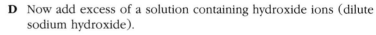

CORROSIVE
Concentrated
hydrochloric
acid

CARE Phenol is corrosive and toxic. Eye protection is essential. Avoid all contact with the skin. Wear protective gloves.

Put a few crystals of phenol in a test tube. Add an equal volume of water, cork the tube and shake.

4 Does phenol dissolve in water?

   D Now add excess of a solution containing hydroxide ions (dilute sodium hydroxide).

5 What happens?

6 A proton-transfer reaction has occurred. What substance has acted as an acid, and what has acted as a base?

   E Now add a few drops of concentrated hydrochloric acid.

7 What happens?

8 Another proton-transfer reaction has occurred. What substance has acted as an acid, and what has acted as a base this time?

9 Explain the reactions that have occurred in terms of the relative positions of hydrochloric acid, phenol and water in table 1.

Experiment 2: Finding the position of benzoic acid in the table

Benzoic acid, C_6H_5COOH, is a white solid which is nearly insoluble in water. Benzoate ions, however, are soluble.

Make a solution of sodium benzoate by dissolving 1.0 g in 10 cm³ water. Divide the solution between three test tubes. To the first tube add 2 cm³ dilute hydrochloric acid, to the second 2 cm³ dilute ethanoic acid, and to the third $2\,cm^3$ of a solution containing ammonium ions (ammonium chloride solution). Record your results and write equations where appropriate.

10 Where should benzoic acid be positioned in the table?

Experiment 3: Acid strength and hydrogen ion concentration

In aqueous solution, acids donate protons to water molecules, forming the oxonium ion, H_3O^+.

$$HA + H_2O \rightleftharpoons H_3O^+ + A^-$$

Oxonium ions are often written simply as $H^+(aq)$.
The stronger the acid HA, the further this equilibrium will lie to the right, and the higher the concentration of $H^+(aq)$.
Prepare four test tubes as follows:

HARMFUL
Ethanol

HIGHLY
FLAMMABLE
Ethanol

Tube 1: $4\,cm^3$ dilute ethanoic acid
Tube 2: $4\,cm^3$ ammonium chloride solution
Tube 3: $4\,cm^3$ water
Tube 4: $4\,cm^3$ ethanol

To each of these tubes add **half a spatula load** of magnesium powder. Compare the reactions in the different tubes.

11 Write a general ionic equation for the reactions that occur.

FLAMMABLE
Magnesium
powder

12 Relate the vigour of each reaction to the acid strength of the liquid in the tube.

Experiment 4: Acid–base indicators

Indicators are substances which change colour according to the pH of the solution they are in. Indicators are themselves weak acids or bases which differ in colour from their conjugates.

For example, phenolphthalein, an indicator which is colourless in acid but pink in alkali, is a weak acid which we might represent as HPh. Unionised acid, HPh, is colourless, but its conjugate base, Ph^-, is pink.

$$HPh(aq) \rightleftharpoons H^+(aq) + Ph^-(aq)$$

colourless   pink

When acid is added, the equilibrium moves to the left and the colourless form is in large excess. When alkali is added, $H^+(aq)$ is removed, the equilibrium moves to the right and the pink form predominates. Hence phenolphthalein is colourless in acid but pink in alkali.

Put $2\,cm^3$ dilute hydrochloric acid in a test tube and add 2 drops of the indicator bromophenol blue, which can be represented as HB.

13 In what form is the indicator present in the tube? What colour is this form? Add excess sodium hydroxide solution.

14 In what form is the indicator now present? What is the colour of this form?
Prepare five test tubes as follows:
Tube 1: $4\,cm^3$ dilute hydrochloric acid
Tube 2: $4\,cm^3$ dilute ethanoic acid
Tube 3: $4\,cm^3$ ammonium chloride solution
Tube 4: 2 or 3 crystals of phenol (**CARE**) dissolved in $4\,cm^3$ water
Tube 5: $4\,cm^3$ water
Add 2 drops of bromophenol blue indicator to each tube and record the colour.

CORROSIVE
Phenol

INVESTIGATION

See Investigation 6

15 Where would you place HB in the table of acids? Why is it not possible to position it exactly?

Practical 11
Electrochemical cells

REQUIREMENTS

Each student, or pair of students, will need:
- Eye protection
- 3 beakers ($100 \, cm^3$)
- 2 wire leads fitted with crocodile clips
- Access to a high resistance voltmeter. The millivolt scale of a pH meter is suitable. It is best to have at least one meter between three or four pairs.
- Strips of filter paper long enough to connect two $100 \, cm^3$ beakers
- Saturated potassium nitrate solution
- Strip of zinc foil about $6 \, cm \times 1 \, cm$
- Strip of copper foil about $6 \, cm \times 1 \, cm$
- Iron nail
- Emery paper
- $1.0 \, mol \, dm^{-3}$ copper sulphate solution ($50 \, cm^3$)
  Dissolve $250 \, g$ hydrated copper(II) sulphate in distilled water and make up to $1 \, dm^3$
- $0.1 \, mol \, dm^{-3}$ copper sulphate solution ($50 \, cm^3$)*
- $0.01 \, mol \, dm^{-3}$ copper sulphate solution ($50 \, cm^3$)*
- $0.001 \, mol \, dm^{-3}$ copper sulphate solution ($50 \, cm^3$)*
- $1.0 \, mol \, dm^{-3}$ zinc sulphate solution ($50 \, cm^3$). (Dissolve $288 \, g$ hydrated zinc sulphate in distilled water and make up to $1 \, dm^3$)
- $1.0 \, mol \, dm^{-3}$ iron(II) sulphate solution (acidified). Dissolve $278 \, g$ hydrated iron(II) sulphate (**irritant**) in $200 \, cm^3$ $1.0 \, mol \, dm^{-3}$ sulphuric acid and make up to $1 \, dm^3$ with distilled water.

*Made by diluting the $1.0 \, mol \, dm^{-3}$ solution as appropriate.

Time required 1–2 double periods

Introduction

Many chemical reactions give out energy. This energy is usually transferred by heating, and when the energy is used, for example to drive an engine, the chemical is called a **fuel**. Occasionally a chemical reaction can be arranged so that the energy is transferred electrically. Such an arrangement is called an **electric cell**.

Procedure

Introductory experiment

Add a little zinc powder to a few cubic centimetres of copper sulphate solution in a test tube. Note everything that happens.

In this reaction, copper(II) ions are being reduced by zinc:

$$Zn(s) + Cu^{2+}(aq) \longrightarrow Zn^{2+}(aq) + Cu(s)$$

Electrons are transferred from zinc atoms to copper ions. If the zinc atoms are kept apart from the copper ions, the electrons transferred from Zn to Cu^{2+} can be made to flow down a wire. In this way, the energy transferred by heat-ing in the simple test tube reaction above can be made available as electricity.

Experiment 1: Constructing a zinc/copper cell

One way of doing this is shown in figure 1 (see next page). A strip of zinc foil is placed in contact with zinc ions, and a strip of copper foil in contact with copper ions. When these two **half-cells** are connected by a wire joining the metal electrodes and a salt bridge connecting the ionic solutions, the follow-ing reactions occur:

In the left-hand beaker $\quad Zn(s) \longrightarrow Zn^{2+}(aq) + 2e^-$

In the right-hand beaker $\quad Cu^{2+}(aq) + 2e^- \longrightarrow Cu(s)$

The electrons flow down the wire from the left-hand to the right-hand beaker, giving an electric current. A potential difference is set up between the two half-cells. This potential difference is at a maximum when no current is flowing, and it is then called the **e.m.f.** of the cell, or E_{cell}. The value of E_{cell} depends on a number of factors, but when the concentrations of zinc and copper ions are both $1.0 \, mol \, dm^{-3}$ and the temperature is $298 \, K$, E_{cell} is said to have its **standard** value, indicated by $E_{cell}^{\ominus}$.

Set up a zinc/copper cell (often called a Daniell cell) as shown in figure 1. Clean the zinc and copper foils with emery before use. Use $1.0 \, mol \, dm^{-3}$ zinc sulphate and $1.0 \, mol \, dm^{-3}$ copper sulphate for the electrolytes, and a strip of filter paper soaked in saturated potassium nitrate solution for the salt bridge. Measure the e.m.f. of the cell using a high-resistance voltmeter. You should be able to predict the polarity of the electrodes before connecting the meter.

1 What is $E_{cell}^{\ominus}$ for the zinc/copper cell?

2 Bearing in mind the relative tendencies of zinc, iron and copper to lose electrons, would you expect a zinc/iron cell to have a greater or a smaller $E^{\ominus}_{\text{cell}}$ than a zinc/copper cell?

Experiment 2: Constructing a zinc/iron cell

IRRITANT
Acidified iron(II)
sulphate solution

Set up a zinc/iron cell using a similar arrangement to the previous one, with a Fe/Fe^{2+} half-cell instead of the copper one. (Keep the copper half-cell for a later experiment.) Use a clean iron nail for the iron electrode and an acidified $1.0\,\text{mol}\,\text{dm}^{-3}$ iron(II) sulphate solution as the electrolyte. Use a fresh salt bridge. You should be able to predict the polarity of the cell before measuring its e.m.f.

3 Write an equation for the reaction occurring in this cell.

4 What is $E^{\ominus}_{\text{cell}}$ for the zinc/iron cell?

5 Assuming that each half-cell in a cell makes a fixed, independent contribution to E_{cell}, use your answers to questions **1** and **4** to predict $E^{\ominus}_{\text{cell}}$ for an iron/copper cell.

Experiment 3: Constructing an iron/copper cell

Set up an iron/copper cell using the Fe/Fe^{2+} and Cu/Cu^{2+} half-cells employed in the previous two experiments. Use a fresh salt bridge. Measure $E^{\ominus}_{\text{cell}}$.

6 How does your measured value for $E^{\ominus}_{\text{cell}}$ compare with your predicted value?

Experiment 4: Effect of concentration on E_{cell}

When current is drawn from a Daniell cell, the reactions occurring at each electrode are:

$$\text{Zn(s)} \longrightarrow \text{Zn}^{2+}(\text{aq}) + 2\text{e}^- \quad \text{and} \quad \text{Cu}^{2+}(\text{aq}) + 2\text{e}^- \longrightarrow \text{Cu(s)}$$

However, when the e.m.f. of the cell is being measured, no current is being drawn and each electrode is at equilibrium:

$$\text{Zn(s)} \rightleftharpoons \text{Zn}^{2+}(\text{aq}) + 2\text{e}^- \quad \text{and} \quad \text{Cu}^{2+}(\text{aq}) + 2\text{e}^- \rightleftharpoons \text{Cu(s)}$$

7 Use Le Chatelier's principle to predict the changes which occur if the ion concentration in each equilibrium is reduced.

8 What will be the effect of decreasing the concentration of copper ions on the tendency of the copper electrode to accept electrons from the zinc?

9 What will be the effect on E_{cell} of decreasing the concentration of copper ions?

Test your prediction in question **9** as follows. Set up a Daniell cell as in the first experiment, and measure E_{cell} with the following concentrations of Cu^{2+}(aq): $0.1\,\text{mol}\,\text{dm}^{-3}$, $0.01\,\text{mol}\,\text{dm}^{-3}$, $0.001\,\text{mol}\,\text{dm}^{-3}$. Use a fresh salt bridge each time. At the lower concentrations, it is very important to pay careful attention to cleanliness in the copper half-cells, as small quantities of impurities will give rise to large errors.

10 Does E_{cell} increase or decrease when Cu^{2+} concentration decreases?

11 Is the relation between E_{cell} and Cu^{2+} concentration a linear one? If not, what form does it take?

12 How would E_{cell} change when Zn^{2+} concentration decreases?

13 The cell shown in figure 2 is an example of a **concentration cell.** Use your experimental results to predict its e.m.f. Check your answer experimentally if you have time.

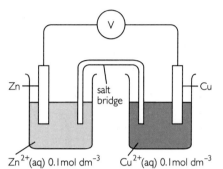

Figure 1
A simple cell.

Zn — salt bridge — Cu

Zn^{2+}(aq) 0.1 mol dm^{-3} Cu^{2+}(aq) 0.1 mol dm^{-3}

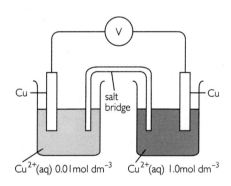

Figure 2
A concentration cell.

Cu — salt bridge — Cu

Cu^{2+}(aq) 0.01 mol dm^{-3} Cu^{2+}(aq) 1.0 mol dm^{-3}

INVESTIGATION

See Investigation 7

Practical 12
Complex formation and competition for cations

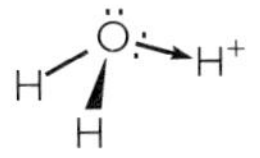

Figure 1
Co-ordinate bonding in an H_3O^+ ion.

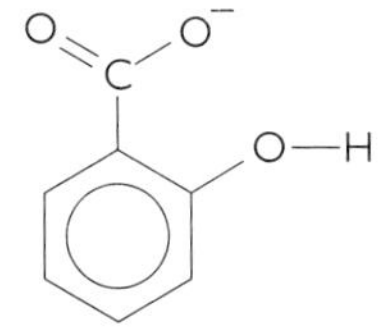

2-hydroxybenzoate ion
(salicylate ion)

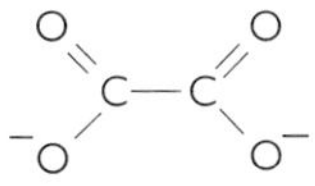

ethanedioate ion
(oxalate ion)

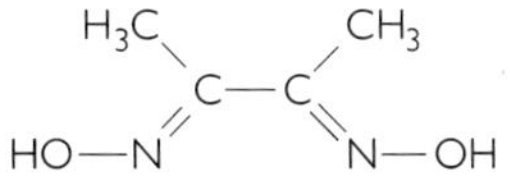

butanedione dioxime
(dimethylglyoximine)

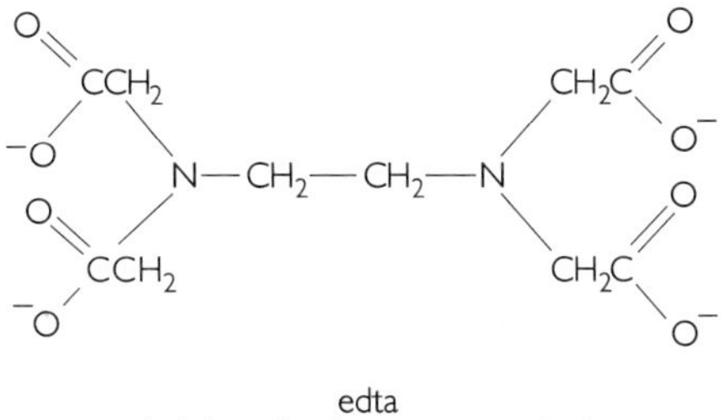

edta
(ethylenediaminetetraacetate ion)

Figure 2
Some polydentate ligands.

Introduction

In aqueous solution, H^+ ions are attached to polar water molecules by co-ordinate bonds forming H_3O^+ ions (figure 1). In the same way, other cations will also exist in aqueous solution as hydrated ions with formulae of the type $[M(H_2O)_n]^{x+}$.

H^+ ions are very small and it is often assumed that each one associates with only one water molecule, but the larger size of other cations enables them to associate with two, four or even six water molecules. For example, Ag^+ ions exist in aqueous solution as $[Ag(H_2O)_2]^+$, Cu^{2+} ions exist as $[Cu(H_2O)_4]^{2+}$ and Fe^{3+} ions exist as $[Fe(H_2O)_6]^{3+}$.

Other polar molecules, besides water, can also co-ordinate with metal cations. Thus, in aqueous ammonia Cu^{2+} exists mainly as $[Cu(NH_3)_4]^{2+}$ and Ag^+ exists as $[Ag(NH_3)_2]^+$. Anions, such as Cl^-, OH^- and $S_2O_3^{2-}$, can also associate with cations in the same way as polar molecules like H_2O and NH_3. Thus, Ag^+ exists as $[Ag(S_2O_3)_2]^{3-}$ in sodium thiosulphate solution and Cu^{2+} ions form $[CuCl_4]^{2-}$ in concentrated hydrochloric acid.

Ions, such as $[Ag(S_2O_3)_2]^{3-}$ and $[Ag(NH_3)_2]^+$, in which a metal ion is associated with a number of anions or neutral molecules are known as **complex ions**. The anions and molecules co-ordinated to the central cation are called **ligands**. Each ligand contains at least one atom bearing a lone pair of electrons which can be donated to the central cation forming a co-ordinate (dative) bond.

Most ligands can form only one co-ordinate bond with a cation. These ligands, which include H_2O, NH_3 and Cl^-, are said to be **unidentate** because they have only 'one tooth' with which to attach themselves to the central cation in a complex. (The word 'dens' in Latin means tooth.) In some cases, however, a ligand can form two or more co-ordinate bonds to the central metal ion and such ligands are said to be **polydentate**, meaning 'many teeth' (figure 2).

Some ligands such as edta (ethylenediaminetetraacetate) in $[Ag(edta)]^{3-}$ can form as many as six co-ordinate bonds with the central ion. The complex ions formed between polydentate ligands and cations are known as **chelates** or **chelated complexes** from the Greek word 'chelos', meaning 'a crab's claw', because the polydentate ligands form a claw-like grip on the central metal ion.

The intention of this practical is to study the formation of complexes and to determine the relative strength with which different ligands form complex ions.

Each student, or pair of students, will need:

- Eye protection
- 6 test tubes
- 2 teat pipettes
- Access to approximately 0.1 mol dm^{-3} solutions of the following:
- Iron(III) chloride (**irritant solid**) (16.2 g $FeCl_3$ in 1 dm^3 solution)
- Potassium thiocyanate (**harmful solid**) (9.7 g KSCN in 1 dm^3 solution)
- Sodium 2-hydroxybenzoate (salicylate) (16.0 g HOC_6H_4COONa in 1 dm^3 solution)
- Edta (disodium salt) (33.6 g $[CH_2N(CH_2COOH).CH_2COONa]_2$ in 1 dm^3 solution)
- Ammonium ethanedioate (oxalate) (**harmful solid**) (14.2 g $(COONH_4)_2.H_2O$ in 1 dm^3 solution)
- Silver nitrate
- Sodium chloride
- Ammonia
- Potassium bromide
- Potassium iodide
- Sodium thiosulphate

Time required 1 double period

EYE PROTECTION MUST BE WORN

Procedure

CARE Eye protection must be worn for all these experiments.

Experiment 1: Complexes in which Fe^{3+} is the central ion

A Put 10 drops of iron(III) chloride solution in a test tube.

1 What complex ion is present? What is its colour and what ligand does it contain?

B Add potassium thiocyanate solution drop by drop until no further change occurs. (Keep half of the resulting solution for part **E**. Use the other half for part **C**.)

2 What is the colour of the solution now and what ligand is present in the complex ion?

C If the solution from **B** is too deeply coloured, dilute it until the true colour of the complex is evident. Now, add sodium 2-hydroxybenzoate (salicylate) solution drop by drop until there is no further change in colour. Keep the solution for part **D**.

3 What is the colour of the solution now? What ligand is now present in the complex ion?

4 Which ligand, NCS^- or $HOC_6H_4COO^-$, competes more strongly for Fe^{3+} ions during complexing?

D Take 10 drops of the solution from **C** and add a solution of edta drop by drop until there is no further colour change.

5 What colour is the edta–Fe(III) complex?

6 Write the ligands NCS^-, $HOC_6H_4COO^-$, edta and water in order of increasing strength of co-ordination with Fe^{3+} ions.

7 Predict what would happen if edta solution were added to the solution obtained in **B**.

E Add edta solution drop by drop to the solution retained in part **B** until there is no further colour change.

8 Was your prediction in question **7** correct?

Experiment 2: Investigating the relative strength of $C_2O_4^{2-}$ as a ligand with Fe^{3+}

Add ammonium ethanedioate (oxalate) solution drop by drop to 10 drops of iron(III) chloride solution until there is no further colour change.

9 What is the colour of the solution? What ligand is present in the complex ion?

Devise test tube experiments to find the strength of the ethanedioate ion $(C_2O_4^{2-})$ as a ligand relative to NCS^-, $HOC_6H_4COO^-$, edta and H_2O. **After checking with your teacher**, carry out the experiments.

10 Describe the experiments you performed and give the results.

11 Write the five ligands in order of increasing strength.

12 What structural features do the strongest co-ordinating ligands have in common?

Experiment 3: Complexes in which Ag^+ is the central ion

Some ligands react with cations to form precipitates of insoluble solids. Ag^+, for example, reacts with Cl^- to form insoluble $AgCl$. These precipitates can be regarded as neutral complexes. Being uncharged, they are less readily hydrated by polar water molecules than charged complexes and so they are less likely to dissolve in water.

Put ten drops of silver nitrate solution into each of six test tubes. To the first tube add ten drops of sodium chloride solution. To the second tube add ten drops of ammonia solution; to the third ten drops of potassium bromide; to the fourth sodium thiosulphate; to the fifth potassium iodide and to the sixth edta solution.

13 Make a table showing the ligand added to each tube and the formula, name, state and colour of each complex ion.

The relative strengths of the ligands used in the last experiment are:

$$edta > I^- > S_2O_3^{2-} > Br^- > NH_3 > Cl^- > H_2O$$

You are about to perform an experiment in which first a solution of sodium chloride, then one of ammonia, then one of potassium bromide, then sodium thiosulphate, then potassium iodide and finally edta are added in turn to a solution of Ag^+ ions.

14 Use the relative strengths of the ligands to predict what will happen.

Add sodium chloride solution drop by drop to ten drops of silver nitrate solution until no further change occurs. To the resulting solution add ammonia solution dropwise until no further change occurs. Now add potassium bromide dropwise until no further change occurs. Carry on in this fashion with first sodium thiosulphate, then potassium iodide and finally edta solution.

15 Were your predictions in question 14 correct?

Practical 13

Determination of the formulae of complex ions

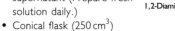
Introduction

Essentially, the determination of the formulae of a complex ion involves measurement of the number of ligands complexing with one metal ion. This can be investigated by several methods, the most important of which are:

a colorimetric methods requiring measurement of the colour intensity of the mixture as the proportion of metal ion to ligand is varied,

b titration methods involving competitive complexing.

The object of this experiment is first to investigate the stoichiometry of the copper(II)/1,2-diaminoethane complex using colorimetry, and then to investigate the stoichiometry of the nickel(II)/edta complex using a complexometric titration.

CARE Eye protection must be worn for experiment 1 and experiment 2.

Experiment 1: Determination of the formula of the copper(II)/1,2-diaminoethane complex by colorimetry

The stoichiometry of a complex ion can be investigated by colorimetry provided there is a significant difference in colour between the simple aqueous ions and the complex. Basic ideas regarding the principles and practice of colorimetry are discussed in the introduction to practical 16. When aqueous Cu^{2+} ions react with 1,2-diaminoethane (H$_2$NCH$_2$CH$_2$NH$_2$), a deeply coloured complex ion is produced. We can write an equation for this reaction as

$$\text{Cu}^{2+}(\text{aq}) + x\text{H}_2\text{NCH}_2\text{CH}_2\text{NH}_2(\text{aq}) \longrightarrow [\text{Cu}(\text{H}_2\text{NCH}_2\text{CH}_2\text{NH}_2)_x]^{2+}(\text{aq})$$

In order to determine the formula of the complex, we must find the value of x. This can be done using the method of continuous variation described below.

Procedure

Take nine test tubes and number them 1 to 9. Using these test tubes, make up mixtures of 0.05 mol dm^{-3} CuSO$_4$ and 0.05 mol dm^{-3} 1,2-diaminoethane with the compositions shown below. Shake each tube to ensure the solutions are thoroughly mixed. Notice that each tube contains a total volume of 12 cm^3.

Test tube number	1	2	3	4	5	6	7	8	9
Vol. of 0.05 mol dm^{-3} CuSO$_4$/cm^3	0.0	2.0	3.0	4.0	6.0	8.0	9.0	10.0	12.0
Vol. of 0.05 mol dm^{-3} 1,2-diaminoethane/cm^3	12.0	10.0	9.0	8.0	6.0	4.0	3.0	2.0	0.0

1 What is the colour of the copper(II)/1,2-diaminoethane complex ion?

2 What is the colour of the filter which would be most suitable for the experiment?

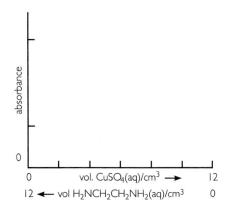

Figure 1

Figure 2
The anion ligand in murexide has the structure shown above.

Follow the usual procedure to obtain zero absorbance (100% transmission) when tube 1, containing only 1,2-diaminoethane solution is placed in the colorimeter. Now measure the absorbance of the other mixtures relative to this zero reading.

3 Plot a graph of absorbance (vertical) against the volume of $0.05 \, mol \, dm^{-3}$ $CuSO_4$ reading from left to right, and, on the same horizontal scale, the volume of $0.05 \, mol \, dm^{-3}$ 1,2-diaminoethane solution reading from right to left (figure 1).

4 What are the volumes of the two solutions which, on mixing, give the maximum colour intensity?

5 In what molar proportions do Cu^{2+} and $H_2NCH_2CH_2NH_2$ react to form the complex?

6 Write an equation for the formation of the complex.

7 Draw the structural formula you would predict for the complex ion and relate this structure to that of $[Cu(NH_3)_4]^{2+}$.

Experiment 2: Determination of the formula of the nickel(II)/edta complex by competitive complexing

Add 5 drops of murexide solution (figure 2) to $5 \, cm^3$ of a $0.1 \, mol \, dm^{-3}$ solution of a nickel(II) salt. Add edta solution to the mixture slowly until no further changes occur.

8 What are the colours of Ni^{2+} ions complexed with **a** water, **b** murexide?

9 Explain the reactions that have occurred in terms of competitive complexing. (Remember that the final colour of the solution is due to the nickel(II)/edta complex and the non-complexed murexide.)

The colour of the nickel(II)/murexide remains as long as there are more than enough Ni^{2+} ions for the edta, because these excess Ni^{2+} ions will form a complex with murexide. As the nickel(II)/murexide complex is removed, the colour of the solution changes and the nickel(II)/edta complex forms. When all the nickel has complexed with edta, the non-complexed murexide appears in the solution.

Consequently, murexide can act as an indicator in nickel(II)/edta titrations.

10 Devise a titration to determine the volume of $0.1 \, mol \, dm^{-3}$ edta which will just react with $20 \, cm^3$ or $25 \, cm^3$ of $0.1 \, mol \, dm^{-3}$ Ni^{2+} salt.

Discuss your suggested method with your teacher before performing a titration. (You will need to add the same proportion of murexide to nickel(II) solution as in the test tube reaction above. Mix the solutions very thoroughly during the titration. Near the end-point, add the edta solution $0.5 \, cm^3$ at a time. Titrate the solution to the same colour that you obtained in the test tube reaction.)

11 How many moles of Ni^{2+} were taken?

12 How many moles of edta reacted with this Ni^{2+}?

13 How many moles of edta react with one mole of Ni^{2+}?

14 What is the formula of the Ni^{2+}/edta complex?

15 Draw a diagram to represent the structure of the Ni^{2+}/edta complex.

Practical 14

Determination of the equilibrium constant for an esterification reaction

Introduction

The practical determination of the equilibrium constant K for a reaction presents some difficulties. To find K for a reaction it is necessary to measure the concentration of reactants and products at equilibrium. Most methods for doing this involve removal of reactant or products, which changes their concentration and shifts the equilibrium. It is therefore ideal to use a method of measuring concentration that does not involve removing any component—colorimetry, for example.

The reaction under consideration here is the esterification of ethanoic acid (acetic acid) by ethanol:

$$CH_3COOH + CH_3CH_2OH \rightleftharpoons CH_3COOCH_2CH_3 + H_2O$$

$$\text{ethanoic acid} \qquad \text{ethanol} \qquad \text{ethyl ethanoate}$$

The reaction is catalysed by H^+ ions. The advantage of studying this particular reaction is that it is kinetically slow, so it is possible to measure the concentration of a reactant by titration (which removes the reactant), without significantly disturbing the equilibrium in the relatively short time it takes to carry out the titration.

Known amounts of acid, alcohol and/or ester are mixed with dilute hydrochloric acid in a stoppered bottle and allowed to reach equilibrium at room temperature. After reaching equilibrium, which takes several days, the mixture is titrated with alkali in order to find the total amount of acid present. After allowing for the presence of the hydrochloric acid catalyst, the amount of ethanoic acid present at equilibrium can be calculated. From this the amounts of the other reagents can be calculated, and hence a value for the equilibrium constant can be found.

Procedure

Preliminary

CARE Eye protection must be worn throughout.
Burettes are set up in the laboratory containing the following:

- ethyl ethanoate (ethyl acetate)
- concentrated ('glacial') ethanoic acid (**CARE Corrosive**)
- approximately $3 \, mol \, dm^{-3}$ HCl
- ethanol
- distilled water

You will be asked to make up one of the mixtures in table 1 (see next page). Get a reagent bottle and make sure it has a well-fitting stopper. Run the liquids into the reagent bottle from the burette, and stopper immediately to prevent evaporation. Shake well, then allow the bottle to stand at room temperature for a week, to allow the mixture to reach equilibrium.

Note that the total volume in each experiment is $10 \, cm^3$.

IRRITANT
Hydrochloric acid

CORROSIVE
Glacial ethanoic acid

HIGHLY FLAMMABLE
Ethanol
Ethyl ethanoate

EYE PROTECTION MUST BE WORN

HARMFUL
Ethanol

After one week

Titrate the whole of the mixture in the bottle with $1.0 \, mol \, dm^{-3}$ sodium hydroxide solution, using phenolphthalein as indicator.

In order to find the exact concentration of the HCl catalyst, titrate $5 \, cm^3$ of the approximately $3 \, mol \, dm^{-3}$ HCl with $1.0 \, mol \, dm^{-3}$ NaOH.

IRRITANT
Sodium hydroxide solution

Table I

Experiment number	HCl/cm³	Water/cm³	Ethyl ethanoate/cm³	Glacial ethanoic acid/cm³	Ethanol /cm³
I	5	0	5	0	0
2	5	I	4	0	0
3	5	2	3	0	0
4	5	3	2	0	0
5	5	0	4	0	I
6	5	0	4	I	0
7	5	0	0	I	4
.8	5	0	0	2	3

Finally, weigh $5 \, cm^3$ of each of the liquids used to make up your mixture (including the HCl).

Finding the equilibrium constant

1 How many moles of ethyl ethanoate were there in your *original* mixture (i.e. before any reaction had occurred)?

2 How many moles of ethanoic acid were there in your original mixture?

3 How many moles of ethanol were there in your original mixture?

4 How many moles of water were there in your original mixture? (Remember to take into account the water present in the dilute HCl. You can find the mass of this by deducting the mass of pure HCl, found by titration, from the mass of $5 \, cm^3$ of $3 \, mol \, dm^{-3}$ HCl.)

5 How many moles of ethanoic acid were there in the mixture *at equilibrium*? (This can be found from the volume of $1.0 \, mol \, dm^{-3}$ NaOH needed to titrate the mixture, after subtracting the volume of NaOH needed to titrate $5 \, cm^3$ of approximately $3 \, mol \, dm^{-3}$ HCl.)

6 How many moles of ethanol were there in the mixture *at equilibrium*? (This can be found from your answer to question **5**, bearing in mind the number of moles of ethanol present in the initial mixture, and using the equation $CH_3COOH + CH_3CH_2OH \rightleftharpoons CH_3COOCH_2CH_3 + H_2O$.)

7 How many moles of ethyl ethanoate were there in the mixture at equilibrium?

8 How many moles of water were there in the mixture at equilibrium?

9 Work out the *concentrations* of water, ethyl ethanoate, ethanol and ethanoic acid in the mixture at equilibrium, using your answers to questions **5–8** and the fact that the total volume of the reaction mixture was $10 \, cm^3$.

10 What is the equilibrium constant for this reaction?

11 Compare your result with those obtained by other members of the group who started with different mixtures. Does the value of the equilibrium constant depend on the starting concentration of the reactants?

12 ΔH for this reaction is $+17.5 \, kJ \, mol^{-1}$. Would you expect the value of K_c to be greater or smaller at 80°C than at room temperature?

13 The yield of ester formed in the reaction between ethanoic acid and ethanol is considerably increased if concentrated sulphuric acid is added to the reactants. Suggest a reason for this.

INVESTIGATION

See Investigation 14

Practical 15

Determination of the order of a reaction

REQUIREMENTS

Each pair of students will need:

- Eye protection
- Burette and stand
- Beaker ($1\,dm^3$)
- Measuring cylinder ($500\,cm^3$)
- Measuring cylinder (25 or $50\,cm^3$)
- Measuring cylinder ($10\,cm^3$)
- Stirring rod
- Pipette ($10\,cm^3$) and safety filler
- Clock or watch with seconds hand
- Graph paper
- Small funnel
- 2 small beakers
- Approximately $0.1\,mol\,dm^{-3}$ H_2O_2 ($30\,cm^3$)
- $0.05\,mol\,dm^{-3}$ $Na_2S_2O_3$ ($100\,cm^3$)
- $1.0\,mol\,dm^{-3}$ H_2SO_4 ($75\,cm^3$)
- $1.0\,mol\,dm^{-3}$ KI ($45\,cm^3$)
- Starch solution ($2\,cm^3$)

Time required 1 double period

Introduction

Consider the reaction

$$x\text{A} + y\text{B} \longrightarrow \text{products}$$

Experiments show that the reaction rate can be related to the concentrations of individual reactants by an equation of the form,

$$\text{Rate} = k[\text{A}]^m[\text{B}]^n$$

This expression is known as the **rate equation** or **rate law** for the reaction under consideration. m and n are constants whose values are usually 0, 1 or 2, and k is the **rate constant** for the reaction.

The index m is known as **the order of the reaction with respect to A**, and n is the order of the reaction with respect to B. The **overall order** of the reaction is $(m + n)$.

The reaction we shall be studying involves hydrogen peroxide and iodide ions in acid solution.

$$H_2O_2(aq) + 2I^-(aq) + 2H^+(aq) \longrightarrow 2H_2O(l) + I_2(aq)$$

The rate equation for this reaction can be written as

$$\text{Rate} = k[H_2O_2]^\alpha[I^-]^\beta[H^+]^\gamma$$

The order of the reaction with respect to one reactant may be investigated by having the other reactants present in large excess so that their concentrations remain effectively constant during the reaction. For example, in this experiment, the order of the reaction with respect to H_2O_2 is investigated by using very much larger concentrations of I^- and H^+.

Under these circumstances the reaction rate can be expressed as:

$$\text{Rate} = k'[H_2O_2]^\alpha,$$

where k' is a modified rate constant which includes the constant concentrations of I^- and H^+.

Principle

The object of this experiment is to determine the order with respect to H_2O_2 for the reaction discussed above.

Hydrogen peroxide is allowed to react with an acidified solution of potassium iodide in the presence of small quantities of starch and sodium thiosulphate solutions.

$$H_2O_2(aq) + 2I^-(aq) + 2H^+(aq) \longrightarrow 2H_2O(l) + I_2(aq)$$

As soon as the iodine is produced, it reacts with thiosulphate and is converted back to iodide ions:

$$I_2(aq) + 2S_2O_3^{2-}(aq) \longrightarrow 2I^-(aq) + S_4O_6^{2-}(aq)$$

When the iodine produced in the reaction is in excess of the sodium thiosulphate, a blue colour suddenly appears as the iodine reacts with starch.

From the amount of $S_2O_3^{2-}$ added, we can calculate the amount of I_2 produced by the time the blue colour appears and hence the amount of H_2O_2 used up.

Knowing the original amount of H_2O_2, we can calculate $[H_2O_2]$ at the time the blue colour appears. The values of $[H_2O_2]$ at different times can then be used to find the order of reaction with respect to H_2O_2.

Procedure

EYE PROTECTION MUST BE WORN

IRRITANT
Dilute sulphuric acid

CARE Eye protection must be worn.
Fill a burette with $0.05\,\text{mol}\,\text{dm}^{-3}$ $Na_2S_2O_3(aq)$.

Put $450\,\text{cm}^3$ of distilled water in a $1\,\text{dm}^3$ beaker and add $25\,\text{cm}^3$ of $1.0\,\text{mol}\,\text{dm}^{-3}$ H_2SO_4, $1\,\text{cm}^3$ of starch solution and $15\,\text{cm}^3$ of $1.0\,\text{mol}\,\text{dm}^{-3}$ KI. Finally, add $2\,\text{cm}^3$ of $0.05\,\text{mol}\,\text{dm}^{-3}$ $S_2O_3^{2-}(aq)$ from the burette. Now, start the reaction by rapidly adding $10\,\text{cm}^3$ of approximately $0.1\,\text{mol}\,\text{dm}^{-3}$ H_2O_2 from a pipette **using a safety filler**. Stir during this addition. (Start timing when half of the H_2O_2 has been added.)

When the I_2 produced in the reaction is in excess of the added $S_2O_3^{2-}$, a blue colour will suddenly appear. Quickly, note the time, add a further $2\,\text{cm}^3$ of $S_2O_3^{2-}(aq)$ and the blue colour will disappear.

Note the time again when the blue colour reappears and add another $2\,\text{cm}^3$ of $S_2O_3^{2-}(aq)$. Continue in this manner until 8–10 readings have been obtained.

Finally, determine the exact concentration of the H_2O_2 as follows. Pipette $10\,\text{cm}^3$ of approximately $0.1\,\text{mol}\,\text{dm}^{-3}$ H_2O_2 into a conical flask **using a safety filler**. Then, add $25\,\text{cm}^3$ of $1.0\,\text{mol}\,\text{dm}^{-3}$ H_2SO_4 and $15\,\text{cm}^3$ $1.0\,\text{mol}\,\text{dm}^{-3}$ KI and titrate this mixture against the $0.05\,\text{mol}\,\text{dm}^{-3}$ $S_2O_3^{2-}(aq)$ using starch as indicator.

1 Why must all other reactants (e.g. KI and H_2SO_4) be in large excess compared with the reactant for which the order is being determined?

2 Why does the concentration of I^- remain constant throughout the whole of the rate study experiment? (**Hint** Look closely at the equations for the reactions involved.)

3 Why does the time interval between appearances of the blue colour become longer?

4 Why is it important to stir during the addition of the H_2O_2?

5 If the H_2O_2 solution is exactly $0.1\,\text{mol}\,\text{dm}^{-3}$ and the $S_2O_3^{2-}$ solution is exactly $0.05\,\text{mol}\,\text{dm}^{-3}$ then:

$10\,\text{cm}^3$ of $0.1\,\text{mol}\,\text{dm}^{-3}$ H_2O_2 will just react with $40\,\text{cm}^3$ of $0.05\,\text{mol}\,\text{dm}^{-3}$ $S_2O_3^{2-}$ during titration. Explain why this is.

6 From the amount of $S_2O_3^{2-}$ added, we can calculate the amount of I_2 produced by the time the blue colour appears and hence the amount of H_2O_2 used up. Knowing the original amount of H_2O_2, we can now calculate the concentration of H_2O_2 at different times.

The concentration of H_2O_2 is most conveniently computed in terms of the volume of $0.05\,\text{mol}\,\text{dm}^{-3}$ $Na_2S_2O_3$ added.

For example, suppose the H_2O_2 was exactly $0.1\,\text{mol}\,\text{dm}^{-3}$. Its initial concentration would then be equivalent to $40\,\text{cm}^3$ of $0.05\,\text{mol}\,\text{dm}^{-3}$ $S_2O_3^{2-}$. Suppose the blue colour first appeared after x seconds, and appeared a second time after y seconds. We can then say:

At $t = 0\,\text{s}$, $40\,\text{cm}^3$ $0.05\,\text{mol}\,\text{dm}^{-3}$ $S_2O_3^{2-}(aq) \propto [H_2O_2]$;
at $t = x\,\text{s}$, when blue colour first appears,

$$(40 - 2) = 38\,\text{cm}^3\ 0.05\,\text{mol}\,\text{dm}^{-3}\ S_2O_3^{2-}(aq) \propto [H_2O_2];$$

at $t = y$ s, when blue colour appears a second time,

$$(40 - 4) = 36 \, \text{cm}^3 \, 0.05 \, \text{mol dm}^{-3} \, S_2O_3^{2-}(\text{aq}) \propto [H_2O_2]; \text{ etc,}$$

$$\Rightarrow \text{At time, } t = 0 \, \text{s}, \ [H_2O_2] \propto 40;$$

$$\text{at time, } t = x \, \text{s}, \ [H_2O_2] \propto 38;$$

$$\text{at time, } t = y \, \text{s}, \ [H_2O_2] \propto 36; \text{ etc.}$$

Record your results in a table similar to table 1. Remember to use your own value for the volume of $S_2O_3^{2-}$ needed to titrate $10 \, \text{cm}^3$ of the approximately $0.1 \, \text{mol dm}^{-3} \, H_2O_2$. This is unlikely to be exactly $40 \, \text{cm}^3$.

Table I

Vol. of 0.05 mol dm^{-3} $S_2O_3^{2-}$ added/cm^3	Vol. of 0.05 mol dm^{-3} $S_2O_3^{2-} \propto [H_2O_2]$/cm^3	Time at which blue colour appears/s
0	40	0
2	38	x
4	36	y

7 If the order of the reaction with respect to reagent X is zero, the corresponding rate equation is

$$\text{Rate} = k[X]^0$$

The **integrated** rate equation for this zero order reaction is

$$[X] = -kt + [X]_0 \qquad \qquad \ldots (1)$$

where $[X]$ is the concentration of substance X at time t; $[X]_0$ is the original concentration of X at time 0 and k is the rate constant for the reaction.
Write similar integrated rate equations relating the concentration of reactant (say $[X]$) and time (t) for first and second order reactions.

8 Investigate whether the reaction is zero order, first order or second order with respect to H_2O_2, by plotting your results for this experiment on suitable graphs. For example, in order to test whether the reaction is zero order, plot $[H_2O_2]$ against t. (See equation (1).) If this gives a straight line, it suggests the reaction is zero order.

Practical 16

Using colorimetry to find the order of the reaction between bromine and methanoic acid

REQUIREMENTS

Each pair of students will need:
- Eye protection
- 0.1 mol dm^{-3} bromine (16 g (5 cm^3) Br$_2$ in 1 dm^3 of solution (25 cm^3))
- 1.0 mol dm^{-3} methanoic acid (46 g (37.7 cm^3) HCOOH in 1 dm^3 of solution (25 cm^3))

CARE Both methanoic acid and bromine are corrosive, fuming liquids capable of causing serious burns. Their solutions should be prepared in a fume cupboard, and protective gloves should be worn.

(The concentrations of these two solutions may need modification with certain colorimeters.)
- Colorimeter with blue, green or turquoise filter
- Distilled water (10 cm^3)
- 2 measuring cylinders (25 or 50 cm^3)
- 1 boiling tube
- 2 matched thin-walled (soda) test tubes for use with the colorimeter
- Stop clock or watch reading in seconds

Time required 1 double period

Introduction

In this practical, the technique of colorimetry is introduced and then used to investigate the reaction between bromine and methanoic acid. Colorimetry can be employed to determine the concentration of any coloured substance. It is particularly useful in the study of reaction rates, where the concentration of a coloured species is constantly changing.

In a colorimeter, a narrow beam of light passes through the solution under test towards a sensitive photocell (figure 1). In most colorimeters, it is possible to select the most appropriate colour and wavelength of light by choosing a particular filter or by adjusting a diffraction grating. The current generated in the photocell is, of course, dependent on the intensity of light transmitted by the solution which in turn depends upon the concentration of coloured solution under test. Thus, the current generated in the photocell will be greatest when the light transmitted by the coloured solution is greatest, i.e. when the coloured solution is least concentrated. Normally, however, the meter is not calibrated to show the light transmitted but the **absorbance**, because this is proportional to the concentration of the coloured solution.

I.e. Absorbance (optical density) ∝ concentration of coloured species.

In the experiment which follows, the coloured species is bromine, so absorbance ∝ [Br$_2$].

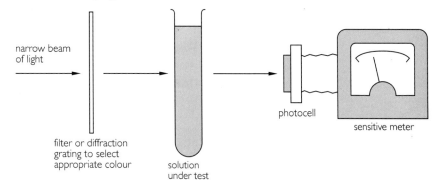

narrow beam of light

filter or diffraction grating to select appropriate colour

solution under test

photocell

sensitive meter

Figure 1
A simplified diagram of a colorimeter.

Principle

The reaction under investigation is

$$Br_2(aq) + HCOOH(aq) \longrightarrow 2Br^-(aq) + 2H^+(aq) + CO_2(g).$$

By using a concentration of methanoic acid which is ten times larger than that of bromine, it is possible to assume that the concentration of methanoic acid is constant throughout the experiment and to see how the concentration of bromine affects the reaction rate. If the reaction is zero order,

$$\frac{-d[Br_2]}{dt} = k_0,$$

where $-d[Br_2]/dt$ represents the reaction rate in terms of the rate of change of concentration of bromine and k_0 is the rate constant for a zero order reaction. Integrating this equation gives:

$$-[Br_2] = k_0 t + \text{constant} \qquad \dots (1)$$

Thus a graph of $[Br_2]$ (or absorbance) against t (time) should give a straight line.

If the reaction is first order with respect to bromine,

$$\frac{-d[Br_2]}{dt} = k_1[Br_2]$$

where k_1 is the rate constant for a first order reaction. Integration of this equation gives

$$-\ln[Br_2] = k_1 t + \text{constant}$$

or $\qquad\qquad\qquad\qquad\qquad\qquad\qquad\qquad\qquad\qquad\qquad\qquad \dots(2)$

$$-\lg[Br_2] = \frac{k_1 t}{2.3} + \text{constant}$$

Thus, a graph of $\lg[Br_2]$ (or lg absorbance) against t (time) should give a straight line.

If the reaction is second order with respect to bromine,

$$\frac{-d[Br_2]}{dt} = k_2[Br_2]^2$$

where k_2 is the rate constant for a second order reaction. Integration of this equation gives:

$$\frac{1}{[Br_2]} = k_2 t + \text{constant} \qquad \dots (3)$$

Thus a graph of $1/[Br_2]$ (or the reciprocal of the absorbance) against t (time) should give a straight line.

By plotting three graphs, one for absorbance against time, one for lg(absorbance) against time and a third for the reciprocal of absorbance against time, we can determine the order of reaction with respect to bromine.

Procedure

EYE PROTECTION
MUST BE WORN

HARMFUL
Bromine solution

CARE Eye protection must be worn.
Switch the sensitivity controls of the colorimeter to a minimum, insert a blue or green filter, switch on and allow five minutes for the instrument to warm up.

Insert a thin-walled test tube containing water into the colorimeter, cover it with a cap and adjust the sensitivity (using the higher sensitivity controls) to give zero absorbance (i.e. 100% transmission). Now, mix $10\,cm^3$ of $1.0\,mol\,dm^{-3}$ methanoic acid with an equal volume of $0.1\,mol\,dm^{-3}$ bromine in a boiling tube and start the stop watch. Shake the mixture gently, transfer some of it to a colorimeter tube and read the absorbance on the colorimeter after 15 seconds, 30 seconds, 45 seconds, 60 seconds, etc. Nine or ten readings should be sufficient.

1 What are the advantages of colorimetry over titrimetric analysis in rate experiments such as this?

2 Why is it necessary to use carefully matched tubes in the colorimeter?

3 Why is a blue or green filter chosen in this experiment? What general principles should be used in choosing a filter for a colorimetric investigation?

4 Tabulate your results. The columns of your table should show time, absorbance, lg(absorbance) and reciprocal of absorbance.

5 Using the same axes (but with different vertical scales), plot graphs of

    a absorbance against time.

    b lg(absorbance) against time.

    c reciprocal of absorbance against time.

6 What is the order of reaction with respect to bromine?

7 Why is the graph not absolutely straight even when there are no experimental errors? (**Hint** What assumption has been made which is not wholly true?)

8 Using the appropriate rate equation, obtain a value for the rate constant for the reaction and state its units.

Practical 17

Determination of the activation energy for the reaction between bromide and bromate(V) ions

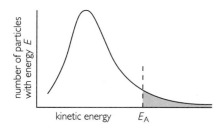

Figure 1

Introduction

During a reaction, bonds are first broken, and others are then formed. Energy is required to break certain bonds and start this process, whether the overall reaction is exothermic or endothermic. Particles will not always react when they collide because they may not possess sufficient energy for the appropriate bonds to break.

A reaction will only occur if the colliding particles possess more than a certain minimum quantity of energy known as the **activation energy, E_A**.

During the 1930's, Zartmann, Ko and others showed that the distribution of kinetic energies amongst the particles of a liquid or gas was similar to that shown in figure 1.

Essentially, the curve is a histogram showing the number of particles within each small range of kinetic energy, and the area beneath the curve is proportional to the total number of particles in that energy range.

Consequently, the number of particles capable of reacting, with energy greater than the activation energy, E_A, is proportional to the shaded area beneath the curve at energies above E_A. Hence the *fraction* of particles with energy greater than E_A is given by the ratio:

$$\frac{\text{(shaded area beneath curve)}}{\text{(total area beneath curve)}}.$$

Using the kinetic theory and probability theory, Maxwell and Boltzmann showed that the fraction of molecules with energy greater than E_A was given by $e^{-E_A/RT}$ where R is the gas constant, T is the absolute temperature and e is the exponential function.

This suggests that at a given temperature:

$$\text{Reaction rate} \propto e^{-E_A/RT}$$

But as k, the rate constant for a reaction, is a measure of the reaction rate, we can write

$$k \propto e^{-E_A/RT}$$

$$\Rightarrow k = Ae^{-E_A/RT}$$

This last expression is called the **Arrhenius equation**, because it was first predicted by the Swedish chemist, Svante Arrhenius in 1889.

Principle

The object of this experiment is to obtain E_A for the reaction between Br^- and BrO_3^- in acid solution.

$$5Br^-(aq) + BrO_3^-(aq) + 6H^+(aq) \longrightarrow 3Br_2(aq) + 3H_2O(l)$$

The time, t, required to the reaction to proceed to a given extent at different temperatures is found by adding a fixed amount of phenol and a small amount of methyl red indicator to the reaction mixture.

The bromine produced during the reaction reacts very rapidly with phenol (forming tribromophenol). Once all the phenol is consumed, any further bromine bleaches the indicator immediately.

Now, as $k \propto$ reaction rate $= \dfrac{\text{concentration change}}{\text{time}}$

and as the concentration change in this experiment is constant,

$$k \propto \frac{1}{\text{time for methyl red to be bleached}}$$

$$\therefore k = \frac{c}{\text{time for methyl red to be bleached}} = \frac{c}{t}$$

where c is a constant and t is the time taken to bleach the methyl red. Hence, $c/t = Ae^{-E_A/RT}$ and if we take logs to base e:

$$\ln\left(\frac{c}{t}\right) = \ln A + \ln e^{-E_A/RT}.$$

$$\Rightarrow \ln c - \ln t = \ln A - \frac{E_A}{RT}$$

$$\Rightarrow \ln t = \ln c - \ln A + \frac{E_A}{RT}$$

$\ln c$ and $\ln A$ are constants, so a graph of $\ln t$ against $1/T$ has a gradient of E_A/R.

Procedure

EYE PROTECTION
MUST BE WORN

IRRITANT
Dilute sulphuric acid

CARE Eye protection must be worn.

Work in pairs.

Using a measuring cylinder, put $10\,\text{cm}^3$ of $0.01\,\text{mol}\,\text{dm}^{-3}$ phenol and $10\,\text{cm}^3$ of the bromide/bromate(V) solution into a boiling tube, and then add 4 drops of methyl red indicator. In a second boiling tube, put $5\,\text{cm}^3$ of $0.5\,\text{mol}\,\text{dm}^{-3}$ H_2SO_4.

Fill a $1\,\text{dm}^3$ beaker with water, warm to about $75°C$ and adjust the heating to keep the temperature of the water steady.

Immerse the two boiling tubes in the water and when their contents reach the water temperature ($\pm1°C$), mix the contents of the tubes and time the reaction until the colour of the methyl red disappears.

Repeat the experiment at about $65°C$, $55°C$, $45°C$, $35°C$, $25°C$ and $15°C$.

1 Arrange your results in a table, as shown

Temperature/°C	Temperature/K	$(1/T)/K^{-1}$	Time taken to bleach methyl red, t/s	ln t

2 Why does the reaction not start until the contents of the boiling tubes are mixed?

3 Write an equation for the reaction between bromine and phenol.

4 What function does the methyl red play in the experiment? (**Hint** It is not acting as an indicator in the accepted sense.)

5 Why is it unsatisfactory to measure the reaction rate at temperatures above $75°C$?

6 Plot a graph of $\ln t$ (vertically) against $1/T$ (horizontally).

7 Measure the gradient of this graph and obtain the value of E_A. ($R = 8.3\,\mathrm{J\,K^{-1}\,mol^{-1}}$)

8 Is the value of E_A positive or negative? What does this signify?

9 How is E_A related to the enthalpy change for the forward reaction? Draw a simple energy diagram to make your answer clear.

10 What effect does E_A have on the equilibrium constant for the Br^-/BrO_3^- reaction?

Practical 18
Periodicity—a practical study of the third period

REQUIREMENTS

- Eye protection
- Samples of elements from period 3
  Because of the hazardous nature of sodium, phosphorus and chlorine, it is best for the teacher to demonstrate these elements. It is important to avoid confusion between phosphorus (stored under water) and sodium (stored under oil), and best not to have both in the laboratory at the same time.
- Simple apparatus to test electrical conductivity
- 1 rack + 4 test tubes
- Full-range indicator paper
- Samples of the following oxides:
  Na_2O (or $NaOH$), MgO, Al_2O_3, SiO_2, P_2O_5
- Access to SO_2 cylinder
- Samples of the following chlorides:
  $NaCl$, $MgCl_2$, $AlCl_3$, PCl_3, SCl_2 (or S_2Cl_2)
- Bunsen burner

Time required 2 double periods

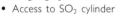

EYE PROTECTION
MUST BE WORN

CORROSIVE
Sodium

FLAMMABLE
Sodium
Magnesium
Phosphorus

TOXIC
Chlorine
White phosphorus

Introduction

The periodic table provides one of the most important unifying patterns to the study of chemistry. The intention of this practical is to study some of the trends in properties across the third period of the periodic table.

A Periodicity in the properties of elements

The properties of the elements show a repeating pattern with increasing atomic number. The most obvious pattern is the steady change from metals on the left to non-metals on the right of each period and then back to metals again.

Procedure

CARE Eye protection must be worn throughout this practical.
Examine samples of the elements in period 3 (Na to Ar) and test the electrical conductivity of those elements for which the results are not given in table 1.

1 Copy and complete table 1. You will have to consult a data book, or section 4.8 in *Chemistry in Context*, Fourth Edition, for boiling point values.

Table 1
The elements of period 3

	Na	Mg	Al	Si	P	S	Cl	Ar
Atomic number								
Physical state and appearance								
Boiling point/°C								
Conductivity at room temperature	good				poor		poor	poor
Structure (giant metallic, giant molecular or simple molecular)								
Type of element (metal, non-metal or metalloid)								

2 How do the boiling points of elements vary across the period from sodium to argon? How are the boiling points related to the structure of the elements?

3 Describe the changes in structure and type of the elements across period 3.

B Periodicity in the properties of oxides

You should know quite a lot about the properties of these compounds already.

4 Copy out table 2, and complete the first three rows.

CARE Avoid skin contact when using Na₂O and P₂O₅.

Examine the solubility of each oxide in water. Add a **very small** measure of each solid to about $3\,cm^3$ of distilled water and shake thoroughly. (In the case of sulphur dioxide, bubble the gas through $3\,cm^3$ of water in a **fume cupboard** for a few seconds.)

If Na₂O is not available, use sodium hydroxide (NaOH) (**CARE Corrosive. Wear protective gloves.**) Some oxides will dissolve easily, but others will not dissolve at all. Test the pH of the solution obtained from each oxide using full-range indicator paper and record your results in table 2.

EYE PROTECTION MUST BE WORN   USE A FUME CUPBOARD

CORROSIVE
Sodium oxide
Phosphorus(V) oxide

TOXIC
Sulphur dioxide

WEAR PROTECTIVE GLOVES

CORROSIVE
Sodium hydroxide

Table 2
Properties of the oxides in period 3

Oxide formula	Na₂O	MgO	Al₂O₃	SiO₂	P₂O₅	SO₂	Cl₂O
State at room temp.							(g)
Appearance							yellow-red gas
Volatility							high
Conductivity of molten oxide	good	good	good	poor	poor	poor	poor
Solubility in water							dissolves readily
pH of solution in water							2
Classification of oxide (acidic, basic or amphoteric)							acidic
Structure of oxide (simple molecular, giant molecular, giant ionic)							simple molecular

5 Which of the oxides of period 3 elements

    a form acidic solutions with water?

    b form alkaline solutions with water?

    c are insoluble in water?

6 Write equations for the reactions of the soluble oxides with water.

If an oxide is insoluble in water, its reactions with acids and alkalis can be used to decide its acid–base character. If it dissolves in acid, it must have reacted with it and can therefore be classified as basic. If the oxide dissolves in alkali, it can be described as acidic. If the insoluble oxide dissolves in both acids and alkalis, it is both basic and acidic. The adjective 'amphoteric' (from a Greek word meaning 'both') is used to describe these oxides.

Examine the solubility of the insoluble oxides in dilute hydrochloric acid and then in dilute sodium hydroxide solution. Remember to use **very small** measures of solid.

7 Write equations for the reactions of the insoluble oxides with hydrochloric acid and sodium hydroxide where appropriate.

8 Complete the last two lines in table 2.

CORROSIVE
Sodium hydroxide solution

9 Describe the following trends in properties of the oxides across period 3:

    a their state;

    b their character (acidic/amphoteric/basic);

    c their structure.

C Periodicity in the properties of chlorides

Examine samples of the chlorides of period 3 elements.

10 Copy out table 3 and complete the first two rows. (You will **not** be expected to test silicon tetrachloride yourself; the results for this are already inserted.)

EYE PROTECTION MUST BE WORN

CORROSIVE
Aluminium chloride
Phosphorus chlorides
Sulphur chlorides

USE A FUME CUPBOARD

CARE Take great care with the chlorides of aluminium, phosphorus and sulphur. Work in a fume cupboard and wear eye protection.

Working in a fume cupboard, warm separate **small** samples of the chlorides gently with a bunsen.

    Investigate the relative volatility of the chlorides and put your results in table 3.

    Investigate the effect of water on each chloride by adding a **small** quantity to about $3\,cm^3$ of distilled water in a test tube.

CARE Eye protection is essential. The reactions of some of the chlorides with water are very vigorous.

Test the pH of the mixture obtained using full-range indicator paper, then complete table 3.

Table 3
Properties of the chlorides in period 3

Element	Na	Mg	Al	Si	P	S
Formula of chloride				$SiCl_4$		
Appearance and state of chloride				colourless liquid		
Volatility of chloride				high		
Action of water on chloride				very vigorous reaction, HCl fumes evolved		
pH of solution of chloride in water				3		
Structure of chloride				simple molecular		

11 Explain, with equations, the action of sodium chloride, aluminium chloride and phosphorus chloride with water.

12 Describe the trends across period 3 in:

    a the formula of the chlorides;

    b the state of the chlorides;

    c the pH of the aqueous chloride solutions;

    d the structure of the chlorides.

Practical 19
A practical study of some Group II elements

Each student, or pair of students, will require:
- Eye protection
- Hard-glass test tubes (8)
- Stopper to fit tubes
- Test tube holders
- Angled glass bend with bung to fit test tube
- Beaker (400 cm^3)
- Funnel
- Universal indicator solution
- Indicator paper
- Filter paper
- Splints
- Magnesium ribbon
- Magnesium powder
- Calcium, granules or turnings
- Barium metal, cut into small pieces (The teacher may prefer to demonstrate the reaction of barium with water.)
- Magnesium oxide
- Calcium hydroxide
- Barium hydroxide
- Hydrated magnesium chloride
- Hydrated calcium chloride
- Hydrated barium chloride
- Magnesium carbonate
- Calcium carbonate
- Barium carbonate
- Lime water

Approximately 0.1 mol dm^{-3} solutions of:
- Mg^{2+} (25 g Mg(NO$_3$)$_2$.6H$_2$O or 20 g MgCl$_2$.6H$_2$O per dm^3)
- Ca^{2+} (25 g Ca(NO$_3$)$_2$.4H$_2$O or 10 g anhydrous CaCl$_2$ per dm^3)
- Ba^{2+} (25 g Ba(NO$_3$)$_2$ or 25 g BaCl$_2$.2H$_2$O per dm^3)

Approximately 1.0 mol dm^{-3} solutions of:
- OH$^-$ (40 g NaOH per dm^3)
- CO$_3^{2-}$ (100 g anhydrous Na$_2$CO$_3$ per dm^3)
- SO$_4^{2-}$ (300 g Na$_2$SO$_4$.10H$_2$O per dm^3) 250 cm^3 of each of these six solutions is enough.

Time required 1–2 double periods

Introduction

The *s*-block of the periodic table contains the most reactive and, in chemical terms, the most typically metallic elements. All the elements in Group I are highly reactive, but those in Group II are slightly less so and show a rather more obvious trend in reactivity. In this practical you will study some of the properties of the elements of Group II and their compounds. The members of the group are shown in table 1.

Table 1

The elements of Group II	
Beryllium	Be
Magnesium	Mg
Calcium	Ca
Strontium	Sr
Barium	Ba
Radium	Ra

We will concentrate on the three elements magnesium, calcium and barium. Beryllium will not be studied because its compounds are extremely toxic and very expensive.

Some physical data concerning the elements of Group II are given in table 2.

1 What type of ion is formed by Group II elements when they react?

2 Why do ionisation energies decrease as you go down Group II?

3 Why do atomic radii increase as you go down Group II?

4 Which of the various sets of data in table 2 gives the most accurate indication of the likely reactivity trend within the group?

Try to use the data in table 2 when interpreting the results of your experimental work.

Table 2
Some properties of the Group II elements

Element	Be	Mg	Ca	Sr	Ba
Electron structure	(He)2s^2	(Ne)3s^2	(Ar)4s^2	(Kr)5s^2	(Xe)6s^2
First ionisation energy/kJ mol^{-1}	900	740	590	550	500
Second ionisation energy/kJ mol^{-1}	1800	1450	1150	1060	970
Third ionisation energy/kJ mol^{-1}	14800	7700	4900	4200	—
Atomic radius (metallic radius)/nm	0.11	0.16	0.20	0.21	0.22
Ionic radius (M^{2+})/nm	0.030	0.065	0.094	0.110	0.134
Hydration energy (M^{2+})/kJ mol^{-1}	—	−1891	−1561	−1414	−1273
Standard electrode potential, $E^{\ominus}$ (M^{2+}(aq)|M(s))/V	−1.85	−2.37	−2.87	−2.89	−2.91

Procedure

EYE PROTECTION
MUST BE WORN

FLAMMABLE IRRITANT HARMFUL
Calcium Calcium Barium
compounds

Magnesium

CARE Eye protection must be worn throughout this practical. Barium and its compounds are poisonous. Handle with care and wash your hands after the practical.

Experiment 1: Reaction of the elements with water

Your teacher may prefer to demonstrate the reaction of barium with water.

Put a very small piece of calcium metal into a large beaker of cold water. Observe the reaction and identify the products. Repeat, using a small piece of clean magnesium ribbon and then a small piece of barium metal.

5 Write equations for any reactions which occur.

6 How do the metals differ in the vigour with which they react with water?

7 In all their reactions the Group II metals behave as reducing agents. What is being reduced in this reaction?

8 Explain the reactivity trend among the three metals in this experiment, using some of the data in table 2.

9 What other factor, not listed in the table, may affect the relative reactivity of the metals with water?

The reaction of magnesium with water was probably very slow. You can investigate this reaction further by setting up the experiment shown in figure 1. Leave the experiment for half an hour or so, then test the products.

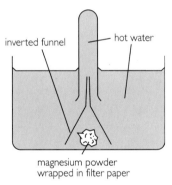

Figure 1
Investigation of the reaction of magnesium with water.

Experiment 2: Acid–base character

HARMFUL EYE PROTECTION
Barium MUST BE WORN
hydroxide

Place a very small quantity (about 0.01 g) of magnesium oxide, calcium hydroxide and barium hydroxide in three separate test tubes. Add 10 cm^3 distilled water to each tube, stopper the tube and shake. Add 2 drops of universal indicator solution to each tube and mix. Record the pH values indicated for the three tubes.

10 How does the acid–base character of the hydroxides vary within the group?

11 Write a general ionic equation to represent the equilibrium between the undissolved solid hydroxide and its aqueous ions.

12 Why is it valid to use magnesium oxide instead of magnesium hydroxide in this experiment?

13 What is 'milk of magnesia' and what is it used for?

14 Look at the values for ionic radius in table 2. Which Group II ion will have the strongest attraction for OH$^-$ ions? What effect will this have on the basic strength of its hydroxide?

Experiment 3: Hydrolysis of the chlorides

Ionic chlorides dissolve in water forming simple hydrated ions. Many covalent and partly covalent chlorides, however, are hydrolysed, giving hydrogen chloride and the oxide or hydroxide. For example, aluminium chloride reacts vigorously with water as follows:

$$AlCl_3 + 3H_2O \longrightarrow Al(OH)_3 + 3HCl$$

The extent of hydrolysis of the Group II chlorides can be estimated by heating the hydrated chloride and testing for hydrogen chloride gas.

Working in a fume cupboard, strongly heat about 1 cm depth of the hydrated chlorides of magnesium, calcium and barium in separate, dry, hard-glass test tubes. Test for the evolution of hydrogen chloride (**CARE toxic**).

15 Are any of the chlorides hydrolysed? Is there a trend in the tendency towards hydrolysis?

16 Which of the chlorides shows the greatest covalent character?
Explain this tendency towards covalency in terms of some of the data in table 2.

TOXIC
Hydrogen chloride

EYE PROTECTION
MUST BE WORN

USE A FUME
CUPBOARD

HARMFUL
Hydrated
barium chloride

IRRITANT
Hydrated
calcium chloride

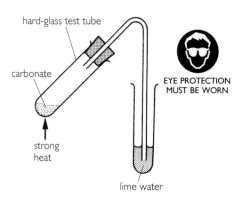

hard-glass test tube

carbonate

strong
heat

lime water

EYE PROTECTION
MUST BE WORN

Figure 2
Investigation of the thermal stability of carbonates.

Experiment 4: Thermal stability of the carbonates

Strongly heat about 1 cm depth of each of the dry carbonates of magnesium, calcium and barium separately in the apparatus shown in figure 2. Continue heating strongly for several minutes. Note how rapidly gas is evolved, and the extent to which the lime water becomes milky. Remember to remove the tube from the lime water as soon as heating is stopped.

17 Write equations for any reactions which occur.

18 What trend do you detect in the thermal stability of the carbonates of the elements of Group II?

Experiment 5: Solubility of some compounds of Group II elements

EYE PROTECTION
MUST BE WORN

IRRITANT
Solution of
hydroxide ions

To investigate the solubility of Group II compounds, solutions containing the appropriate anions and cations are mixed. If the compound is insoluble, a precipitate will form.

Put 2 cm³ of a 0.1 mol dm⁻³ solution of each of the Group II cations under investigation (Mg^{2+}, Ca^{2+}, Ba^{2+}) in separate test tubes. Add an equal volume of a 1.0 mol dm⁻³ solution of hydroxide ions, and mix. Remember, do **not** put your thumb over the tube when mixing. Note whether a precipitate is formed, and if so, how dense it is. Repeat the experiment twice, using first a 1.0 mol dm⁻³ solution of sulphate ions and then a 1.0 mol dm⁻³ solution of carbonate ions, instead of the hydroxide ions. Tabulate your results.

19 What trends do you notice in the solubility of

a hydroxides,

b sulphates,

c carbonates?

If you have time, you could extend this experiment by investigating the solubility of some other compounds—say chromates and oxalates. You might then be able to formulate a more general rule concerning solubility trends within the group.

20 Using the results and conclusions you have derived from this practical, predict the following properties of **a** beryllium, **b** strontium, and their compounds:

   i reaction with water

   ii acid–base character of the hydroxide

   iii tendency of the chloride to hydrolyse

   iv thermal stability of the carbonate

   v solubility of the hydroxide

   vi solubility of the carbonate

   vii solubility of the sulphate

Practical 20
Aluminium and its compounds

REQUIREMENTS

- Eye protection
- Rack with four test tubes
- Small beaker
- Full-range indicator paper
- Hard-glass test tube with hole in its base
- Bunsen burner
- Aluminium turnings
- Aluminium powder
- Magnesium ribbon
- Dilute hydrochloric acid
- Dilute sodium hydroxide
- Mercury(II) chloride solution (0.1 mol dm^{-3})
- Chlorine generator with anhydrous $CaCl_2$ drying tube
- Ceramic wool
- Anhydrous aluminium chloride
- Anhydrous magnesium chloride
- Magnesium oxide
- Aluminium oxide
- Solution of Al^{3+}, 0.1 mol dm^{-3}
- Solution of Mg^{2+}, 0.1 mol dm^{-3}

Time required 1–2 double periods

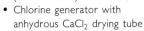

EYE PROTECTION
MUST BE WORN

Introduction

Aluminium has been variously described as a metalloid, a 'poor metal' and an 'amphoteric metal'. The intention of this experiment is to explore these descriptions of aluminium and to compare the chemistry of aluminium and its compounds with that of magnesium and its compounds.

Much of the chemistry of aluminium compounds is dictated by the charge density of the Al^{3+} ion, which is so highly polarising that many aluminium compounds are covalent. (See *Chemistry in Context*, Fourth Edition, section 16.2.) Furthermore, the energy required to form Al^{3+} from Al is so large that Al^{3+} only forms in combination with anions of high charge density such as O^{2-} and F^-, or when it is hydrated as $[Al(H_2O)_6]^{3+}$.

CARE Eye protection must be worn for all the experiments in this practical.

Experiment 1: Reaction with dilute hydrochloric acid

Add about 5 cm^3 of dilute hydrochloric acid to a few aluminium turnings in a test tube. If the aluminium has not started to react after five minutes, warm the mixture gently.

Repeat the test using magnesium ribbon in place of aluminium turnings (**CARE**).

1 Explain your observations giving appropriate equations.

2 Look up the standard electrode potentials of hydrogen, aluminium and magnesium. These suggest that both aluminium and magnesium should react readily with dilute hydrochloric acid. What explanation can you offer for the slow reaction of aluminium?

Experiment 2: Reaction with dilute sodium hydroxide solution

CORROSIVE
Sodium hydroxide
solution

FLAMMABLE
Aluminium powder

Add about 5 cm^3 of dilute sodium hydroxide solution to a few aluminium turnings (or a spatula measure of aluminium powder if this is available). If there is no action after five minutes, warm **carefully**.

3 Record your observations and identify the gas evolved.

4 Write an equation for the reaction which occurs.

5 Repeat the test using magnesium ribbon in place of aluminium and compare the two reactions.

6 Why should aluminium pans never be cleaned with washing soda (sodium carbonate)? (**Hint** Test the pH of sodium carbonate solution.)

Experiment 3: Reaction with oxygen

TOXIC
Mercury(II)
chloride

CARE Mercury compounds are very poisonous.
Place a piece of aluminium foil in a small beaker and cover it with mercury(II) chloride solution.

Leave it for a few minutes and then wash the foil with distilled water. Leave the wet foil in the air for a few minutes.

7 Describe and explain your observations with appropriate equations.

8 Why does mercury(II) chloride solution clean the surface of the aluminium foil so effectively? (How does $HgCl_2(aq)$ react with Al_2O_3 and Al? **Hint** Test the pH of $HgCl_2(aq)$ with full-range indicator paper.)

9 The processes, $Al \longrightarrow Al^{3+}$ and $O_2 \longrightarrow O^{2-}$ are both very endothermic. Why then does Al_2O_3 form and why is it so stable?

10 Why does aluminium not corrode away in air like iron?

11 What are the principal uses of aluminium? On what properties of aluminium (besides its resistance to corrosion) do these uses depend?

Experiment 4: Reaction with chlorine

USE A FUME
CUPBOARD

CORROSIVE
Anhydrous aluminium
chloride

TOXIC
Chlorine

CARE This experiment must be performed in a fume cupboard.
Arrange the apparatus in figure 1 in a fume cupboard. Clamp the tube horizontally, heat the aluminium and then pass chlorine over the heated metal. Once the reaction has started, remove the bunsen so that the vigour of the reaction can be observed. Try to collect the product at the end of the tube.

When the test tube has cooled, remove the product (aluminium chloride, Al_2Cl_6) and keep it for the next experiment.

12 Describe and explain your observations.

13 Why is the plug of ceramic wool used?

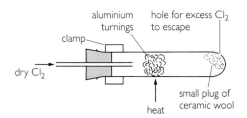

Figure 1
Reaction with chlorine.

Experiment 5: Comparing aluminium chloride and magnesium chloride

USE A FUME
CUPBOARD

(1) *Effect of heating the anhydrous chlorides*
Heat a spatula measure of anhydrous aluminium chloride in a test tube **in a fume cupboard**. Heat the sample, **gently** at first, and then more strongly. Repeat the experiment using anhydrous magnesium chloride.

14 Describe the effect of heating Al_2Cl_6 and $MgCl_2$. What does this suggest about the bonding and structure in each chloride?

15 Draw dot and cross diagrams to represent the electronic structure of Al_2Cl_6 and $MgCl_2$.

(2) *Action of water on the anhydrous chlorides*
CARE Eye protection must be worn. Use a fume cupboard for this experiment.
Put one spatula measure of anhydrous aluminium chloride in a test tube and add water drop by drop.

EYE PROTECTION
MUST BE WORN

16 Describe what happens. Does the tube become warm? What is the final pH of the solution?

17 Write an equation for the reaction of Al_2Cl_6 with water. Repeat the experiment with anhydrous magnesium chloride.

18 Compare the action of water on Al_2Cl_6 and $MgCl_2$.

Experiment 6: Comparing the acid–base character of aluminium oxide and magnesium oxide

Examine the reaction of small quantities of aluminium oxide and magnesium oxide with water and test the pH of the solutions obtained.

19 Describe the results of your tests. Can either of these oxides be described as alkaline?

CARE Eye protection must be worn when warming with dilute acid or alkali in the following tests.

Examine the reactions of these oxides first with dilute hydrochloric acid and then with dilute sodium hydroxide. Use only a small quantity (about 0.1 g) of the oxide and see if it dissolves on warming with 3 cm³ of dilute hydrochloric acid and then with 3 cm³ of dilute sodium hydroxide.

20 Which of these oxides can be described as

   a basic, **b** acidic, **c** amphoteric?

21 Write equations for the reactions which occur when aluminium oxide and magnesium oxide are warmed with dilute hydrochloric acid and dilute sodium hydroxide.

Experiment 7: Comparing the acid–base properties of hydrated Al^{3+} and Mg^{2+} ions

In solution, Al^{3+} and Mg^{2+} ions are thought to be hydrated by six water molecules as $[Al(H_2O)_6]^{3+}$ and $[Mg(H_2O)_6]^{3+}$ respectively. These hydrated ions can act as Brønsted–Lowry acids by donating protons as follows:

$$[Al(H_2O)_6]^{3+} + H_2O \rightleftharpoons [Al(H_2O)_5OH]^{2+} + H_3O^+$$

$$[Mg(H_2O)_6]^{2+} + H_2O \rightleftharpoons [Mg(H_2O)_5OH]^+ + H_3O^+$$

Pour 3 cm³ of 0.1 mol dm⁻³ Al^{3+}(aq) into one test tube and 3 cm³ of 0.1 mol dm⁻³ Mg^{2+}(aq) in another. Test the pH of each solution using full range indicator paper.

22 Which is the stronger Brønsted–Lowry acid: hydrated Al^{3+} or hydrated Mg^{2+}? Explain your results.

Add dilute sodium hydroxide to the 3 cm³ of 0.1 mol dm⁻³ Al^{3+}(aq) until the precipitate which forms has dissolved.

23 Describe and explain what happens. Write equations where appropriate. (The full formula of the precipitate is $Al(OH)_3(H_2O)_3$ and the final state of Al^{3+} is as aqueous $[Al(OH)_4(H_2O)_2]^-$.)

24 Why is $[Al(OH)_4(H_2O)_2]^-$ soluble in water, whilst $Al(OH)_3(H_2O)_3$ is insoluble?

Repeat the last test using 0.1 mol dm⁻³ Mg^{2+}(aq) in place of 0.1 mol dm⁻³ Al^{3+}(aq).

25 Describe and explain what happens. Why does the precipitate remain insoluble in excess sodium hydroxide in this case?

26 What are the main differences between the chemistry of aluminium and its compounds and that of magnesium and its compounds?

27 Is aluminium best described as a metalloid, a 'poor metal' or an 'amphoteric metal'? Explain your answer.

EYE PROTECTION
MUST BE WORN

CORROSIVE
Sodium hydroxide
solution

INVESTIGATION

See Investigation 9

Practical 21
The halogens

The intention of this practical is to compare the properties and reactions of the halogens, a group of reactive non-metals in the periodic table.

CARE Eye protection must be worn at all times in this practical.

A Preparation of the halogens

All the methods of preparing halogens involve oxidising halide ions.

$$2Hal^- \longrightarrow Hal_2 + 2e^-$$

CARE Particular care is needed in the following experiments. Use a fume cupboard, and do not use greater quantities than those given.

Action of manganese(IV) oxide or potassium manganate(VII) on concentrated hydrohalic acid (HCl, HBr, HI)

Warm $1\,cm^3$ of concentrated hydrochloric acid (**CARE**) with a spatula measure of manganese(IV) oxide.

1 Describe what happens and write an equation (or half-equations) for the reaction occurring.

Add a few drops of concentrated hydrochloric acid to half a spatula measure of potassium manganate(VII).

CARE Make quite sure you are using hydrochloric acid. Other concentrated acids can have dangerous reactions with potassium manganate (VII).

2 Write an equation (or half-equations) for the reaction occurring.

3 Compare the action of manganese(IV) oxide and potassium manganate(VII) as oxidising agents in these two simple experiments.

4 Write the halide ions in order of their ease of oxidation.

5 Explain the relative ease of oxidation of the halide ions.

B Physical properties of the halogens

6 Use a data book to make a table comparing the colour, state at room temperature, melting point and boiling point of the halogens fluorine, chlorine, bromine and iodine.

7 What trends are evident in the physical properties of the halogens as their relative atomic mass increases?

EYE PROTECTION
MUST BE WORN

USE A FUME
CUPBOARD

CORROSIVE
Concentrated
hydrochloric acid

HARMFUL
Potassium
manganate(VII)
Manganese(IV)
oxide

OXIDISING
Potassium
manganate(VII)

C Chemical properties of the halogens

Experiment 1: Reactions of halogens with water

Working in a fume cupboard, pass chlorine through $5\,cm^3$ of water for a few seconds. Test the pH of the resulting solution with full-range indicator paper.

8 What conclusion can you draw concerning chlorine water from this test?

9 Chlorine water contains dissolved chlorine, together with a mixture of two acids which are formed when chlorine reacts with water. What are these two acids called? Write an equation for the reaction of chlorine with water.

CARE Keep the bromine bottle in a fume cupboard and avoid skin contact by wearing protective gloves. If any bromine is spilt, neutralise it immediately with a solution of sodium thiosulphate(VI).

Shake **one drop** of bromine with $5\,cm^3$ of water in a test tube until the bromine dissolves. Test the resulting solution with full-range indicator paper.

Repeat the experiment using a small crystal of iodine in place of the bromine.

10 Compare the ease with which the three halogens dissolve in water, the pH of their resulting solutions and their action as bleaching agents.

11 What specific uses does chlorine have as a bleach?

Experiment 2: Solubility of the halogens in 1,1,1-trichloroethane

Shake $3\,cm^3$ of chlorine water, $Cl_2(aq)$, with $1\,cm^3$ of 1,1,1-trichloroethane in a test tube.

Repeat the experiment using first $3\,cm^3$ of bromine water and then a small crystal of iodine in place of the $3\,cm^3$ of chlorine water.

12 Tabulate and explain your observations in the three simple experiments.

Experiment 3: Halogens as oxidising agents

(1) Reactions with hydrogen sulphide
CARE Experiment 3 must be carried out in a fume cupboard.

Pass hydrogen sulphide from a Kipp's apparatus through $3\,cm^3$ of chlorine water. Compare the final solution with clear chlorine water.

13 Describe what happens and write an equation for the reaction which occurs.

Repeat the experiment using bromine water in place of chlorine water.

14 Compare the reactions of bromine and chlorine with hydrogen sulphide.

(2) Reactions with iron(II) sulphate solution
Put $3\,cm^3$ of iron(II) sulphate into each of two test tubes. To one test tube add $3\,cm^3$ of $Cl_2(aq)$ and to the other $3\,cm^3$ of water. This second test tube acts as a control.

15 What is a 'control'?

16 What do you observe in

a the first tube,

b the control tube?

EYE PROTECTION MUST BE WORN

USE A FUME CUPBOARD

TOXIC
Chlorine

WEAR PROTECTIVE GLOVES

USE A FUME CUPBOARD

CORROSIVE
Bromine

HARMFUL
Iodine

Iodine

EYE PROTECTION MUST BE WORN

IRRITANT
Chlorine water

Bromine water

HARMFUL
1,1,1-Trichloroethane

EYE PROTECTION MUST BE WORN

USE A FUME CUPBOARD

HIGHLY FLAMMABLE
Hydrogen sulphide

TOXIC
Hydrogen sulphide

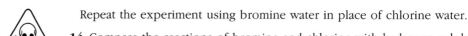

Investigate whether Fe^{2+} ions have been oxidised to Fe^{3+} by adding $1\,cm^3$ of sodium hydroxide solution to each tube.

17 What evidence does the addition of sodium hydroxide provide for the oxidation of Fe^{2+} ions by chlorine?

18 Write an equation for the reaction of chlorine with iron(II) sulphate.

Repeat the experiment using $Br_2(aq)$ in place of $Cl_2(aq)$.

19 Describe and explain the reactions of $Br_2(aq)$.

Experiment 4: Relative reactivity of the halogens as oxidising agents

Investigate the action of $Cl_2(aq)$ on

    a KBr(aq),

    b KI(aq),

and then the action of $Br_2(aq)$ on

    a KCl(aq),

    b KI(aq).

Use $3\,cm^3$ of each reacting solution and then shake each of the four resulting solutions with $1\,cm^3$ of 1,1,1-trichloroethane.

20 Tabulate the results of the four tests showing the solutions mixed, the changes which occur before 1,1,1-trichloroethane is added, and the final colour of the 1,1,1-trichloroethane layer.

21 Write equations for the reactions where appropriate.

22 What is the order of the halogens as oxidising agents?

23 Look up the electrode potentials of the halogens for the Hal_2/Hal^- systems. Do these confirm your deductions about their relative oxidising power?

INVESTIGATIONS

See Investigations 10 and 11

Practical 22
The oxidation states of vanadium and manganese

Introduction

The atoms of transition metals have electrons of similar energy in both the $3d$ and $4s$ levels. This means that one particular element can form a number of different stable ions by losing or sharing different numbers of electrons. Thus, all the transition metals in the first series (titanium to copper) can exhibit two or more oxidation states in their compounds. The intention of this experiment is:

   A to investigate the chemistry of vanadium and manganese;

   B to apply a knowledge of electrode potentials to the reactions studied;

   C to prepare some vanadium and manganese compounds in their less common oxidation states.

1 The electronic structure of vanadium is (Ar) $3d^3\,4s^2$. Write the electronic structures of V^+, V^{2+} and V^{3+}.

2 Which of these ions has the most stable electronic structure? Explain your answer.

3 Vanadium(III) compounds are much more common than vanadium(II) and vanadium(I) compounds. What factors are responsible for this?

CARE Eye protection must be worn throughout this practical.

Oxidation states of vanadium

Step-by-step conversion of vanadium(V) to vanadium(II)

CARE Vanadium compounds are toxic.

Dissolve 1 g of ammonium vanadate(V) (NH_4VO_3) in $10\,cm^3$ of $2\,mol\,dm^{-3}$ sodium hydroxide solution in a boiling tube and then add $20\,cm^3$ of $1.0\,mol\,dm^{-3}$ sulphuric acid. This solution contains dioxovanadium(V) ions, VO_2^+, in acid solution.

$$VO_3^-(aq) + 2H^+(aq) \longrightarrow VO_2^+(aq) + H_2O(l)$$

Now add a few pieces of granulated zinc to the mixture. Close the boiling tube with a rubber bung and shake until no further changes occur. Remove the bung to release pressure from time to time.

4 Describe what happens as the tube is shaken.

5 Copy and complete table 1, recording the colours of the various oxidation states to which vanadium is successively reduced. (**Note** The first green colour which you see is a mixture of the original vanadium(V) solution and vanadium(IV).)

Table 1

Oxidation states of vanadium

Ion	VO_2^+	VO^{2+}	V^{3+}	V^{2+}
Name	dioxovanadium(V) ion	oxovanadium(IV) ion	vanadium(III) ion	vanadium(II) ion
Oxidation state				
Colour				

The standard electrode potentials for the reactions involved are:

$$VO_2^+ + 2H^+ + e^- \longrightarrow VO^{2+} + H_2O \qquad E^\ominus = +1.00\,V$$

$$VO^{2+} + 2H^+ + e^- \longrightarrow V^{3+} + H_2O \qquad E^\ominus = +0.32\,V$$

$$V^{3+} + e^- \longrightarrow V^{2+} \qquad E^\ominus = -0.26\,V$$

$$Zn^{2+} + 2e^- \longrightarrow Zn \qquad E^\ominus = -0.76\,V$$

6 Explain why zinc is capable of reducing VO_2^+ to V^{2+}.

7 Which of the stages in the reduction of vanadium(V) to vanadium(II) would you expect to be achieved least readily? Explain your answer.

EYE PROTECTION MUST BE WORN

CORROSIVE Concentrated nitric acid

When no further colour changes occur, filter the mixture to obtain $5\,cm^3$ of the final solution. Now add concentrated nitric acid drop by drop to the $5\,cm^3$ of filtrate, shaking carefully.

8 Describe what happens. To which oxidation state does nitric acid oxidise vanadium(II)?

9 Are your results consistent with standard electrode potentials? Explain.

$$NO_3^- + 2H^+ + e^- \longrightarrow NO_2 + H_2O \qquad E^\ominus = +0.80\,V$$

Oxidation states of manganese

You have possibly met and used the following compounds of manganese already: potassium manganate(VII), $KMnO_4$ (also called potassium permanganate), manganese(IV) oxide, MnO_2, and manganese(II) sulphate, $MnSO_4$.

10 Prepare an oxidation number chart for manganese and write MnO_4^-, MnO_2, and Mn on the appropriate lines of the chart.

The commonest oxidation states of manganese are +7, +4 and +2. In the next experiment, we shall investigate the preparation of manganese(VI) and manganese(III) compounds.

The preparation of manganese(VI) compounds

11 Use the following electrode potentials to predict whether Mn(VI) might be prepared by reacting Mn(VII) with Mn(IV) in *acid* solution. Explain your answer.

In acid:

$$MnO_4^- + e^- \longrightarrow MnO_4^{2-} \qquad E^\ominus = +0.56\,V$$

Mn(VII)   Mn(VI)

$$4H^+ + MnO_4^{2-} + 2e^- \longrightarrow MnO_2 + 2H_2O \qquad E^\ominus = +2.26\,V$$

Mn(VI)   Mn(IV)

12 Would increasing the concentration of either MnO_4^- or H^+ improve the chances of preparing Mn(VI)? Explain.

13 Explain why the reaction is more likely to yield Mn(VI) in *alkaline* solution.

14 Do the following electrode potentials suggest that Mn(VI) might be prepared from Mn(VII) and Mn(IV) in *alkaline* solution? Explain.

In alkali:

$$MnO_4^- + e^- \longrightarrow MnO_4^{2-} \qquad E^\ominus = +0.56\,V$$

$$2H_2O + MnO_4^{2-} + 2e^- \longrightarrow MnO_2 + 4OH^- \qquad E^\ominus = +0.59\,V$$

15 Would increasing the concentration of either MnO_4^- or OH^- improve the chance of preparing Mn(VI)?

Test your predictions as follows. Put $10\,cm^3$ portions of $0.01\,mol\,dm^{-3}$ $KMnO_4$ into each of two boiling tubes. Add $5\,cm^3$ of dilute sulphuric acid to one tube and $5\,cm^3$ of dilute sodium hydroxide to the other. Now add a little manganese(IV) oxide to each tube and shake for two minutes. Filter each mixture into a clean test tube.

16 In which tube has a reaction occurred? (The colour of Mn(VI) is green.)

To the green solution add $5\,cm^3$ of dilute sulphuric acid.

17 Describe and explain what happens.

The preparation of manganese(III) compounds

18 Use the following electrode potentials to predict whether Mn(III) could be prepared by reacting Mn(II) and Mn(IV) in *acid* solution. Explain your answer.

In acid:

$$4H^+ + MnO_2 + e^- \longrightarrow Mn^{3+} + 2H_2O \quad E^{\ominus} = +0.95\,V$$
$$Mn^{3+} + e^- \longrightarrow Mn^{2+} \quad\quad\quad E^{\ominus} = +1.51\,V$$

19 Would increasing the concentration of H^+ or Mn^{2+} improve the chance of preparing Mn(III)? Explain.

20 Use the following electrode potentials to predict whether Mn(III) could be prepared by reacting Mn(II) and Mn(IV) in *alkaline* solution.

In alkali:

$$2H_2O + MnO_2 + e^- \longrightarrow Mn(OH)_3 + OH^- \quad E^{\ominus} = +0.20\,V$$
$$Mn(OH)_3 + e^- \longrightarrow Mn(OH)_2 + OH^- \quad E^{\ominus} = -0.10\,V$$

21 Would increasing the concentration of OH^- improve the chance of preparing Mn(III)? Explain.

22 Write an overall equation for the reaction including state symbols. Why is the rate of this reaction very slow?
Another possible way of obtaining Mn(III) is by reacting Mn(II) with Mn(VII).

In acid:

$$8H^+ + MnO_4^- + 5e^- \longrightarrow Mn^{2+} + 4H_2O \quad E^{\ominus} = +1.51\,V$$
$$Mn^{3+} + e^- \longrightarrow Mn^{2+} \quad\quad\quad\quad E^{\ominus} = +1.51\,V$$

23 Do these electrode potentials suggest that Mn^{3+} could be obtained by reacting MnO_4^- with Mn^{2+}? Explain.

24 Would increasing the concentration of acid improve the chance of preparing Mn(III)?

Procedure
Dissolve 0.5 g of hydrated manganese(II) sulphate in about $2\,cm^3$ of dilute sulphuric acid and add 10 drops of concentrated sulphuric acid. Cool the test tube in cold water and then add 5 drops of $0.1\,mol\,dm^{-3}$ potassium manganate(VII).

CORROSIVE
Concentrated
sulphuric acid

EYE PROTECTION
MUST BE WORN

25 Describe what happens. What is the colour of aqueous Mn^{3+} ions?

Pour the final solution into $50\,cm^3$ of water.

26 Describe and explain what happens.

Practical 23
Copper

Introduction

Before looking at the two oxidation states of copper, carry out some simple test tube experiments to remind yourself of some of the basic reactions of this metal.

A Introductory experiments

CARE Eye protection must be worn throughout this practical.

a Hold a piece of clean copper foil with tongs and heat it in a bunsen flame.

b Drop one copper turning into $2 \, cm^3$ of dilute nitric acid and warm. Identify the gas evolved.

c Add dilute sodium hydroxide solution drop by drop to $2 \, cm^3$ of copper sulphate solution, until the sodium hydroxide is in excess.

d Add ammonia solution drop by drop to $2 \, cm^3$ of copper sulphate solution until the ammonia is in excess.

e Add concentrated hydrochloric acid drop by drop to $2 \, cm^3$ of copper sulphate solution. Continue adding concentrated hydrochloric acid until no further changes occur, then add water gradually, again until no further changes occur.

1 For each of the reactions **a** to **c**, decide what has been formed and write an equation.

2 Reaction **d** finally results in the formation of a complex ion containing Cu^{2+} and ammonia.

$$Cu(H_2O)_4^{2+}(aq) + 4NH_3(aq) \rightleftharpoons Cu(NH_3)_4^{2+}(aq) + 4H_2O(l)$$
pale blue $\qquad\qquad\qquad\qquad\qquad$ deep blue

Explain your observations in reaction **d** in terms of this equilibrium.

3 Reaction **e** also involves the formation of a complex ion—in this case the ligand is Cl^-:

$$Cu(H_2O)_4^{2+}(aq) + 4Cl^-(aq) \rightleftharpoons CuCl_4^{2-}(aq) + 4H_2O(l)$$
pale blue $\qquad\qquad\qquad\qquad\qquad$ green

Intermediate ions such as $[CuCl_3(H_2O)]^-$ may also be formed. Explain your observations in reaction **e** in terms of this equilibrium.

4 What is the oxidation state of copper in all the compounds formed in these introductory experiments?

5 What other oxidation states does copper have besides this one?

The atomic number of copper is 29, and its 29 electrons are arranged in orbitals thus:

$$1s^2 2s^2 2p^6 3s^2 3p^6 3d^{10} 4s^1$$

6 How many electrons would you expect a copper atom to lose in forming its compounds, in view of what you know about the tendency of atoms to achieve stable electron structures?

7 Does it surprise you that the commonly encountered oxidation state of copper is 2+? Explain.

8 Given the electron structure of the Cu^+ ion, what colour would you expect copper(I) compounds to be?

The electronic structure of copper suggests that its stable oxidation state should be 1+, yet experience shows that the 2+ state is the more stable under normal conditions. Nevertheless, Cu(I) compounds do exist, and in this practical you will prepare some of them and examine their reactions. Your results may help you understand why, under normal conditions, Cu(II) is more common than Cu(I).

B Copper(I) and copper(II)

Experiment 1: The preparation of copper(I) oxide

Copper(I) oxide is normally made by reducing Cu^{2+} ions in alkaline solution. This reaction forms the basis of Fehling's and Benedict's tests for reducing sugars.

CORROSIVE
Sodium hydroxide solution

EYE PROTECTION MUST BE WORN

CARE Eye protection must be worn.
Put about $5\,cm^3$ of copper(II) sulphate solution in a boiling tube. In a separate boiling tube mix $5\,cm^3$ of sodium hydroxide solution and about 1 g of potassium sodium tartrate (Rochelle salt). Add this solution to the copper(II) sulphate until the precipitate formed at first just dissolves. You now have Fehling's solution. Now add about 1 g of glucose to the mixture and boil until an orange-red precipitate forms.

Allow the precipitate to settle (centrifuge if necessary), then decant the solution and wash the precipitate with distilled water. Keep the precipitate for use in experiment **2**.

The orange-red precipitate is copper(I) oxide.

HARMFUL
Copper(I) oxide

9 What substance acted as the reducing agent in converting Cu(II) to Cu(I)?

10 What is the purpose of the tartrate ions in this experiment?

11 Would you describe copper(I) oxide as stable or unstable relative to copper(II) oxide under normal conditions? Give your evidence.

Experiment 2: The reactions of copper(I) oxide and copper(II) oxide with acids

IRRITANT
Dilute sulphuric acid

Dilute nitric acid

EYE PROTECTION MUST BE WORN

Put a small quantity (about 0.1 g) of your copper(I) oxide in each of three test tubes. Put a similar amount of copper(II) oxide in each of three further tubes. Use the tubes to investigate the reaction of each oxide with dilute hydrochloric acid, dilute sulphuric acid and dilute nitric acid in turn. Add the acid slowly to the oxide until acid is present in excess, then warm gently and observe **carefully** to see what is formed. (In some cases there is more than one product.)

12 Tabulate your observations.

13 What generalisation can you make about the reactions of copper(I) oxide with acids?

14 What evidence is there that **a** Cu^+ ions, **b** Cu^{2+} ions are formed when copper(I) oxide reacts with dilute sulphuric acid?

15 What other product is formed in the reaction of copper(I) oxide with dilute sulphuric acid?

16 What happens to the Cu^+ ion when copper(I) oxide reacts with dilute sulphuric acid?

17 Is the reaction with dilute nitric acid similar? If not, why not?

18 What is the oxidation state of copper in the product from the reaction of copper(I) oxide with dilute hydrochloric acid?

Your results in experiment **2** should show that copper(I) can exist under certain conditions but under other conditions the Cu^+ ion disproportionates.

19 What is meant by disproportionation?

20 To what does Cu^+ disproportionate in the reaction of copper(I) oxide with dilute sulphuric acid?

21 Under what circumstances do copper(I) compounds remain stable without disproportionating?

The relative stability of copper(I) and copper(II) is discussed further in *Chemistry in Context* Fourth Edition, section 20.10.

Experiment 3: The preparation of copper(I) chloride

The Cu^+ ion normally disproportionates in aqueous solution, though it is quite stable under non-aqueous conditions. Copper(I) chloride is insoluble, so it is not subject to the disproportionation that Cu^+ undergoes in aqueous solution. Furthermore, copper(I) forms a complex ion, $CuCl_2^-$, in the presence of excess chloride ions, and this increases the stability of copper(I) chloride relative to copper(II) chloride. All this means that copper(I) chloride is quite stable and easily prepared. In fact, it can be prepared by reversing the normal disproportionation of copper(I) and reacting copper(II) with copper metal.

EYE PROTECTION
MUST BE WORN

HARMFUL
Copper(I) chloride

CARE Eye protection must be worn.
Put about 0.5 g of copper(II) oxide in a boiling tube and add 5–10 cm³ of concentrated hydrochloric acid. Warm, preferably in a fume cupboard, to obtain a clear green solution of copper(II) chloride. Now add about 1 g of copper turnings and boil gently for five minutes or so. Filter the resulting solution into about 200 cm³ of distilled water in a beaker. Allow the precipitate of copper(I) chloride to settle, then decant off the water.

22 Write an equation for the formation of copper(I) chloride from copper metal and copper(II) chloride.

23 Does copper(I) chloride appear to be a typical transition metal compound? Compare your answer with the answer you gave to question **8**.

24 What similarities are there between copper(I) chloride and silver chloride, AgCl? Why is it reasonable to expect copper(I) chloride to resemble silver chloride?

25 Bearing in mind the comparison between copper(I) chloride and silver chloride, predict the effect of ammonia solution on solid copper(I) chloride.

Test your prediction by adding a few cubic centimetres of ammonia solution to a little solid copper(I) chloride in a test tube.

26 Record your results and try to explain what has happened.

Although copper(I) chloride is insoluble in water, it forms a soluble complex ion in the presence of excess chloride ions:

$$CuCl(s) + Cl^-(aq) \rightleftharpoons CuCl_2^-(aq)$$

CORROSIVE
Concentrated
hydrochloric
acid

Add $2\,cm^3$ of concentrated hydrochloric acid (**CARE**) to a small amount of your copper(I) chloride in a test tube. Note what happens, then pour the contents of the tube into about $50\,cm^3$ of cold water in a small beaker.

27 Record your observations and explain them in terms of the equilibrium between CuCl and $CuCl_2^-$.

28 Re-examine the copper(I) chloride. Are there any signs of reversion to the copper(II) state?

Experiment 4: The thermal decomposition of copper(II) halides

USE A FUME
CUPBOARD

The previous experiments show that copper(I) chloride is reasonably stable with respect to copper(II) chloride. Perhaps copper(II) chloride will decompose to copper(I) chloride when it is heated.

Working in a fume cupboard, heat very small samples of anhydrous copper(II) chloride and anhydrous copper(II) bromide in separate hard-glass ignition tubes. Heat gently at first, then more strongly. Observe closely to see if any gases are evolved, and note the appearance of the residues.

IRRITANT
Anhydrous
copper(II)
bromide

TOXIC
Anhydrous
copper(II)
chloride

29 Do the halides decompose on heating? Write equations for any reactions that occur.

30 Which halide decomposed more readily?

31 How stable would you expect copper(II) iodide to be relative to copper(I) iodide?

Experiment 5: The preparation of copper(I) iodide

Add $3\,cm^3$ of potassium iodide solution to $3\,cm^3$ of copper(II) sulphate solution in a test tube. Note carefully what happens, and allow the contents of the tube to settle. Add sodium thiosulphate solution to the tube until the solution is clear and you can tell the colour of the solid that has been formed.

32 What substances are produced when KI reacts with $CuSO_4$? Write an equation for the reaction.

33 Does the result of this reaction agree with your answer to question **31**?

34 In this practical you have encountered copper in both oxidation states, +1 and +2. Summarise the conditions which favour the existence of each of the two oxidation states.

35 Is copper a transition metal?

INVESTIGATION

See Investigation 20

Practical 24
Identifying cations

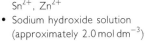

EYE PROTECTION
MUST BE WORN

EYE PROTECTION
MUST BE WORN

CORROSIVE
Concentrated
hydrochloric
acid

IRRITANT
Dilute
nitric acid

HARMFUL
Barium chloride

IRRITANT
Calcium chloride

TOXIC
Copper chloride

Introduction

Many common cations can be identified from the colour of their hydroxides and/or the colour they produce during flame tests.

The intention of this practical is to develop a simple, systematic method of identifying the following cations, provided there is only one cation present in the substance under test:
Al^{3+}, Ag^+, Ba^{2+}, Ca^{2+}, Cr^{3+}, Cu^{2+}, Fe^{2+}, Fe^{3+}, K^+, Mg^{2+}, Mn^{2+}, Na^+, NH_4^+, Ni^{2+}, Pb^{2+}, Zn^{2+}.

CARE Eye protection must be worn throughout.

Appearance

The colour of a substance may give a clue to its identity and the cation it contains, as shown in table 1 below.

Table 1
The colours of substances and their constituent cations

Colour	Inference
White or colourless	probably does not contain a transition metal cation
Not white or transparent	probably contains a transition metal cation
Blue	possibly Cu^{2+}, Ni^{2+}
Green	possibly Cu^{2+}, Cr^{3+}, Fe^{2+}, Ni^{2+}
Yelllow	possibly Fe^{3+}

Preparing a solution of the substance

If you are provided with a solid, it is most convenient to carry out a flame test on this, but you will need to make an aqueous solution of the substance before other tests are carried out.

Put one spatula-full of the substance (i.e. 0.2 g–0.4 g) in a test tube and shake this with about 5 cm^3 of distilled water. If the solid will not dissolve in the cold, warm gently.

If the solid is insoluble in water, try cold and then hot dilute nitric acid. If this fails, consult your teacher. It may be necessary to use concentrated hydrochloric acid.

Flame tests

CARE Eye protection must be worn for flame tests.
Dip a nichrome wire in concentrated hydrochloric acid and then heat it in a roaring bunsen flame until it no longer gives colour to the flame. The wire is now clean. Mix a little barium chloride with concentrated hydrochloric acid on a watch glass, moisten the wire with this solution and hold the wire in the

bunsen flame. Clean the wire thoroughly again and repeat the test with the chlorides of Ca^{2+}, Cu^{2+}, Mg^{2+}, K^+ and Na^+ in turn.

1 What are the flame colours (if any) of the following metal ions?

a Ba^{2+} **b** Ca^{2+} **c** Cu^{2+} **d** Mg^{2+} **e** K^+ **f** Na^+

2 Why do certain metal ions give flame colours in this way?

3 One of the six metal ions tested gives no flame colour. Why is this?

Testing with sodium hydroxide solution

EYE PROTECTION
MUST BE WORN

CORROSIVE
Sodium hydroxide
solution

HARMFUL
Solutions of
lead(II) compounds
Solutions of
barium compounds

Add a few drops of sodium hydroxide solution to $3\,cm^3$ of a solution containing $Al^{3+}(aq)$.

4 What happens? Write an equation for the reaction.

5 Does the precipitate remain or dissolve when *excess* NaOH(aq) is added?

Repeat the experiment with solutions containing the following cations in place of Al^{3+}:
Ag^+, Ba^{2+}, Ca^{2+}, Cr^{3+}, Cu^{2+}, Fe^{2+}, Fe^{3+}, K^+, Mg^{2+}, Mn^{2+}, Na^+, NH_4^+, Ni^{2+}, Pb^{2+}, Sn^{2+}, Zn^{2+}.

Record your results in a table similar to table 2. (The table has been completed for Al^{3+} to show you what is required.) Write the formulae and colours of precipitates, write equations for reactions and say whether precipitates remain or dissolve when excess sodium hydroxide is added.

Table 2
Reactions of cations with sodium hydroxide solution

Cation tested	What happens when a few drops of NaOH(aq) are added to $3\,cm^3$ of the cation solution?	What happens when excess NaOH(aq) is added?
Al^{3+}	white precipitate of $Al(OH)_3$ forms. $Al^{3+}(aq) + 3OH^-(aq) \rightarrow Al(OH)_3(s)$	white precipitate dissolves forming a clear solution $Al(OH)_3(s) + OH^-(aq) \rightarrow Al(OH)_4^-(aq)$

6 Which cations give no precipitate with NaOH(aq)?

7 How can these three cations be distinguished using flame tests?

8 Which cations give a white precipitate with NaOH(aq) which remains with excess NaOH(aq)?

9 How can these three cations be distinguished using flame tests?

10 Which cations give distinctive coloured precipitates with NaOH(aq)?

Al^{3+}, Pb^{2+}, Sn^{2+} and Zn^{2+} give white precipitates with NaOH(aq) which dissolve in excess. These four ions cannot be distinguished by flame tests.

Precipitate further samples of $Al(OH)_3$, $Pb(OH)_2$, $Sn(OH)_2$ and $Zn(OH)_2$. Filter each precipitate and heat a sample of it to dryness. Copy out and complete table 3.

Table 3

Precipitate	Colour before heating	What happens on heating?	Colour after heating
$Al(OH)_3$			
$Pb(OH)_2$			
$Sn(OH)_2$			
$Zn(OH)_2$			

11 How can Al^{3+}, Pb^{2+}, Sn^{2+} and Zn^{2+} be distinguished?

Identifying the cation in an unknown substance

Use the information you have gathered in the previous tests to identify the cation in each of the unknown substances provided by your teacher.

Further work

If time permits, develop a table similar to the one that you have obtained for the reactions of cations with NaOH, showing their reactions with ammonia solution.

Practical 25
Alkanes

Introduction

The alkanes form the simplest family of hydrocarbons and can be regarded as the basic skeletons to which functional groups are attached in more complex organic compounds. They are in many ways the most important homologous series, because they are the principal constituents of crude oil, from which most organic chemical products are derived.

In this practical you will investigate some of the physical and chemical properties of alkanes. You will be working with a number of different alkanes or mixtures of alkanes.

Methane, CH_4	Natural gas from the laboratory gas taps is a good source. (North Sea gas is about 95% methane, most of the remainder being higher alkanes.)
Hexane, C_6H_{14}	Cyclohexane is a good substitute if hexane is not available. Cycloalkanes have very similar properties to straight-chain alkanes.
Medicinal paraffin	A liquid mixture of long-chain alkanes.
Paraffin wax	A solid mixture of long-chain alkanes.

CARE Eye protection must be worn throughout this practical.

Physical properties

Volatility

Use a data book to answer the following questions.

1 What are the boiling points of methane and hexane?

2 Which is the first straight-chain alkane to be liquid at room temperature and pressure?

3 Which alcohol has a boiling point closest to that of hexane? Comment on your answer.

Solubility

Put $2\,cm^3$–$3\,cm^3$ of hexane in a test tube and add about twice this volume of water. Shake, then stand the tube in a rack.

4 Does hexane dissolve in water? Suggest a reason why the two liquids behave in this way.

5 Is hexane more or less dense than water?

6 Use a data book to discover how the densities of straight-chain alkanes change as their relative molecular masses increase.

- Eye protection
- Rack and 4 test tubes
- Boiling tube
- Beaker ($250\,cm^3$)
- Small glass trough or large beaker
- Hard-glass watch glass
- Boiling tubes fitted with bungs and glass bends as in figure 1
- Aluminium foil
- Glass wool
- Splints
- Access to a bright light source (ideally sunlight, but a high intensity lamp or even a fluorescent light will do)
- Hexane or cyclohexane
- Paraffin oil (medicinal paraffin)
- Paraffin wax
- Bromine. Sodium thiosulphate solution (approximately $1\,mol\,dm^{-3}$ should also be available for dealing with bromine spills)
- Concentrated sulphuric acid
- Bromine water
- Potassium manganate(VII) (potassium permanganate) solution, about $0.1\,mol\,dm^{-3}$
- Dilute sodium hydroxide
- **Access to a fume cupboard**

Time required 1–2 double periods

EYE PROTECTION MUST BE WORN

HARMFUL
Hexane
Cyclohexane

HIGHLY FLAMMABLE
Hexane
Cyclohexane

Chemical properties

Action of some common reagents on hexane

EYE PROTECTION
MUST BE WORN

CORROSIVE
Concentrated
sulphuric acid

Sodium
hydroxide solution

HARMFUL
Bromine water

Use about $2\,cm^3$ of hexane with $2\,cm^3$ of the reagent in each case, shake carefully and look for any signs of a chemical reaction having occurred.

Investigate the reaction of hexane (a typical alkane) with

a bromine water,

b potassium manganate(VII) solution,

c sodium hydroxide solution,

d concentrated sulphuric acid (**CARE**).

7 Does hexane react with any of the above substances under normal laboratory conditions?

8 The alkanes used to be called the **paraffins**. Suggest why this name was used.

9 In which substance is bromine more soluble—hexane or water? Why?

10 In which substance is potassium manganate(VII) more soluble—hexane or water? Why?

The experiments you have carried out suggest that with common reagents under ordinary laboratory conditions, alkanes are very unreactive. Alkanes are not, however, completely inert. If they were they would not be very useful to humans.

Reaction of hexane with bromine

EYE PROTECTION
MUST BE WORN

WEAR PROTECTIVE
GLOVES

USE A FUME
CUPBOARD

CORROSIVE
Bromine

CARE Bromine is corrosive and toxic. Wear eye protection and protective gloves and work in a fume cupboard when adding the bromine. If any bromine is spilt, neutralise it immediately with a solution of sodium thiosulphate(VI).

Put $2\,cm^3$ of hexane in each of two test tubes. Add **one drop** of bromine (not bromine water) to each tube.

Wrap aluminium foil around one of the tubes so that it is light-proof, then stand the two tubes side by side in a test tube rack. Leave the rack in bright sunlight or near to a bright light source for 5–10 minutes, then examine the appearance of each tube. Look for any signs of a gas being evolved.

11 Under what conditions does hexane react with bromine?

12 What inorganic product is formed in this reaction?

13 Write a structural formula for one possible organic product of the reaction.

14 What type of reaction is this?

Combustion of alkanes

HIGHLY
FLAMMABLE
Methane

Fill a boiling tube with methane from the gas tap. Stopper the tube and stand it in a rack. Light a splint, unstopper the tube and apply the lighted splint to the mouth of the tube.

15 Write a balanced equation for the reaction which occurs.

16 Would you expect the same result if you held the tube upside down and lighted the gas? Explain your answer.

Put a small piece of paraffin wax on a hard-glass watch glass and apply a lighted splint to it.

17 Can the wax be easily ignited?

18 Why is wax harder to ignite than methane, even though they both contain alkanes?

19 Why does a candle have a wick?

Cracking of alkanes

At high temperatures, the atoms in an alkane molecule vibrate rapidly. If the temperature is high enough, the vibration becomes sufficiently vigorous for chemical bonds to break. This breakage of the C–C bonds in alkanes leads to the formation of smaller hydrocarbon fragments, and is called **cracking.** The temperature required for cracking can be reduced by the use of solid catalysts.

Set up the apparatus shown in figure 1.

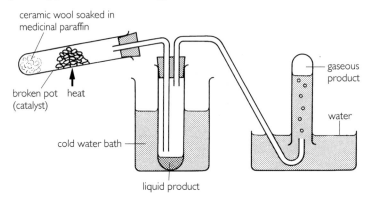

Figure 1
Cracking medicinal paraffin.

CARE Wear eye protection. When heating the tube, beware of melting the rubber bung, and make sure the delivery tube does not become blocked. Beware of suck-back: remove the delivery tube from the water when you stop heating or when the gas ceases to be evolved.

Heat the broken pot strongly and warm the medicinal paraffin gently so that a steady steam of vapour passes over the hot catalyst. Continue until a few cubic centimetres of liquid product have collected, by which time you should have collected several tubes of gas.

Shake some of the gas with a few drops of bromine water.

20 What happens? What structural feature does the gaseous product's molecule contain?

Test the gaseous product with a burning splint.

Compare the appearance and viscosity of the liquid product with that of the paraffin oil. Shake a little of the liquid product with an equal volume of bromine water in a stoppered tube.

21 What evidence is there that the liquid product contains smaller molecules than the original paraffin oil?

22 Eicosane ($C_{20}H_{42}$) is a typical alkane present in paraffin oil. Write an equation (using structural formulae) to represent one possible outcome of the cracking of eicosane.

23 Why are cracking reactions of this sort important in the petrochemical industry?

24 What would you expect to happen if you repeated the cracking experiment using the liquid product instead of paraffin oil? Test your prediction if you have time.

25 Summarise the important physical and chemical properties of alkanes that you have encountered in this practical. Where appropriate give an example of the industrial, social or environmental importance of that property.

INVESTIGATION

See Investigation 12

Practical 26
Alkenes

REQUIREMENTS

For the preparation and reactions of ethene, each student, or pair of students, will need:
- Eye protection
- Ceramic wool
- Ethanol
- Teat pipette
- Bunsen burner
- Porous pot
- Hard-glass test tube fitted with bung and delivery tube
- 4 test tubes
- Beaker (250 cm^3 or 400 cm^3)
- Dilute bromine water
- Dilute potassium manganate(VII) (about 0.1 mol dm^{-3})
- Dilute sulphuric acid
- Sodium carbonate solution (about 0.1 mol dm^{-3})

For the preparation and reactions of cyclohexene:
- Eye protection
- Round-bottomed flask or pear-shaped flask (50 cm^3 or 100 cm^3)
- Still-head
- Thermometer (0–110°C) and holder
- Liebig condenser
- Collecting (receiving) vessel
- Beaker (250 cm^3 or 400 cm^3)
- Cyclohexanol
- Concentrated phosphoric(V) acid
- Measuring cylinder (10 cm^3)
- Separating funnel
- Rack and 3 test tubes
- Small conical flask
- Small crucible
- Teat pipette
- Saturated sodium chloride solution
- Anhydrous calcium chloride
- Ceramic wool
- Bromine water
- Dilute potassium manganate(VII) (about 1.0 mol dm^{-3})
- Dilute sulphuric acid
- Concentrated sulphuric acid
- Cyclohexane

Time required 2–3 double periods

Introduction

The intention of this practical is to prepare a gaseous and a liquid alkene and to look at some of their important reactions.

Preparing alkenes

Although large quantities of ethene and propene are obtained industrially from cracking reactions, the most convenient method of preparing small amounts of any alkene is by the dehydration of the corresponding alcohol. In this experiment you will prepare ethene and cyclohexene from ethanol and cyclohexanol respectively.

1 What is meant by the term dehydration?

2 Write equations for the preparation of **a** ethene and **b** cyclohexene by dehydration of their corresponding alcohols.

3 What is the most commonly used dehydrating agent?
(We could use this reagent or concentrated phosphoric(V) acid to dehydrate alcohols, but in preparing ethene from ethanol we shall use a catalytic dehydrating agent such as aluminium oxide, silicon(IV) oxide or porous pot.)

4 Porous pot is made from clay. What elements will it contain?

Preparing ethene from ethanol

CARE Eye protection must be worn throughout this practical.
Arrange the apparatus as in figure 1. Heat the porous pot with a small flame. Do **not** heat the ceramic wool directly. **Remember to remove the delivery tube from the water when you are not heating or when bubbles cease.**

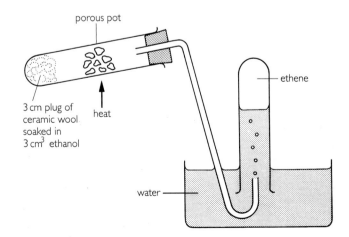

EYE PROTECTION MUST BE WORN

HIGHLY FLAMMABLE
Ethanol
Ethene

Figure 1
Preparing ethene from ethanol.

This will prevent suck-back occurring. Discard the first test tube of gas and then collect three or four test tubes of ethene.

5 Why is the ceramic wool not heated directly?

6 Why must the delivery tube be removed from the water when you are not heating?

7 Why should you discard the first test tube of gas?

Reactions of ethene

EYE PROTECTION
MUST BE WORN

(1) Burning

Ignite the ethene in one test tube.

8 Describe the flame and write an equation for the combustion.

(2) Reaction with bromine

IRRITANT
Bromine water

Dilute sulphuric acid

Add 1 cm^3 of dilute bromine water to a test tube of ethene. Cork the tube and shake.

9 Describe what happens, write an equation for the reaction and name the product.

(3) Reaction with potassium manganate(VII)

Add 1 cm^3 of dilute sulphuric acid and 3 drops of potassium manganate(VII) solution to a test tube of ethene. Cork the tube and shake.

10 Describe what happens.
The potassium manganate(VII) oxidises ethene to ethane-1,2-diol and other products.

11 What has the KMnO$_4$ been converted to?
Repeat this test using 1 cm^3 of sodium carbonate solution in place of dilute sulphuric acid.

12 What happens this time?

13 Is the KMnO$_4$ reduced to the same product as before? Explain your answer.

Preparing cyclohexene from cyclohexanol

The aims of this experiment are:

A to prepare cyclohexene by dehydrating cyclohexanol using concentrated phosphoric(V) acid;

B to introduce the method for purification of an organic liquid.

14 Concentrated phosphoric(V) acid is preferred to concentrated sulphuric acid as a dehydrating agent for alcohols because it gives a higher yield of alkene. Why does concentrated sulphuric acid gave a lower yield of alkene? (**Hint** What side reactions occur with concentrated sulphuric acid?)

Preparation

CORROSIVE
Phosphoric(V)
acid

HIGHLY
FLAMMABLE
Cyclohexanol

Cyclohexene

EYE PROTECTION
MUST BE WORN

Put 10 cm^3 of cyclohexanol in a small round-bottomed flask. *Slowly* add 4 cm^3 of concentrated phosphoric(V) acid and **mix thoroughly** by swirling the flask cautiously. Now arrange the apparatus as in figure 2 (see next page).

Heat the mixture in a water bath at 70°C for 15 minutes. Raise the temperature and **distil very slowly, so that all the cyclohexene vapour is condensed by the condenser**. Collect the distillate which comes over between 70°C and 90°C.

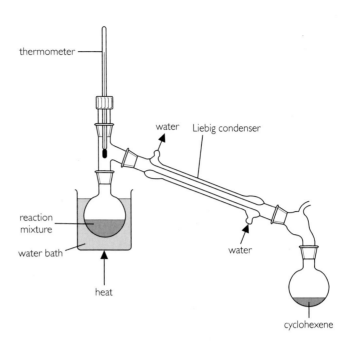

Figure 2
Preparing cyclohexene from cyclohexanol.

Purification

IRRITANT
Anhydrous
calcium chloride

Pour the distillate into a separating funnel and shake it with an equal volume of saturated sodium chloride solution.

Allow the two layers to separate and then run off the lower aqueous layer. Transfer the top layer (cyclohexene) to a small conical flask and add a few pieces of anhydrous calcium chloride. Mix the contents of the flask until the liquid is clear.

Finally, decant the alkene into a clean flask and re-distil it, collecting the liquid which distils between 81°C and 85°C. (The boiling point of cyclohexene is 83°C.) Use your sample of cyclohexene in the experiments below.

15 Name two impurities present in the cyclohexene before purification.

16 What impurities are removed from the impure cyclohexene when it is shaken with sodium chloride solution? (Sodium chloride solution is used rather than water because it is denser than water and will separate from the cyclohexene more rapidly after shaking.)

17 Why is the cyclohexene mixed with anhydrous calcium chloride?

18 What are the three key stages in purifying an organic liquid?

19 What mass of cyclohexene did you obtain?
Use the equation for the dehydration of cyclohexanol to calculate the theoretical yield of cyclohexene. (Assume that the phosphoric(V) acid is present in excess.)

20 What is your percentage yield of cyclohexene?

Reactions of cyclohexene

**EYE PROTECTION
MUST BE WORN**

(1) Burning

Burn 1 *drop* of cyclohexene on a small tuft of ceramic wool in a crucible.

21 Suggest four products formed when the cyclohexene burns.

22 Write an equation for the complete combustion of cyclohexene (C_6H_{10}) in excess oxygen.

(2) Reaction with bromine

Add 1 cm³ of bromine water to 3 drops of cyclohexene in a test tube. Cork the tube and shake.

23 Describe what happens, write an equation for the reaction and name the product.

(3) Reaction with potassium manganate(VII)

Add 1 cm³ of dilute sulphuric acid and 3 drops of potassium manganate(VII) solution to 3 drops of cyclohexene in a test tube. Cork the tube and shake.

24 Describe and explain what happens.

(4) Reaction with concentrated sulphuric acid

CORROSIVE
Concentrated
sulphuric acid

Add 3 drops of concentrated sulphuric acid (**CARE**) to 3 drops of cyclohexene.

25 Describe what happens, write an equation and name the product.

26 Many of the reactions of alkenes involve addition. What do you understand by the term 'addition reaction'?

27 Why do alkenes readily undergo addition reactions?

Further reactions

HIGHLY
FLAMMABLE
Cyclohexane

If time permits, carry out the reactions again, using cyclohexane in place of cyclohexene.

28 Account for the differences in reactivity between cyclohexene (a typical alkene) and cyclohexane (a typical alkane).

Practical 27
Aromatic compounds

REQUIREMENTS

Each student, or pair of students, will require:

Part I
- Eye protection
- Cyclohexane
- Cyclohexene
- Methylbenzene
- Bromine water
- Dilute sulphuric acid
- Dilute potassium manganate(VII) solution (about $0.1\,mol\,dm^{-3}$)
- Rack with 4 test tubes

Part 2
- Eye protection
- Methyl benzoate
- Concentrated sulphuric acid
- Concentrated nitric acid
- Ice
- Ethanol
- Conical flask ($100\,cm^3$)
- Measuring cylinder ($10\,cm^3$)
- Beaker ($250\,cm^3$ or $400\,cm^3$)
- 2 small beakers ($100\,cm^3$ or $150\,cm^3$)
- Rack with 2 test tubes
- Teat pipette
- Thermometer ($0°C–110°C$)
- Buchner funnel and flask
- Filter paper
- Melting point tube
- Access to balance
- Acess to melting point apparatus
- Access to suction pump

Time required 2 double periods

HARMFUL
Bromine water

IRRITANT
Dilute
sulphuric acid

HARMFUL
Methylbenzene

HIGHLY
FLAMMABLE
Cyclohexane
Cyclohexene
Methylbenzene

Introduction

The most important, and the prototype, aromatic compound is benzene. Indeed, aromatic compounds are normally considered to be those compounds with chemical properties similar to benzene.

1 Write down the full structural formulae of benzene, cyclohexane, cyclohexene and methylbenzene.

2 Which of these compounds are

   a alkanes,   **c** cyclic compounds,

   b aromatic compounds,   **d** unsaturated hydrocarbons?

3 What reactions would you expect an unsaturated hydrocarbon to undergo with

   a bromine water,   **b** dilute acidified potassium manganate(VII)?

Benzene is toxic and its use is illegal in school and college laboratories. However, the typical reactions of benzene are also given by methylbenzene, which is safe to use with adequate precautions.

A Addition reactions

Reaction with bromine water

Add $1\,cm^3$ of bromine water to separate $1\,cm^3$ samples of methylbenzene, cyclohexane and cyclohexene. Shake all three mixtures thoroughly.

4 Make a table of your results. Describe what happens in each case, write equations where appropriate and name the products of any reactions.

Reaction with acidified potassium manganate(VII)

Add $1\,cm^3$ of dilute sulphuric acid and $1\,cm^3$ of dilute potassium manganate(VII) solution to separate $1\,cm^3$ samples of methylbenzene, cyclohexane and cyclohexene. Shake all three mixtures thoroughly.

5 Make a table of your results. Describe what happens in each case, write equations where appropriate and name the products of any reactions.

6 Benzene is an unsaturated compound yet it does not react with bromine water or with dilute acidified potassium manganate(VII). Why is this so?

The characteristic reactions of benzene and other aromatic hydrocarbons involve substitution, because this type of reaction retains the delocalised π-electron system of the aromatic nucleus (see *Chemistry in Context*, Fourth Edition, sections 29.6 and 29.7). Addition reactions involving disruption of the aromatic ring do, however, occur (see *Chemistry in Context*, Fourth Edition, section 29.8).

7 State the conditions, name the products and write equations for the addition reactions between benzene and

a hydrogen,

b chlorine.

What are the important uses of the products of these two reactions?

B Substitution reactions

One of the most important substitution reactions of aromatic compounds is nitration. The intention of this experiment is:

A to illustrate the technique of nitration;

B to demonstrate the method of purifying an organic solid.

The compound chosen for nitration is methyl benzoate, a relatively simple derivative of benzene, of relatively low toxicity, which is used in commercial heat meters. Methyl benzoate can be nitrated readily with the usual nitric acid/sulphuric acid nitrating mixture. The product is solid methyl 3-nitrobenzoate.

(1) Preparation of methyl 3-nitrobenzoate

HARMFUL
Methyl benzoate

EYE PROTECTION MUST BE WORN

CARE Eye protection must be worn.
Measure $2.5\,cm^3$ of methyl benzoate into a small conical flask and then dissolve it in $5\,cm^3$ of concentrated sulphuric acid. When the liquid has dissolved, cool the mixture in ice.
Prepare the nitrating mixture by carefully adding $2\,cm^3$ of concentrated sulphuric acid to $2\,cm^3$ of concentrated nitric acid and then cool this mixture in ice as well.

CORROSIVE
Concentrated sulphuric acid

Concentrated nitric acid

CARE These acids are corrosive.
Now add the nitrating mixture drop by drop from a teat pipette to the solution of methyl benzoate. (Do not allow the nitrating mixture to get into the rubber teat.) Stir the mixture with a thermometer and keep the temperature below 10°C. When the addition is complete, allow the mixture to stand at room temperature for another 15 minutes.

After this time, pour the reaction mixture on to about 25 g of crushed ice and stir until all the ice has melted and crystalline methyl 3-nitrobenzoate has formed.

(2) Purification of the methyl 3-nitrobenzoate

Filter the crystals using a Buchner funnel, wash them thoroughly with cold water and then transfer them to a small beaker.

Now, recrystallise the product from the minimum volume of hot ethanol. Warm $15\,cm^3$ of ethanol to about 50°C by immersing it in a beaker of hot water. The hot water should be obtained using an electric kettle or from a hot water tap. **There should be no naked flames in the laboratory whilst ethanol is being used.** Dissolve all the crystals in the minimum volume of this hot ethanol. Allow the solution to cool to room temperature, then immerse the beaker in iced water to complete the crystallisation of methyl 3-nitrobenzoate.

HIGHLY FLAMMABLE
Ethanol

Filter the crystals, dry them between filter papers and then weigh them. Record the mass obtained. Finally, obtain the melting point of the crystals. (Pure methyl 3-nitrobenzoate melts at 77.5°C.)

8 What conditions employed during the preparation help to prevent further nitration of the product to a dinitro-derivative?

9 Give the names and structural formulae of two nitro-compounds that are very likely to contaminate the impure crystals of methyl 3-nitrobenzoate.

10 How do the conditions for nitration of methyl benzoate differ from those for the nitration of benzene?

11 Why were the crystals washed with water before recrystallisation?

12 What happens during a recrystallisation to

    a impurities, **b** the main product?

13 How is loss of the product kept to a minimum during recrystallisation?

14 What are the usual stages in the purification of an organic solid?

15 How many moles of **a** methyl benzoate, **b** nitric acid, were used in the preparation of methyl 3-nitrobenzoate? (Assume that concentrated nitric acid is pure HNO_3 and that its density is $1.5\,g\,cm^{-3}$. Assume that the density of methyl benzoate is $1.1\,g\,cm^{-3}$.) Which reactant is present in excess?

16 What is the theoretical yield of methyl 3-nitrobenzoate that should be obtained?

17 What is your actual percentage yield?

Practical 28
Bromobutane

REQUIREMENTS

Each student, or pair of students, will need:

- Eye protection
- Pear-shaped flask (50 cm^3)
- Round flask (50 cm^3)
- Condenser
- Still-head
- Tap funnel to fit still-head (doubles as separating funnel)
- Thermometer (0°C–110°C) and holder
- Measuring cylinder (25 cm^3)
- Teat pipette
- Rack with 3 test tubes
- Beaker (250 cm^3)
- Butan-1-ol
- Sodium bromide
- Concentrated sulphuric acid
- Anhydrous sodium sulphate
- Concentrated hydrochloric acid
- Ethanol
- Dilute nitric acid
- Dilute sodium hydroxide
- Silver nitrate solution, approximately 0.1 mol dm^{-3} (4 g in 250 cm^3)
- Sodium bromide solution, approximately 0.1 mol dm^{-3} (2.5 g in 250 cm^3)

Time required 3 double periods

Introduction

In this practical you will prepare 1-bromobutane in as high a yield and as pure a state as possible. You will meet several of the experimental techniques commonly used in the preparation of an organic liquid. Having prepared a sample of 1-bromobutane, you will investigate some of its chemical reactions.

Principle

Halogenoalkanes are normally prepared from their corresponding alcohol by a nucleophilic substitution reaction. The reagents most frequently used are hydrogen halides or phosphorus halides (e.g. PCl_5, PCl_3).

1 Draw the structure of the alcohol from which 1-bromobutane can be made, and indicate which bond must be broken.

Hydrogen halides and phosphorus halides show acidic properties. In the presence of an acid, the OH group of an alcohol becomes protonated, by virtue of the lone pairs of electrons on the oxygen atom:

$$R\text{–}\underset{..}{\overset{..}{O}}H + H^+ \longrightarrow R\text{–}\underset{\underset{H}{|}}{\overset{+}{O}}\text{–}H$$

2 Explain why acidic conditions favour the required bond cleavage.

In practice, a mixture of concentrated sulphuric acid and bromide ions is normally used instead of hydrogen bromide. The mechanism is the same, except that the initial protonation of the OH group is by H_2SO_4 rather than HBr.

3 Outline the mechanism of the reaction between hydrogen bromide and an alcohol to produce a bromoalkane.

4 The preparation of 2-bromo-2-methylpropane (an isomer of 1-bromobutane) by a similar method requires much less severe conditions than the preparation you will carry out here. Standing at room temperature for twenty minutes gives a good yield. Suggest a reason for this difference in the light of your proposed mechanism.

5 Give one example of an alternative preparation of monohalogenoalkanes that does not involve a substitution reaction. Could this method be readily applied to the preparation of 1-bromobutane?

You will be preparing 1-bromobutane by the reaction of butan-1-ol with a mixture of sodium bromide and concentrated sulphuric acid. The 1-bromobutane prepared in this way will be impure, even after distilling it off from the reaction mixture, and a lot of your time will be spent in purifying the crude product. Impurities will include:

• unreacted butan-1-ol
• oxides and oxyacids of sulphur
• bromine
• hydrogen bromide
• water
• butoxybutane
• but-1-ene

Butan-1-ol is soluble in concentrated hydrochloric acid, so the first stage of purification is to shake with this reagent. Excess hydrochloric acid, and other acidic impurities are then removed by shaking with a base, sodium hydrogencarbonate. The 1-bromobutane is then dried using anhydrous sodium sulphate, and finally distilled to remove remaining impurities.

Procedure

Preparation of 1-bromobutane

CARE Eye protection must be worn throughout this practical.
Put 10 g sodium bromide, 7.5 cm³ (6 g) butan-1-ol and 10 cm³ water in a 50 cm³ pear-shaped flask. The mass of butan-1-ol used should be known so that you can calculate your final percentage yield. Fit the flask with a reflux condenser, and place a funnel in the top as shown in figure 1.

Surround the flask with a beaker of cold water to cool it during the addition of concentrated sulphuric acid. Put 10 cm³ of this acid in the tap funnel (**CARE**). Gradually add it to the reaction mixture, carefully swirling the apparatus from time to time to mix well.

Remove the funnel from the reflux condenser and the flask from the water bath. Set the apparatus over a tripod and gauze and heat gently over a low bunsen flame so that the mixture reflexes gently for 30–45 minutes. The flask now contains crude bromobutane, which must be distilled from the reaction mixture.

Allow the flask to cool and rearrange the apparatus for distillation as shown in figure 2. (The thermometer is not essential at this stage.) Boil the mixture in the flask and collect the distillate in a measuring cylinder. A form of 'steam distillation' takes place—bromobutane and water distil simultaneously and form separate layers in the measuring cylinder. Continue the distillation until the upper organic layer in the flask has disappeared. Dismantle, then clean and dry your apparatus.

The distillate in the measuring cylinder has an organic and an aqueous layer. Before the bromobutane in the organic layer can be purified, the aqueous layer must be removed and discarded. In order to avoid discarding the wrong layer, it is essential to think carefully which layer is which. One way to decide is by using the densities given in table 1. If you are still not sure which is the aqueous layer, run in a few drops of water and note which layer they enter.

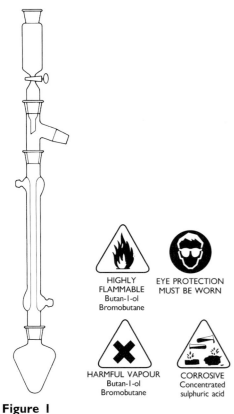

Figure 1
Apparatus for refluxing with addition.

HIGHLY FLAMMABLE
Butan-1-ol
Bromobutane

EYE PROTECTION MUST BE WORN

HARMFUL VAPOUR
Butan-1-ol
Bromobutane

CORROSIVE
Concentrated sulphuric acid

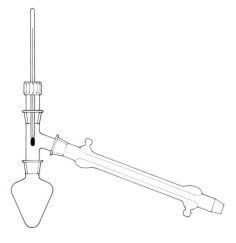

Figure 2
Apparatus for distillation.

Table 1

Liquid	Density/g cm⁻³
Water	1.0
Butan-1-ol	0.81
1-Bromobutane	1.3
Concentrated hydrochloric acid	1.2

CORROSIVE
Concentrated
hydrochloric acid

EYE PROTECTION
MUST BE WORN

Use a teat pipette to remove the water layer. You now need to shake the crude product with concentrated hydrochloric acid to remove unreacted butanol.

CARE Eye protection must be worn.

Put the organic layer in a small tap funnel then pour $10\,cm^3$ of concentrated hydrochloric acid into the measuring cylinder you used to receive the distillate—this will wash out any traces of the crude product. Pour the acid into the tap funnel. Stopper the funnel and shake well, releasing the pressure occasionally. Allow the two layers to separate, decide which is the acid layer and discard it. Run the organic layer into a clean measuring cylinder.

You must now remove excess hydrogen chloride and other acid impurities by shaking with a base. Put the bromobutane in a clean tap funnel. Rinse out the measuring cylinder with $10\,cm^3$ of sodium hydrogencarbonate solution, and pour this into the tap funnel. Stopper and shake the funnel cautiously, **regularly releasing pressure caused by the formation of carbon dioxide**. Allow the layers to separate, decide which is the bromobutane layer and run it into a $50\,cm^3$ round flask.

The bromobutane is cloudy because of the presence of water and must now be dried. Add anhydrous sodium sulphate in small quantities, swirling after each addition, until the liquid is perfectly clear.

Finally the bromobutane must be distilled to remove any remaining organic impurities. Set up the apparatus for distillation and transfer the bromobutane to the distillation flask, making sure that the sodium sulphate remains behind. Distil the bromobutane, collecting the fraction with boiling range $100-104°C$ (the boiling point of 1-bromobutane is $102°C$). Find the mass of bromobutane collected.

6 Write a balanced equation for the overall reaction.

7 Calculate the maximum mass of 1-bromobutane that could be formed from the $6\,g$ of butan-1-ol you used.

8 Calculate your percentage yield of 1-bromobutane.

9 Why are the reagents added in the particular order suggested?

10 Why is butan-1-ol much more soluble in concentrated hydrochloric acid than in water?

11 Why is sodium hydrogencarbonate used to remove acid impurities, rather than a stronger base like sodium hydroxide?

Reactions of 1-bromobutane

Experiment 1: Action of aqueous silver ions

EYE PROTECTION
MUST BE WORN

Bromobutane is insoluble in water. In order to investigate its effect on aqueous silver ions, ethanol is used as a mutual solvent, since it dissolves both silver ions and bromobutane.

Add a few drops of bromobutane to $2\,cm^3$ of ethanol, then add $2\,cm^3$ of aqueous silver nitrate. Observe the reaction mixture for a few minutes. Repeat the experiment using sodium bromide solution instead of the solution of bromobutane in ethanol.

12 What does this experiment suggest about the way bromine is bonded in

    a bromobutane

    b sodium bromide?

13 What happens when the bromobutane is left to stand for a few minutes in the presence of aqueous silver ions? Why does this happen?

Experiment 2: Reaction with hydroxide ions

CORROSIVE
Dilute
sodium
hydroxide

IRRITANT
Dilute
nitric acid

Put $2\,cm^3$ of dilute sodium hydroxide in a test tube. Add a few drops of bromobutane and warm very gently. Acidify with dilute nitric acid to neutralise the sodium hydroxide and then add $2\,cm^3$ of silver nitrate solution.

14 What happens? How do hydroxide ions react with 1-bromobutane?

15 Why must the sodium hydroxide be neutralised before adding silver nitrate solution?

16 What are the products of reactions between 1-bromobutane and

    a ammonia,

    b ethoxide ions, $CH_3CH_2O^-$,

    c cyanide ions, CN^-?

17 What type of reactions are those referred to in questions **14** and **16**?

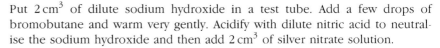

INVESTIGATION

See Investigation 13

Practical 29

Nucleophilic substitution reactions of halogenoalkanes

REQUIREMENTS

Each student, or pair of students, will need:
- Eye protection
- Rack and 9 test tubes
- Labels
- Beaker (250 cm^3)
- Thermometer (0°C–100°C)
- Measuring cylinder (10 cm^3)
- Stop-clock
- 1-Chlorobutane*
- 1-Bromobutane*
- 1-Iodobutane*
- 2-Bromobutane*
- 2-Bromo-2-methylpropane*
- Ethanol
- Silver nitrate solution, approximately 0.1 mol dm^{-3} (dissolve 4.25 g in 250 cm^3 of distilled water)
- Sodium iodide
- Propanone (acetone)

* With a separate dropping pipette for each bottle.

Time required 1 double period

Introduction

The carbon–halogen bond in halogenoalkanes is polarised:

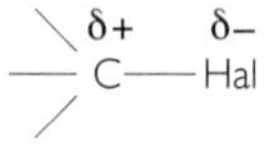

The positive charge on the carbon atom makes it attractive to negatively charged groups or **nucleophiles**. Such groups may attack the carbon, displacing the halogen as a halide ion and resulting in a nucleophilic substitution reaction.

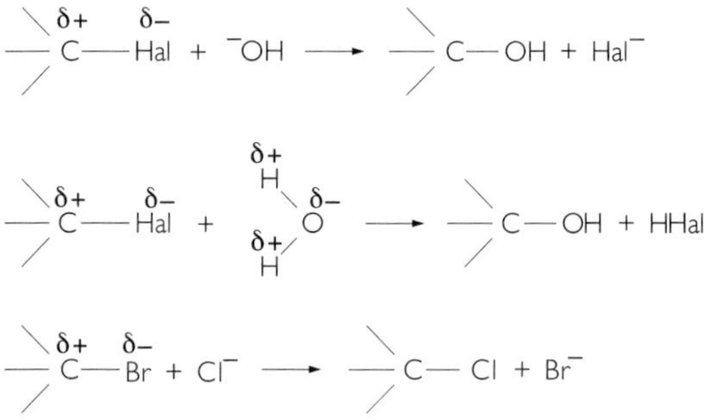

In this practical we will investigate the mechanisms of some nucleophilic substitution reactions by making simple qualitative comparisons of reaction rates.

Procedure

Experiment 1: Effect of the halogen atom on the rate of hydrolysis

In this experiment you will compare the rates of hydrolysis of 1-chlorobutane, 1-bromobutane, and 1-iodobutane.

$$CH_3CH_2CH_2CH_2Hal + H_2O \longrightarrow CH_3CH_2CH_2CH_2OH + H^+ + Hal^-$$

The rate of the reaction can be followed by carrying it out in the presence of silver ions. The halogenoalkanes, being covalently bonded, give no precipitate of silver halide, but as the reaction proceeds and halide ions are produced, a precipitate of silver halide gradually appears:

$$Ag^+(aq) + Hal^-(aq) \longrightarrow AgHal(s)$$

Halogenoalkanes are insoluble in water, so the reaction is carried out in the presence of ethanol, which acts as a mutal solvent for the halogenoalkane and silver ions.

HARMFUL
1-Bromobutane
1-Iodobutane

HIGHLY FLAMMABLE
Ethanol
1-Chlorobutane

EYE PROTECTION MUST BE WORN

CARE Eye protection must be worn. Ethanol is highly flammable. Do not have any naked flames near the tubes or the ethanol bottle.

Set up three labelled test tubes as described in table 1.

Table 1
Tubes for experiment 1

Tube 1	Tube 2	Tube 3
1 cm^3 ethanol	1 cm^3 ethanol	1 cm^3 ethanol
2 drops 1-chlorobutane	2 drops 1-bromobutane	2 drops 1-iodobutane

Stand the tubes in a beaker of water at about 50°C and put a tube containing 5 cm^3 of 0.1 mol dm^{-3} silver nitrate solution in the same beaker. Leave the tubes for about 10 minutes so that they reach the temperature of the bath. Add 1 cm^3 of the silver nitrate solution to each of tubes 1, 2 and 3, working quickly and noting the time. Shake each tube to mix the contents and observe the tubes over the course of the next five minutes or so.

1 Which halogenoalkane undergoes hydrolysis fastest? Which is slowest?

2 Which halogenoalkane has the most polar carbon–halogen bond?

3 Is differing polarity the reason for the different rates of hydrolysis?

4 Suggest a possible explanation for the different rates of hydrolysis using the bond energies shown in table 2.

Table 2
Average bond energies for the carbon–halogen bonds in halogenoalkanes

Bond	Average bond energy/kJ mol^{-1}
C–Cl	339
C–Br	284
C–I	218

Theoretical background: the mechanism of nucleophilic substitution

Consider the substitution reaction:

$$R_2 - \underset{\underset{R_3}{|}}{\overset{\overset{R_1}{|}}{C}} - Br + {}^-OH \longrightarrow R_2 - \underset{\underset{R_3}{|}}{\overset{\overset{R_1}{|}}{C}} - OH + Br^-$$

(R$_1$, R$_2$, and R$_3$ are alkyl groups or hydrogen atoms.) Studies of the kinetics of nucleophilic substitution suggest that these reactions can proceed by two possible mechanisms.

Step-by-step mechanism

In this case, it is proposed that a two-step mechanism is involved:

$$R_2 - \underset{\underset{R_3}{|}}{\overset{\overset{R_1}{|}}{C}} - Br \xrightarrow{\text{slow}} R_2 - \underset{\underset{R_3}{|}}{\overset{\overset{R_1}{|}}{C}}{}^+ + Br^-$$

intermediate carbocation

$$R_2 - \underset{\underset{R_3}{|}}{\overset{\overset{R_1}{|}}{C}}{}^+ + {}^-OH \xrightarrow{\text{fast}} R_2 - \underset{\underset{R_3}{|}}{\overset{\overset{R_1}{|}}{C}} - OH$$

The first step, which is relatively slow, involves bond cleavage to form the intermediate carbocation. The carbocation is very unstable and reactive, so the second step is fast. The overall rate of the reaction is determined by the slow first step — the **rate-determining step**. (See *Chemistry in Context*, Fourth Edition section 25.11 for further discussion of this.)

Single-step mechanism

Here it is proposed that the reaction occurs in a single step. The OH⁻ ion is attracted to the central carbon atoms, and as it moves in, it repels the Br atom. At some 'middle' stage in the reaction, Br and OH are both partially bonded to the carbon, the OH on its way in and the Br on its way out. This is the **transition state** of the reaction. It is **not** a reaction intermediate which exists independently, but simply the middle stage in a continuous process during which the OH⁻ moves in and the Br⁻ moves out.

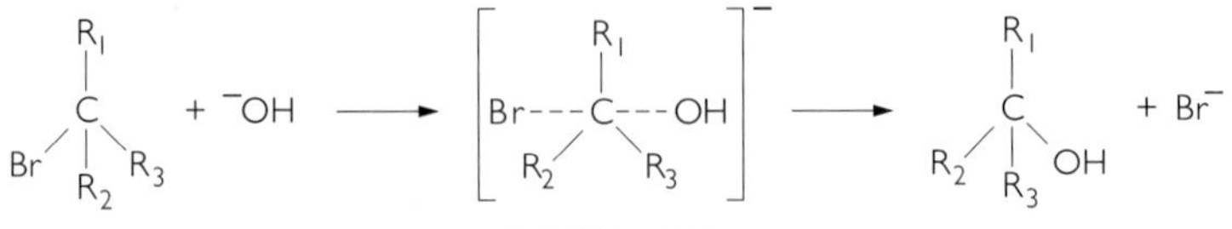

transition state

Factors determining which mechanism operates in practice

In many nucleophilic substitution reactions, both of the proposed mechanisms can and do operate, but in most cases one proceeds much faster than the other. The faster mechanism can often be taken as the mechanism for that reaction. In the experiments which follow you will investigate some of the factors which determine the particular mechanism for a given reaction.

Two of the most important factors are the structure of the halogenoalkane and the nature of the solvent.

A Structure of the halogenoalkane

In the first, two-step mechanism, the rate of the reaction is determined by the ease with which the intermediate carbocation forms. If the substituent groups R_1, R_2, and R_3 are all alkyl groups rather than H atoms, they will tend to donate electrons, stabilising the carbocation and favouring its formation.

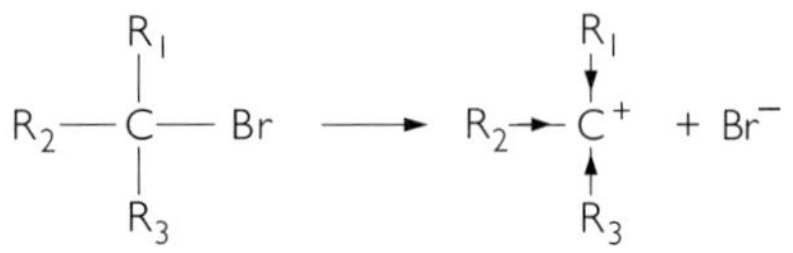

If some or all of R_1, R_2, and R_3 are hydrogen atoms, the formation of the carbocation will be less favoured, so the rate of the overall reaction will be slower. Thus, the two-step mechanism is favoured by the presence of substituent alkyl groups. The reverse applies in the case of the single-step mechanism, which is favoured by the presence of substituent hydrogen atoms.

B Nature of the solvent in which the reaction is carried out

Polar solvents, particularly water, favour ion formation and therefore the two-step mechanism. Conversely, the single-step mechanism is favoured in non-polar solvents.

Experiment 2: Effect of the structure of the carbon skeleton on the reaction mechanism and reaction rate

The experimental method is similar to that in experiment **1**. In this case, instead of varying the halogen atom for a given carbon skeleton, we will vary the structure of the alkane skeleton keeping the same halogen, bromine. The bromoalkanes used are

| 1-bromobutane | 2-bromobutane | 2-bromo-2-methylpropane |

The general reaction is the same as in experiment **1**:

$$RBr + H_2O \longrightarrow ROH + H^+ + Br^-$$

(using RBr to represent the bromoalkane involved).

Table 3
Tubes for experiment 2

Tube 1	Tube 2	Tube 3
1 cm^3 ethanol	1 cm^3 ethanol	1 cm^3 ethanol
2 drops 1-bromobutane	2 drops 2-bromobutane	2 drops 2-bromo-2-methylpropane

EYE PROTECTION MUST BE WORN

Set up three labelled test tubes as described in table 3, above. In this experiment it is satisfactory to work at room temperature.

Add 1 cm^3 of 0.1 mol dm^{-3} silver nitrate solution to each tube, working quickly and noting the time. Shake each tube to mix the contents. Observe the tubes over the course of the next five minutes or so.

5 Which bromoalkane is hydrolysed fastest? Which is slowest?

6 Bearing in mind that the solvent in this experiment is a 1:1 mixture of ethanol and water (the water coming from the silver nitrate solution), which mechanism is likely to be favoured? Explain your answer.

7 Which bromoalkane would be most favoured by the mechanism you have proposed in your answer to question **6**? Which would be least favoured? Explain your answer.

8 Explain the observed relative rates of hydrolysis of the three bromoalkanes.

Experiment 3: Effect of the solvent on the reaction mechanism and the reaction rate: the Finkelstein reaction

Experiments **1** and **2** have involved hydrolysis reactions in aqueous solution. It is, of course, impossible to carry out hydrolysis in a non-aqueous solvent, but by using a substitution reaction known as Finkelstein's reaction you can investigate the rate of a simple nucleophilic substitution reaction in a non-aqueous solvent, propanone. The reaction is the substitution of a bromide ion by an iodide ion:

$$RBr + I^- \longrightarrow RI + Br^-$$

The source of I$^-$ is sodium iodide. Sodium iodide is soluble in propanone, but sodium bromide is not. As bromide ions are produced in the reaction, they combine with sodium ions to form a precipitate of sodium bromide.

$$RBr(pr) + Na^+(pr) + I^-(pr) \longrightarrow RI(pr) + NaBr(s)$$

[(pr) indicates that the substance is in solution in propanone.]

This reaction can therefore be followed by timing the rate of appearance of the sodium bromide precipitate.

EYE PROTECTION
MUST BE WORN

HIGHLY
FLAMMABLE
Propanone

CARE Propanone is highly flammable. Do not have any naked flames near the tubes or the propanone bottle.

Dissolve 1 g of sodium iodide in 15 cm^3 of propanone. This solution is called Finkelstein's Reagent.

Put 5 cm^3 of the reagent into each of three labelled test tubes and stand the tubes in a beaker of water at 35°C. Leave the tubes for 10 minutes to reach the temperature of the water bath.

Working quickly and noting the time, add 8 drops of 1-bromobutane to the first tube, 8 drops of 2-bromobutane to the second and 8 drops of 2-bromo-2-methylpropane to the third. Observe the three tubes over the course of the next 5 minutes or so.

9 Which bromoalkane undergoes nucleophilic substitution by iodide ions fastest? Which is slowest?

10 Bearing in mind that the solvent in this experiment is propanone, which reaction mechanism is likely to be favoured? Explain your answer.

11 Which bromoalkane would be most favoured by the mechanism you have proposed in your answer to question **10**? Which would be least favoured? Explain your answer.

12 Explain the observed order of reaction rate of the three bromoalkanes.

INVESTIGATION

See Investigation 13

Practical 30
Alcohols

REQUIREMENTS

Each student, or pair of students, will need:
- Eye protection
- Rack with 4 test tubes
- Teat pipette
- Ethanol
- Methanol
- Propan-2-ol
- Full range indicator paper
- Sodium, cut into small pieces
- Small beaker ($100\,cm^3$)
- Bunsen burner
- Splint
- Concentrated sulphuric acid
- Glacial ethanoic (acetic) acid
- 2-Hydroxybenzoic (salicyclic) acid
- Phosphorus pentachloride
- Silver nitrate solution (about $0.1\,mol\,dm^{-3}$)
- Dilute sulphuric acid
- Potassium dichromate(VI) solution (about $1\,mol\,dm^{-3}$)
- About $20\,cm$ of medium gauge copper wire wound into a spiral at one end
- **Access to a fume cupboard**

Time required 2 double periods

Introduction

Alcohols are organic compounds with the general formula: $R_2 - \underset{\underset{R_3}{\big/}}{\overset{\overset{R_1}{\big|}}{C}} - OH$

R_1, R_2 and R_3 may be hydrogen or any alkyl or aryl group. Most alcohols can be regarded as alkanes in which a hydrogen atom has been replaced by an –OH group. Examples are ethanol (CH_3CH_2OH), propan-2-ol ($CH_3CHOHCH_3$) and cyclohexanol ($C_6H_{11}OH$).

The intention of this practical is to compare the physical properties of alcohols with those of other organic compounds of similar relative molecular mass and then to look at some of their typical chemical properties.

Comparing the physical properties of alcohols, alkanes and ethers

1 Copy out and complete table 1 below using a data book.

Table 1
Comparing the physical properties of ethanol, methoxymethane and propane

Compound	Relative molecular mass	Structural formula	Melting point/°C	Boiling point/°C	Relative solubility in water
Ethanol					
Methoxymethane					
Propane					

2 Explain the relative volatilites of ethanol, methoxymethane and propane.

3 Explain the relative solubilites in water of ethanol, methoxymethane and propane.

4 Why has ethanol been compared with methoxymethane and propane rather than ethoxyethane and ethane?

Investigating the chemical properties of alcohols

CARE Eye protection must be worn throughout this practical.

(1) Reactions in which the O–H bond breaks

Reactions of alcohols involving cleavage of the O–H bond can be compared with similar reactions for water.

EYE PROTECTION
MUST BE WORN

HIGHLY
FLAMMABLE
Ethanol

CORROSIVE
Sodium

Sodium

Reaction with sodium

Put 1 cm³ of ethanol in a test tube and add one small, **rice grain-sized** piece of sodium. Try to identify the gas produced. **Dispose of the remaining solution carefully because it is very corrosive.**

5 Describe what happens. Is the reaction of sodium with ethanol more or less vigorous than the reaction of sodium with water?

6 Describe and explain what happens when a piece of damp indicator paper is added to the sodium/ethanol mixture.

7 Write equations for the reactions of sodium with **a** water, **b** ethanol.

8 Explain the relative reactivities of ethanol and water with sodium.

CORROSIVE
Glacial ethanoic acid

Concentrated sulphuric acid

EYE PROTECTION
MUST BE WORN

Reaction with organic acids—esterification

Put 10 drops of ethanol in a test tube and add 10 drops of glacial ethanoic (acetic) acid. Carefully, add 6 drops of concentrated sulphuric acid, and then warm the mixture, without boiling, for 5 minutes. Now, pour the contents of the test tube into about 50 cm³ of water in a beaker, and smell cautiously.

9 Why must the mixture not be boiled?

10 The product, ethyl ethanoate (acetate) is an ester. Describe its smell.

11 Why does the smell of the ester become more prominent after the mixture is poured into water?

12 Write an equation for the reaction between ethanol and ethanoic acid, clearly showing the structure of the ester.

13 How does sulphuric acid catalyse this reaction?

14 What uses has ethyl ethanoate?

Repeat the experiment using 2-hydroxybenzoic acid (salicylic acid) in place of ethanoic acid. (Use approximately equal volumes of solid 2-hydroxybenzoic acid and ethanol.)

HARMFUL
2-Hydroxybenzoic acid

15 What is the name of the ester produced? What does it smell like?

16 This ester is a constituent of 'oil of wintergreen'. What is this oil used for?

17 How and why has isotopic labelling been used in the study of esterification reactions? (See *Chemistry in Context*, Fourth Edition, section 33.5.)

(2) Reactions in which the C–OH bond breaks

Reaction with phosphorus halides

USE A FUME
CUPBOARD

EYE PROTECTION
MUST BE WORN

CORROSIVE
Phosphorus pentachloride

CARE The reaction produces corrosive fumes. Work in a fume cupboard. Add a *little* phosphorus pentachloride to 10 drops of ethanol. Collect some of the fumes evolved in a teat pipette and identify them by bubbling into silver nitrate solution.

When the fumes have subsided and the reaction is complete, pour the contents of the tube into 50 cm³ of water in a beaker and cautiously smell the product, which is an alkyl halide.

18 What gas is evolved when phosphorus pentachloride reacts with ethanol?

19 Write equations for the reactions of ethanol with

    a phosphorus pentachloride,

    b phosphorus trichloride.

Reactions with concentrated hydrohalic acids

The reactions between alcohols and concentrated hydrohalic acids (or halide ions in concentrated sulphuric acid) are important in the preparation of alkyl halides. The preparation of 1-bromobutane in practical 28 uses this procedure.

20 Write an equation or equations for the preparation of 2-bromopropane using potassium bromide, concentrated sulphuric acid and an appropriate alcohol.

(3) Reactions of the $-CH_2OH$ and $>CHOH$ groups

Alcohols with a $-CH_2OH$ group can be oxidised first to an aldehyde containing

the $-C\overset{\displaystyle O}{\underset{\displaystyle H}{\diagup}}$ group, and then to a carboxylic acid with the $-C\overset{\displaystyle O}{\underset{\displaystyle OH}{\diagup}}$ group.

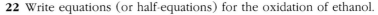

alcohol   aldehyde

carboxylic acid

Alcohols with a $>CHOH$ group can be oxidised to ketones containing the $>C=O$ group. Further oxidation is difficult.

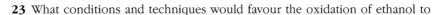

alcohol   ketone

Oxidation with acidified potassium dichromate(VI)

IRRITANT
Dilute
sulphuric acid

EYE PROTECTION
MUST BE WORN

Add 10 drops of dilute sulphuric acid and 5 drops of potassium dichromate(VI) solution to 5 drops of ethanol. Mix thoroughly and then warm the mixture. Smell cautiously.

21 Describe what happens and explain the colour changes.

22 Write equations (or half-equations) for the oxidation of ethanol.

23 What conditions and techniques would favour the oxidation of ethanol to

    a ethanal rather than ethanoic acid,

HIGHLY
FLAMMABLE
Methanol

TOXIC
Methanol

Propan-2-ol

    b ethanoic acid rather than ethanal?

Repeat the experiment using first methanol and then propan-2-ol in place of ethanol.

24 Write equations (or half-equations) for the oxidation of methanol and propan-2-ol. Name the oxidation products. (**Note** The final oxidation products from methanol are carbon dioxide and water.)

Catalytic oxidation of alcohols

Warm 10 drops of methanol in a test tube (**CARE: highly flammable**) and then heat a clean copper spiral to red heat in a roaring bunsen flame.

25 What do you notice as the red-hot spiral is moved out of the hot bunsen flame? Write an equation for the reaction which occurs. Now introduce the red-hot spiral into the methanol vapour in the test tube.

26 Observe the copper spiral carefully and explain the changes in colour which take place on its surface. (**Hint** Methanol is oxidised to methanal (formaldehyde).)

27 Explain how the copper acts as a catalyst in the oxidation of methanol by air.

(Industrially, methanal is manufactured by passing a mixture of methanol vapour and air over a catalyst of silver, rather than copper, at 450°C–600°C.)

Practical 31
Phenol

Introduction

Phenol contains the same functional group as ethanol and other aliphatic alcohols. However, the benzene ring has a marked effect on the behaviour of the hydroxyl group, OH, so many of the properties of phenol are very different from those of ethanol. In this practical you will examine some of the differences between these two hydroxy-compounds. There will also be the opportunity to prepare phenyl benzoate and to use some of the standard techniques employed in purifying a solid organic compound and in testing its purity.

Phenol

Procedure

CARE Phenol is toxic and highly corrosive. Avoid all skin contact and wear protective gloves. Eye protection must be worn throughout this practical.

Experiment 1: Combustion

Working in a fume cupboard, set fire to a small crystal of phenol on a piece of broken porcelain held in tongs.

1 With what sort of flame does phenol burn?

2 What does ethanol look like when it burns?

3 Explain the differences in the flames seen when ethanol and phenol burn.

Experiment 2: Acidic nature

Add a spatula-full of phenol to 5 cm³ of water in a test tube. Stopper the tube and shake. Remove the stopper and warm the tube in a beaker of hot water. Note what occurs, then cool the tube and again note what happens.

4 How does the solubility of phenol in water compare with that of ethanol in water?

To the cooled tube add a little sodium hydroxide solution and mix thoroughly.

5 Is phenol more soluble in aqueous sodium hydroxide than in water? If so, why?

Now add a little concentrated hydrochloric acid (**CARE**).

6 Describe and explain what happens.

Make a stock solution of phenol by putting a spatula-full of phenol into a boiling tube and half-filling with water.

Test a portion of the solution with universal indicator. For comparison, test a solution of ethanol in water with universal indicator.

7 Explain why ethanol and phenol differ in acidity.

REQUIREMENTS

Each student, or pair of students, will need:
- Eye protection
- Rack and 4 test tubes (one fitted with a stopper)
- Boiling tube
- Beaker (250 cm³)
- Conical flask (250 cm³), fitted with a bung
- Broken porcelain
- Tongs
- Spatula
- Evaporating basin
- Melting point tube and access to apparatus for melting point determination
- Glass rod
- Buchner funnel and flask
- Filter paper
- Access to suction pump
- Phenol
- Universal indicator paper
- Concentrated hydrochloric acid
- Concentrated sulphuric acid
- Ethanol
- Sodium metal, ready cut into pieces about the size of a grain of rice
- Benzoyl chloride (keep in fume cupboard)
- Bromine water
- Iron(III) chloride solution (about 0.1 mol dm⁻³)
- Benzene-1,2-dicarboxylic acid anhydride (phthalic anhydride)
- **Access to a fume cupboard**
- Protective gloves

Time required 2 double periods

EYE PROTECTION MUST BE WORN

WEAR PROTECTIVE GLOVES

USE A FUME CUPBOARD

CORROSIVE
Phenol

TOXIC
Phenol

CORROSIVE
Sodium hydroxide solution
Concentrated hydrochloric acid

HIGHLY FLAMMABLE
Ethanol

EYE PROTECTION
MUST BE WORN

CORROSIVE
Sodium

FLAMMABLE
Sodium

Experiment 3: Reaction with sodium

Dissolve a few crystals of phenol in a few cubic centimetres of ethanol. **Working in a fume cupboard**, put the solution in an evaporating basin and add a piece of sodium **about the size of a grain of rice (CARE)**. Observe the reaction and try to decide what is formed. Compare the reaction with that of a similar-sized piece of sodium with ethanol alone. **Destroy any sodium left over, in excess ethanol**.

8 Write an equation for the reaction of phenol with sodium.

9 Use your knowledge of the relative acid strengths of phenol and ethanol to explain why the reaction of sodium with the two compounds differs in vigour.

Experiment 4: Esterification

Phenol differs from ethanol in the ease with which it forms esters. Ethyl esters are readily formed by heating ethanol with a carboxylic acid in the presence of concentrated sulphuric acid, but phenyl benzoate, for example, cannot be prepared by heating phenol with benzoic acid and concentrated sulphuric acid. The benzoic acid must be activated by converting it to benzoyl chloride, which readily reacts with phenol in basic conditions to give a good yield of phenyl benzoate.

phenol   benzoyl chloride   phenyl benzoate   + HCl

This is sometimes called the Schotten–Baumann reaction.

10 Why is phenol more difficult to esterify than ethanol?

11 Why is benzoyl chloride effective in esterifying phenol?

In the experiment which follows you will prepare phenyl benzoate in this way and, if time permits, purify your sample and check its purity by measuring its melting point.

USE A FUME
CUPBOARD

EYE PROTECTION
MUST BE WORN

CORROSIVE
Benzoyl chloride

IRRITANT
Benzoyl chloride
vapour

HIGHLY
FLAMMABLE
Ethanol

CARE Benzoyl chloride is harmful and corrosive and its vapour irritates the eyes. Avoid spilling the liquid or releasing the vapour outside the fume cupboard.
Fit a $250\,cm^3$ conical flask with a stopper, **which must fit tightly so reagents cannot leak out of the flask**. Put 5 g of phenol in the flask. Add $90\,cm^3$ of $2\,mol\,dm^{-3}$ sodium hydroxide solution. **Working in a fume cupboard**, carefully add $9\,cm^3$ of benzoyl chloride.

Put the stopper in the flask and shake vigorously. Leave for 10 minutes, shaking from time to time. Phenyl benzoate separates out as white crystals.

Filter off the crystals using a Buchner funnel, working in a fume cupboard because some unreacted benzoyl chloride may still be present. Wash the crystals several times with water, breaking up any lumps using a glass rod.

The crystals can now be purified by recrystallisation. Dissolve them in the minimum possible quantity of hot ethanol in a boiling tube, heating the ethanol in a water-bath at about 60°C. **There must be no flames nearby.** (Get the hot water from a tap or kettle.) Now allow the solution to cool so that the crystals separate out and can be filtered off, leaving impurities behind in the solution.

The purity of your sample can be assessed by measuring its melting point. Seal a melting point tube at one end, then put into it a few crystals of your sample. The tube must now be heated slowly until the sample melts, at which point the temperature is noted. To do this you may use an electrical melting point apparatus or hot oil—your teacher will show you the details of whichever method you are to use. Remember to heat the tube very slowly, otherwise you may 'overshoot' and get an inaccurate value for the melting point.

12 Record the melting point of your crystals. The melting point of pure phenol benzoate is 71°C.

13 What can you say about the purity of your own sample?

Experiment 5: Complexing reactions

EYE PROTECTION
MUST BE WORN

Add a few drops of iron(III) chloride solution to an aqueous solution of phenol. Repeat the reaction using ethanol instead of phenol.

14 Describe the characteristic colour given by phenol and Fe^{3+}.

15 What is the cause of this colour?

Experiment 6: Substitution reactions of phenol

HARMFUL
Bromine
water

EYE PROTECTION
MUST BE WORN

Add bromine water drop by drop to an aqueous solution of phenol, until it is present in excess.

16 What happens?

17 Use a text book to find the formula of the product, and write an equation for the reaction.

18 Ethanol has no reaction with bromine water. Explain the difference between the two compounds in this respect.

Experiment 7: Preparation of phenolphthalein

The indicator phenolphthalein can be prepared by the reaction between phenol and benzene-1,2-dicarboxylic anhydride (phthalic anhydride):

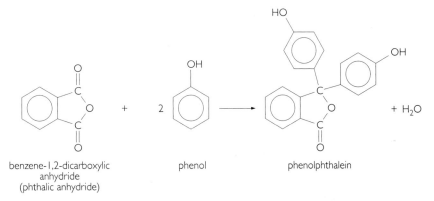

benzene-1,2-dicarboxylic anhydride (phthalic anhydride)   phenol   phenolphthalein

EYE PROTECTION
MUST BE WORN   WEAR PROTECTIVE GLOVES

CORROSIVE
Concentrated sulphuric acid
Sodium hydroxide solution

IRRITANT
Benzene-1,2-dicarboxylic anhydride

Mix 0.5 g of phenol and 0.5 g of benzene-1,2-dicarboxylic anhydride in a test tube and heat the mixture with 1 drop of concentrated sulphuric acid (**CARE**). Cool and then carefully add a little dilute sodium hydroxide solution. Investigate the colour change that occurs when the solution is acidified.

19 Phenolphthalein is a weak acid which dissociates in the following way:

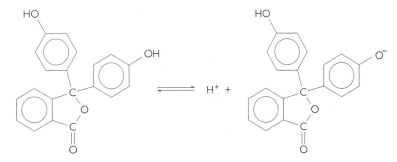

What are the colours of the undissociated and dissociated forms respectively?

20 Summarise the main differences between phenol and ethanol.

Practical 32
Carbonyl compounds

REQUIREMENTS

Each student, or pair of students, will require:
- Eye protection
- Rack with 4 test tubes
- Ethanal (acetaldehyde)
- Aqueous methanal (40% solution—formalin)
- Propanone (acetone)
- Glucose
- Saturated sodium hydrogensulphite solution
- Concentrated sodium hydroxide solution (Dissolve 30 g of NaOH (**corrosive**) in 100 cm³ of water.)
- Ice
- Salt
- Hydrogen chloride generator (Add concentrated sulphuric acid to sodium chloride (rock salt).)
- 2,4-Dinitrophenylhydrazine solution—Brady's reagent (Dissolve 2 g of 2,4-dinitrophenylhydrazine (**toxic, and explosive when dry**) in 4 cm³ of concentrated sulphuric acid (**corrosive**) and add carefully, with cooling, 30 cm³ of methanol (**flammable, toxic**). Warm gently to dissolve any undissolved solid and then add 10 cm³ of water.)
- 2 mol dm⁻³ sulphuric acid
- Ethanol

The following solutions:
- Potassium dichromate(VI) (about 0.1 mol dm⁻³)
- Silver nitrate (about 0.1 mol dm⁻³)
- Dilute ammonia

continued on next page

FLAMMABLE
Propanone

HARMFUL
Sodium hydrogensulphite solution

EYE PROTECTION MUST BE WORN

Introduction

Carbonyl compounds contain the carbonyl group, $>C=O$, which is the functional group in both aldehydes such as ethanal (acetaldehyde) and ketones such as propanone (acetone). The reactions of the carbonyl group are important to organic chemists, as the group is common in biological molecules, particularly carbohydrates such as glucose and ribose. Carbonyl compounds are also used in the manufacture of plastics and as organic solvents.

The double bond between C and O in the carbonyl group, like the double bond in alkenes, consists of a σ-bond and a π-bond. Unlike the C=C group, however, the carbonyl group does not have an even electron distribution between the two atoms and there is a greater electron density near the more electronegative oxygen atom (figure 1).

Figure 1
Electron density in the carbonyl bond.

A Addition reactions of carbonyl compounds

The electron distribution in the carbonyl bond makes the carbon atom attractive towards nucleophiles which attack and bond to it, breaking the π-bond and resulting in addition. With a general nucleophile, $\ddot{X}$–Y

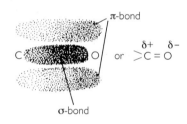

1 Bearing in mind that the first stage of addition involves attack on the $\overset{\delta+}{C}$, predict the relative reactivity of methanal, ethanal and propanone.
(**Hint** The methyl group is electron-donating in these compounds.)

CARE Eye protection must be worn throughout this practical

Reactions with sodium hydrogensulphite

To 2 cm³ of propanone, add 1 cm³ of saturated sodium hydrogensulphite solution, $NaHSO_3(aq)$, a little at a time. Shake thoroughly to ensure mixing after each addition. Judge whether a reaction has taken place by seeing if it gets hot, and then cool the mixture in a stream of cold water.

- Fehling's solution (Mix equal volumes of solutions A and B. Store solutions A and B separately because the mixture will deteriorate.)
- Solution A Dissolve 17 g of $CuSO_4.5H_2O$ in 250 cm³ of water.
- Solution B Dissolve 86 g of potassium sodium tartrate (Rochelle salt) and 30 g of NaOH (**corrosive**) in 250 cm³ of water. Warming may be necessary.
- Teat pipette
- Watch glass
- Small beaker (150 cm³ or 250 cm³)
- Bunsen burner
- Tripod
- Gauze
- Filter paper
- Melting point tubes
- Access to melting point apparatus
- **Access to fume cupboard**

Time required 2–3 double periods

USE A FUME CUPBOARD   TOXIC Methanal   EYE PROTECTION MUST BE WORN

HARMFUL Ethanal   HIGHLY FLAMMABLE Ethanal   CORROSIVE Concentrated sodium hydroxide

2 Describe what happens during this reaction.

3 Draw a full structural formula for the hydrogensulphite ion.

4 Write an equation for the reaction of propanone with sodium hydrogensulphite.

Repeat the experiment using ethanal in place of propanone.

5 Why does the propanone hydrogensulphite crystallise more readily than the ethanal hydrogensulphite?

6 Why are these carbonyl hydrogensulphite addition compounds fairly soluble in water?

7 Why are carbonyl hydrogensulph*ate* compounds (hydrogensulphate ion is HSO_4^-) more difficult to prepare than carbonyl hydrogensulph*ite* compounds?

B Polymerisation of carbonyl compounds

Carbonyl compounds, like alkenes, can undergo self-addition (polymerisation) by addition across the C=O double bond. Ketones are not reactive enough to polymerise easily, but aldehydes can readily be converted to a variety of addition polymers.

Polymerisation of methanal (formaldehyde)

CARE Work in a fume cupboard. Methanal vapour causes severe irritation of skin and eyes.
Put 10 drops of methanal solution on a watch glass and warm this over a beaker of hot water.

8 Describe what happens.

The residue which forms is poly(methanal).

$$-CH_2-O-CH_2-O-CH_2-O-CH_2-O-$$

A plastic made from poly(methanal) has been used to replace metal in machine parts such as gear wheels and clips.

Working in a fume cupboard, scrape some of the poly(methanal) into a test tube and investigate the action of heat on it.

Polymerisation of ethanal

9 Ethanal, unlike methanal, requires chemical reagents to induce polymerisation. Is this consistent with the relative reactivities of the two compounds? Explain.

Ethanal resin

Warm 10 drops of ethanal with 3 cm³ of concentrated sodium hydroxide solution (**CARE: very corrosive**).

10 Describe what happens and smell the product cautiously.

C Condensation reactions of carbonyl compounds

In some cases, the addition reactions of carbonyl compounds are followed by the elimination of a molecule of water. Many of these elimination reactions involve derivatives of ammonia with the general formula $X-NH_2$.

$$\text{C}=\text{O} + \text{H}_2\text{N}-\text{X} \longrightarrow -\overset{|}{\underset{|}{\text{C}}}-\text{N}\overset{OH}{\underset{X}{\diagdown}}^{H} \longrightarrow \text{C}=\text{N}\diagdown_X + \text{H}_2\text{O}$$

This sort of reaction, in which two molecules combine with the elimination of water, is an example of a **condensation** or **addition–elimination** reaction.

The most useful reagent for low molecular mass carbonyl compounds is 2,4-dinitrophenylhydrazine:

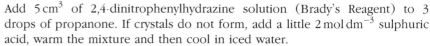

The products of condensation reactions between 2,4-dinitrophenylhydrazine and carbonyl compounds are crystalline solids with well-defined melting points. They are therefore useful in identifying individual carbonyl compounds.

Preparation of propanone 2,4-dinitrophenylhydrazone

Add 5 cm^3 of 2,4-dinitrophenylhydrazine solution (Brady's Reagent) to 3 drops of propanone. If crystals do not form, add a little 2 mol dm^{-3} sulphuric acid, warm the mixture and then cool in iced water.

If time permits, filter off the crystals, wash them with a little water, dry them between filter papers and then recrystallise them from ethanol. Determine their melting point and compare your value with the accepted value of 128°C for the melting point of propanone 2,4-dinitrophenylhydrazone.

11 Describe the appearance of propanone 2,4-dinitrophenylhydrazone crystals.

12 Write an equation for the reaction between propanone and 2,4-dinitrophenylhydrazine.

Other carbonyl compounds react in a similar manner to propanone.

D Oxidation of carbonyl compounds

Aldehydes possess a hydrogen atom attached to their carbonyl group. This hydrogen is activated by the carbonyl group and is readily oxidised to −OH. Aldehydes are therefore readily oxidised to carboxylic acids.

Ketones, however, have no hydrogen atom joined directly to the carbonyl group, so they are not readily oxidised.

13 What would you expect to be the order of ease of oxidation of methanal, ethanal and propanone?

(1) Oxidation by acidified dichromate(VI)

Compare the ease of oxidation and hence the reducing power of methanal, ethanal and propanone by adding 5 drops of each substance *in turn* to 2 drops of potassium dichromate(VI) solution and 10 drops of dilute sulphuric acid. If nothing happens in the cold, warm gently.

14 Write the carbonyl compounds (methanal, ethanal and propanone) in order of increasing reducing power. Do your results agree with your answer to question **13**?

15 Write equations (or half-equations) for the reactions which have occurred.

TOXIC
2,4-Dinitrophenylhydrazine

EYE PROTECTION
MUST BE WORN

CORROSIVE
Sulphuric
acid

HIGHLY FLAMMABLE
Ethanol

IRRITANT
Sulphuric
acid

HIGHLY
FLAMMABLE
Ethanal
Propanone

EYE PROTECTION
MUST BE WORN

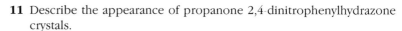
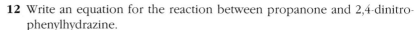

(2) Oxidation by diamminosilver(I) ions (Tollen's reagent)

Put $3\,cm^3$ of silver nitrate solution into a *clean* test tube and add dilute ammonia solution drop by drop until the precipitate of silver oxide just dissolves. The clear solution contains $[Ag(NH_3)_2]^+$ ions. Add 10 drops of ethanal and warm the resulting mixture in a beaker of hot water. **Rinse out the test tube immediately afterwards.**

16 Describe and explain what happens. Write an equation (or half-equations) for the reaction which occurs.

Repeat the experiment using first methanal and then propanone in place of ethanal.

17 How do the reactions of methanal and propanone compare with that of ethanal?

(3) Oxidation by Fehling's solution (copper(II) ions complexed with tartrate ions)

Put $3\,cm^3$ of Fehling's solution in a boiling tube and add 10 drops of ethanal. Boil the mixture gently and note the formation of copper(I) oxide.

CORROSIVE
Fehling's
solution

18 Fehling's solution contains Cu^{2+} ions in an alkaline solution of tartrate ions. The tartrate ions complex with Cu^{2+} ions and prevent the precipitation of copper(II) hydroxide. Describe and explain what happens when ethanal reacts with Fehling's solution. Write an equation (or half-equations) for the reaction which occurs. (In your equation represent the complexed copper(II) ion as Cu^{2+} for simplicity.)

E Sugars—naturally occurring carbonyl compounds

Sugars are sweet-tasting soluble carbohydrates.

The most obvious feature of their structures is the presence of large numbers of −OH groups.

19 What do you understand by the term 'carbohydrate'?

20 Why are carbohydrates very soluble in water?

As well as showing the properties of hydroxy compounds, sugars such as glucose show many properties that are typical of carbonyl compounds. The carbonyl properties of glucose arise from the fact that it can exist in an 'open-chain' form as well as its normal 'ring' form, as shown below. In aqueous solution about 1% of glucose molecules exist in the open-chain form which carries the aldehyde group.

ring form   open-chain form

(1) Condensation with 2,4-dinitrophenylhydrazine

Carry out the experiment in part **C** (condensation reactions of carbonyl compounds), using half a spatula measure of glucose in $1\,cm^3$ of water in place of 3 drops of propanone.

21 Describe the appearance of the crystals which form, and write an equation for the reaction between glucose and 2,4-dinitrophenylhydrazine. (Use the open-chain formula for glucose in this equation.)

(2) Oxidation by diamminosilver(I) ions (Tollen's reagent)

Carry out experiment **2**, in part **D** (oxidation of carbonyl compounds), using half a spatula measure of glucose in $1\,cm^3$ of water in place of 10 drops of ethanal. **Rinse out the test tube immediately after the reaction**.

22 Describe and explain what happens.

(3) Oxidation by Fehling's solution

Fehling's test has been used to detect sugar in the urine of people suffering from diabetes. The pancreas of these patients produces insufficient insulin to cope with the sugar in their diet. This means that sugar accumulates in the blood and, when it reaches a certain concentration, it is excreted by the kidneys and appears in the urine.

Carry out experiment **3**, in part **D**, using half a spatula measure of glucose in $1\,cm^3$ of water in place of 10 drops of ethanal.

23 Describe and explain what happens. Depending on the concentration of glucose, the solution may simply turn green, produce a fine yellow precipitate or give a dark red precipitate.

Practical 33
Carboxylic acids

REQUIREMENTS

Each student, or pair of students, will require:

- Eye protection
- Rack and 6 hard-glass test tubes
- 2 boiling tubes
- Evaporating basin
- Beaker (250 cm³)
- Dropping pipette
- Splints
- Universal indicator paper (pH I to 4 or full range I to 14) or, better, access to a pH meter
- Access to a refrigerator
- **Access to a fume cupboard**
- Concentrated (glacial) ethanoic (acetic) acid
- Concentrated methanoic (formic) acid
- Solid ethanedioic acid (oxalic acid)
- 2 mol dm⁻³ ethanoic acid (dilute 116 cm³ of glacial ethanoic acid (**corrosive**) to I dm³ with distilled water)
- 0.1 mol dm⁻³ ethanoic acid (dilute 5.8 cm³ of glacial ethanoic acid to I dm³ with distilled water)
- 0.1 mol dm⁻³ ethanol in water (dilute 1.5 cm³ of ethanol to 250 cm³ with distilled water)
- 0.1 mol dm⁻³ hydrochloric acid (dilute 8.6 cm³ of concentrated acid (**corrosive**) to I dm³ with distilled water)
- Phosphorus pentachloride (keep in fume cupboard)
- Pentanol (amyl alcohol)
- Concentrated sulphuric acid
- Ethanol
- Dilute sodium hydroxide
- Dilute hydrochloric acid
- Dilute ammonia
- Potassium manganate(VII) (potassium permanganate) (0.1 mol dm⁻³)
- Iron(III) chloride (ferric chloride) (0.1 mol dm⁻³)
- Sodium ethanoate (0.1 mol dm⁻³)

Time required 2–3 double periods

EYE PROTECTION MUST BE WORN

CORROSIVE
Glacial ethanoic acid

Introduction

Carboxylic acids contain the functional group $-C{\overset{\displaystyle OH}{\underset{\displaystyle O}{}}}$. They have important industrial uses, and occur widely in nature, both free and combined as esters, particularly in fats and oils.

In this practical you will begin by considering some of the properties of ethanoic acid, a typical carboxylic acid, and then look at some of the unusual properties of methanoic acid and ethanedioic acid. The structural formulae of these acids are shown in table 1.

Table I
Structural formulae of methanoic, ethanoic and ethanedioic acids

Systematic name	Other name	Structural formula	
Methanoic acid	formic acid	$H-C{\overset{O}{\underset{OH}{}}}$	HCOOH
Ethanoic acid	acetic acid	$CH_3-C{\overset{O}{\underset{OH}{}}}$	CH₃COOH
Ethanedioic acid	oxalic acid	$HO{\overset{O}{}}C-C{\overset{O}{}}OH$	(COOH)₂

Procedure

CARE Eye protection must be worn throughout this practical.

(1) The properties of ethanoic acid as a typical carboxylic acid

CARE Concentrated (glacial) ethanoic acid is corrosive. Any spills should be washed away immediately with plenty of water.

Experiment 1: Physical properties of glacial ethanoic acid
Put a test tube of glacial ethanoic acid in a refrigerator and observe after an hour.

1 What happens? Why is concentrated ethanoic acid called 'glacial'?

Cautiously smell the vapour from a bottle of glacial ethanoic acid. Hold the bottle at a distance, fill your lungs with air and waft the vapour towards your nose.

2 Is the smell familiar? How did the original name 'acetic acid' come to be used for what we now call ethanoic acid?

Test the solubility of glacial ethanoic acid in water.

3 Is the acid soluble in water? Explain your answer in terms of the structure of the acid.

4 Would you expect octadecanoic acid, $C_{17}H_{35}COOH$ to be soluble in water? Explain your answer.

Experiment 2: Acidic properties of ethanoic acid

EYE PROTECTION MUST BE WORN

Using universal indicator paper, or preferably a pH meter, measure the pH of $0.1\,mol\,dm^{-3}$ solutions of

a ethanol

b ethanoic acid

c hydrochloric acid.

5 Record your results and list these compounds in order of increasing acid strength.

6 Would you classify ethanoic acid as a strong or a weak acid?

7 What explanation can you give for the difference in acid strength between ethanol and ethanoic acid?

Measure the pH of a $0.1\,mol\,dm^{-3}$ solution of sodium ethanoate.

8 Why might sodium ethanoate be expected to be neutral?

9 Is it neutral in fact? If not, why not?

CORROSIVE
Sodium hydroxide solution

IRRITANT
Dilute ethanoic acid

Put $10\,cm^3$ of $2\,mol\,dm^{-3}$ sodium hydroxide solution in an evaporating basin. Add $5\,cm^3$ of $2\,mol\,dm^{-3}$ ethanoic acid and **cautiously** smell the resulting mixture.

10 Can ethanoic acid still be smelled? If not, why not?

Add a further $5\,cm^3$ or so of $2\,mol\,dm^{-3}$ ethanoic acid to the evaporating basin, until the acid is just in excess. (How can you test whether it is in excess?) Evaporate the contents of the evaporating basin over a beaker of boiling water until all the water has left the basin and white crystals remain. (This may take some time. Get on with another part of the practical while you are waiting.)

11 Identify the white crystals and write an equation for the reaction that has occurred.

Put a few of the crystals in a test tube and add a few cm^3 of dilute hydrochloric acid. Gently warm the tube and **cautiously** smell the vapour coming off.

12 What has been formed? Explain the reaction that has occurred in terms of your answer to question **5**.

Experiment 3: Reaction of ethanoic acid with phosphorus pentachloride

CORROSIVE
Phosphorus pentachloride
Glacial ethanoic acid

USE A FUME CUPBOARD

.EYE PROTECTION MUST BE WORN

CARE Phosphorus pentachloride is corrosive and reacts violently with water. Do not let it come into contact with water, and avoid spills. Stopper the reagent bottle immediately after use.

Working in a fume cupboard, put $2\,cm^3$ of **concentrated** (glacial) ethanoic acid in a boiling tube. Carefully add about $0.5\,g$ of phosphorus pentachloride.

13 What evidence is there that a reaction has occurred?

14 Give the formula of the organic product of this reaction and write an equation. (Consult a text book if necessary.)

15 How does phosphorus pentachloride react with *ethanol*? How does this reaction resemble the reaction of phosphorus pentachloride with ethanoic acid?

Experiment 4: Reaction of ethanoic acid and ethanoates with neutral iron(III) chloride

EYE PROTECTION
MUST BE WORN

USE A FUME
CUPBOARD

Aqueous Fe^{3+} ions give a characteristic colour with ethanoate ions, but only in neutral solution.

Prepare a neutral solution of iron(III) chloride (which is often acidic) as follows. Add ammonia solution dropwise to a few cubic centimetres of iron(III) chloride solution, until a faint precipitate just begins to form. Filter or decant the solution from the precipitate and then, **working in a fume cupboard**, gently warm the solution to drive off excess ammonia. You now have a neutral solution of iron(III) chloride.

Put $2-3\,cm^3$ of sodium ethanoate solution in a test tube and add a few drops of neutral iron(III) chloride solution. (Sodium ethanoate is used here instead of ethanoic acid because it is nearly neutral.)

16 What colour is given by ethanoate ions with neutral iron(III) chloride?

17 What other organic compounds give a characteristic colour with iron(III) chloride? What colour do they give?

Experiment 5: Esterification

CORROSIVE
Concentrated
sulphuric acid

Concentrated
ethanoic acid

HARMFUL
Pentanol

EYE PROTECTION
MUST BE WORN

Put $2\,cm^3$ of pentanol (amyl alcohol) in a boiling tube and add $1\,cm^3$ of concentrated sulphuric acid. Add a few drops of concentrated (glacial) ethanoic acid and warm the tube gently with shaking (**CARE**). Allow the tube to cool a little, then pour the contents into a beaker containing about $50\,cm^3$ of cold water. **Cautiously** smell the vapour.

18 Describe the smell of the vapour.

19 The pentanol you used may have been a mixture of isomers of formula $C_5H_{11}OH$. Using pentan-1-ol as a representative example, name and write the structural formula of the ester that has been formed.

20 Write an equation for the reaction.

21 What is the purpose of the sulphuric acid in this reaction?

22 Why is the reaction mixture poured into cold water before smelling?

23 Give the names and structural formulae of the esters that would have been formed if

   a ethanol had been used instead of pentanol.

   b propanoic acid had been used instead of ethanoic acid.

Experiment 6: Oxidation

Put $2\,cm^3$ of glacial ethanoic acid in a test tube. Add a few drops of potassium manganate(VII) solution and warm gently.

24 Are there any signs of reaction?

25 Is ethanoic acid easily oxidised?

Experiment 7: Dehydration

Put $2\,cm^3$ of concentrated sulphuric acid in a boiling tube and warm it **gently** (**CARE**). Now add a few drops of glacial ethanoic acid to the warm sulphuric acid and observe carefully to see if any gas is evolved. If a gas comes off, attempt to identify it.

26 Is ethanoic acid readily dehydrated by concentrated sulphuric acid?

The reactions of ethanoic acid that you have seen in the first part of the practical are typical of carboxylic acids in general. Methanoic acid and ethanoic acid are not typical, however, and you will now look at some of their properties.

(2) Some properties of methanoic acid

CARE Methanoic acid is corrosive and its vapour is irritant. Eye protection must be worn.

CORROSIVE
Methanoic acid
Concentrated
sulphuric acid

EYE PROTECTION
MUST BE WORN

Experiment 8: Physical properties
Investigate the smell (**CARE**) and the solubility of methanoic acid.

27 Are these properties similar to those of ethanoic acid?

Experiment 9: Esterification
Repeat the esterification experiment, as in experiment **5**, using ethanol instead of pentanol and methanoic acid instead of ethanoic acid.

28 Describe the smell of the vapour.

29 Name and write the structural formula of the ester that has been formed.

30 Does methanoic acid behave in a similar way to ethanoic acid in this reaction?

HIGHLY
FLAMMABLE
Ethanol

Experiment 10: Oxidation
Repeat the oxidation experiment, as in experiment **6**, using methanoic acid instead of ethanoic acid.

31 Are there signs of reaction?

32 Is methanoic acid easily oxidised? If so, to what?

Experiment 11: Dehydration
Repeat the dehydration experiment, as in experiment **7**, using methanoic acid instead of ethanoic acid.

33 Is methanoic acid readily dehydrated? If so, what is formed?

(3) Some properties of ethanedioic acid

CARE Ethanedioic acid is harmful and irritant.

EYE PROTECTION
MUST BE WORN

IRRITANT
Ethanedioic
acid

HARMFUL
Ethanedioic
acid

Experiment 12: Physical properties
Investigate the smell and the solubility of ethanedioic acid.

34 Compare the volatility of ethanedioic acid with that of methanoic and ethanoic acids.

35 Relate any difference in volatility to the structure of ethanedioic acid.

36 Compare the solubility of ethanedioic acid with that of the other two acids. Attempt to explain any differences.

Experiment 13: Esterification
Repeat the esterification experiment as in experiment **5**, using ethanol instead of pentanol and ethanedioic acid instead of ethanoic acid.

37 Describe the smell of the vapour.

38 Name and write the structural formula of the ester that has been formed.

39 Is the volatility of this ester similar to the volatility of the ethanoate and methanoate esters you prepared?

40 Explain your answer to question **39** in view of the difference in volatility between ethanedioic acid and the other two acids.

HIGHLY
FLAMMABLE
Ethanol

Experiment 14: Oxidation

Repeat the oxidation experiment, as in experiment **6**, using an aqueous solution of ethanedioic acid instead of ethanoic acid.

41 Are there signs of reaction?

42 Is ethanedioic acid easily oxidised? If so, to what?

Experiment 15: Dehydration

Repeat the dehydration experiment, as in experiment **7**, using ethanedioic acid instead of ethanoic acid.

43 Is ethanedioic acid readily dehydrated? If so, what is formed?

44 Draw up a table summarising the reactions of carboxylic acids and showing the results for each of the three acids in this practical.

INVESTIGATION

See Investigation 15

Practical 34
Amines

REQUIREMENTS

Each student, or pair of students, will need:
- Eye protection
- Rack with 4 test tubes
- Teat pipette
- 2 small beakers (100 cm³)
- Universal indicator paper
- Boiling tube
- Thermometer (0°C–110°C)
- Butylamine
- Phenylamine
- Ethanoyl chloride (acetyl chloride)
- Ammonium chloride
- Sodium nitrate
- Concentrated hydrochloric acid
- Phenol
- 2-Naphthol
- Bromine water
- Ice

The following solutions at usual bench concentration:
- Dilute ammonia
- Dilute hydrochloric acid
- Dilute sodium hydroxide
- Copper(II) sulphate solution (about 0.1 mol dm⁻³)

Access to a fume cupboard

EYE PROTECTION
MUST BE WORN

Time required 2 double periods

USE A FUME
CUPBOARD

WEAR PROTECTIVE
GLOVES

TOXIC
Phenylamine

FLAMMABLE
Butylamine

IRRITANT
Butylamine

Introduction

Amines are one of the most important groups of organic nitrogen-containing compounds. They can be regarded as derivatives of ammonia in which one or more of the hydrogen atoms in NH_3 is replaced by aryl or alkyl groups. If only one of the hydrogen atoms in NH_3 is substituted, we get a compound of the form RNH_2, called a primary amine. The simplest primary amines are CH_3NH_2, methylamine, and $CH_3CH_2NH_2$, ethylamine.

1 Write full structural formulae for ammonia, butylamine and phenylamine (aniline).

2 Which simple substance would you expect amines to resemble?

3 Predict two properties of butylamine.

Free amines are relatively rare in nature, but they do occur in decomposing protein such as meat and fish. Normally the $-NH_2$ group is associated with other functional groups and in this respect it forms an important part of proteins. Compounds containing the $-NH_2$ group are important in the manufacture of drugs, dyes and nylon.

The intention of this practical is to consider the properties of an alkylamine (butylamine) and an arylamine (phenylamine) and to compare their properties with those of ammonia. Butylamine is chosen because it is a liquid and not too volatile. Phenylamine is also a liquid, colourless when pure, but the sample you use is likely to be dark-coloured due to atmos-pheric oxidation.

CARE Eye protection must be worn throughout this practical.

A Reactions of amines as bases

CARE Phenylamine is toxic and harmful by skin absorption. Avoid all skin contact. Wear protective gloves and work in a fume cupboard. Butylamine is flammable and an irritant.

(1) Reaction with water and indicators

Shake 2 drops of butylamine and 2 drops of phenylamine separately with 2 cm³ of water. Now test each of these solutions and a solution of ammonia with universal indicator paper.

4 Comment on the solubility of the amines in water and account for any differences in solubility.

5 Comment on the basic strength of the amines relative to ammonia and account for any differences in their strength as bases.

(2) Reaction with dilute hydrochloric acid

Shake 2 drops of butylamine and 2 drops of phenylamine separately with 2 cm³ of dilute hydrochloric acid.

6 Describe what happens.

7 Write equations for the reactions which have occurred.

8 Explain the different solubility of phenylamine in water and in dilute hydrochloric acid.

Add dilute sodium hydroxide to the solution of phenylamine in hydrochloric acid until the mixture is alkaline.

9 Describe and explain what happens.

CORROSIVE
Sodium
hydroxide solution

B Reactions of amines as ligands

Reaction with copper(II) sulphate solution

Add ammonia solution dropwise to $2\,cm^3$ of copper(II) sulphate solution until the ammonia is present in excess.

10 Describe and explain what happens. Write equations for the reactions which occur.

Repeat the experiment using first butylamine and then phenylamine in place of ammonia solution.

11 Describe and explain what happens. Do the amines react in a similar fashion to ammonia?

C Reactions of amines as nucleophiles

(1) Reaction with ethanoyl chloride and benzoyl chloride

CARE Work in a fume cupboard. Eye protection must be worn.

Ammonia and amines can act as nucleophiles in attacking the positive centres in molecules such as ethanoyl chloride, CH_3COCl, and benzoyl chloride, C_6H_5COCl. For example, ammonia reacts very vigorously with ethanoyl chloride, forming ethanamide.

USE A FUME
CUPBOARD

EYE PROTECTION
MUST BE WORN

CORROSIVE
Ethanoyl chloride
Benzoyl chloride

FLAMMABLE
Ethanoyl
chloride

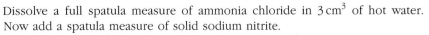

ethanamide

12 Would you expect phenylamine to react with ethanoyl chloride more or less vigorously than ammonia? Explain your answer.

Carefully add $1\,cm^3$ of ethanoyl chloride dropwise to an equal volume of phenylamine in a boiling tube, shaking after the addition of each drop.

13 Describe what happens.

14 Write an equation for the reaction which occurs. Name the solid organic product.

(2) Reaction with nitrous acid

Dissolve a full spatula measure of ammonia chloride in $3\,cm^3$ of hot water. Now add a spatula measure of solid sodium nitrite.

15 Describe and explain what happens. (The reaction can be regarded as one between ammonia and nitrous acid, these two substances being formed by the reaction between ammonium ions and nitrite ions:

$$NH_4^+ + NO_2^- \longrightarrow NH_3 + HNO_2.)$$

HARMFUL
Ammonium
chloride

OXIDISING
Sodium
nitrite

TOXIC
Sodium
nitrite

CORROSIVE
Concentrated
hydrochloric acid

Put 3 drops of butylamine in a test tube and add concentrated hydrochloric acid dropwise until a clear solution is formed. Dilute the mixture to $3\,cm^3$ with water, add a spatula measure of sodium nitrite and warm gently. Repeat the experiment using phenylamine in place of butylamine.

16 Describe and explain what happens. Write equations for the reactions which occur.

The reactive group in nitrous acid is thought to be the nitrosyl cation, NO^+. When amines react with nitrous acid, they first form the diazonium ion, $R-\overset{+}{N}\equiv N$.

$$RNH_2 + NO^+ \longrightarrow R-\overset{+}{N}\equiv N + H_2O$$

Unless the diazonium ion is stabilised in some way, it decomposes forming nitrogen and the new carbocation R^+, which takes part in a variety of further reactions.

$$R-\overset{+}{N}\equiv N \longrightarrow R^+ + N_2$$

In the case of arylamines, such as $C_6H_5NH_2$, stabilisation of the diazonium ion can occur by delocalisation of electrons from the benzene ring, provided the temperature of the reactants is kept below 10°C. The diazonium salts that form are useful reactive intermediates, as the following experiment shows.

Make a solution of 2 drops of phenylamine in $2\,cm^3$ of dilute hydrochloric acid and add it to about $5\,cm^3$ of a crushed ice/water mixture at 5°C–10°C. Add to this mixture a spatula measure of sodium nitrite and stir well to ensure that the solid dissolves. This solution contains the benzenediazonium ion, $C_6H_5-\overset{+}{N}\equiv N$.

Use the solution to prepare azo dyes as follows.

CARE Phenol is corrosive. Avoid skin contact and wear gloves and eye protection in experiment A which follows.

WEAR PROTECTIVE GLOVES

CORROSIVE
Phenol

EYE PROTECTION MUST BE WORN

A Dissolve a spatula measure of phenol in $2\,cm^3$ of dilute sodium hydroxide solution. Cool this solution to below 5°C and add the diazonium solution drop by drop.

B Repeat the test using 2-naphthol in place of phenol.

17 Describe what happens in each case. Write equations for the reactions which occur. (See *Chemistry in Context*, Fourth Edition, section 34.7.)

18 Why is it so important to keep the solutions below 10°C in these reactions?

D Reactions of the aromatic ring in phenylamine

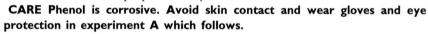

Put 3 drops of phenylamine in a test tube and add concentrated hydrochloric acid drop by drop until the phenylamine dissolves (**CARE**). Now add bromine water dropwise until no further change occurs.

19 Describe what happens. Write an equation for the reaction which occurs.

20 Why can phenylamine undergo substitution with bromine so much more easily than benzene?

HARMFUL
Bromine water

CORROSIVE
Concentrated
hydrochloric acid

EYE PROTECTION MUST BE WORN

Practical 35
Polymers

REQUIREMENTS

Each student, or pair of students, will require:

- Eye protection
- Rack and 4 test tubes
- 2 boiling tubes
- Beaker (400 cm³)
- Beaker (100 cm³)
- Glass rod
- Tweezers
- 2 disposable polystyrene cups (normal, not expanded polystyrene)
- Cotton wool
- Broken porcelain
- Tongs
- Sharp knife or scissors
- **Access to a fume cupboard**
- Access to an oven
- Phenylethene (styrene)
- Di(dodecanoyl)peroxide (lauroyl peroxide)
- 5% solution (freshly prepared) of decanedioyl dichloride (sebacoyl chloride) in 1,1,1-trichloroethane (10 cm³)
- 5% solution of 1,6-diaminohexane in water (10 cm³)
- 40% aqueous solution of methanal (formalin)
- Urea
- Polystyrene chips, or fragments of a polystyrene cup, toy etc.
- Natural rubber, small pieces
- Urea–methanal plastic, small pieces (pieces of a broken white electrical fitting such as a plug or a socket would do)
- 1,1,1-Trichloroethane

continued on next page

EYE PROTECTION
MUST BE WORN

USE A FUME
CUPBOARD

HIGHLY
FLAMMABLE
Di(dodecanoyl)
peroxide

IRRITANT
Phenylethene
Di(dodecanoyl)
peroxide

Introduction

This practical is in two parts. In the first part you will prepare some representative polymers. In the second part you will investigate the way in which the molecular structure of a polymer can influence its physical properties. You may find it helpful to refer to *Chemistry in Context*, Fourth Edition, sections 28.7 and 28.8, during this practical and in answering the questions.

A The preparation of some polymers

Polymers can be classified in a number of ways. One way is to group them according to the type of chemical reaction by which they are prepared. Thus, there are **addition polymers** and **condensation polymers**.

1 Explain the terms 'addition' and 'condensation' as applied to chemical reactions.

Polymers differ in the way in which they behave when heated. **Thermoplastic** materials soften on heating and harden again on cooling. **Thermosetting** materials set hard on heating and cannot be softened or melted. Strong heating only tends to decompose them.

2 Name one article made from a thermoplastic material and one made from a thermosetting material.

The strength and elasticity of polymers varies widely. Highly elastic polymers are called **elastomers. Fibres** have low elasticity and high tensile strength. Intermediate between elastomers and fibres are **plastics**.

3 Name one elastomer, one plastic and one fibre.

CARE Eye protection must be worn throughout this practical.

The preparation of an addition polymer—polystyrene

Polystyrene, systematically called poly(phenylethene), is made by polymerising phenylethene (styrene), whose formula is shown below. A catalyst, di(dodecanoyl) peroxide (lauroyl peroxide) is needed to speed up the polymerisation, which is otherwise very slow.

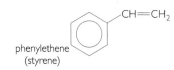

phenylethene
(styrene)

Working in a fume cupboard, put 10 cm³ of phenylethene in a boiling tube. Add about 0.2 g of di(dodecanoyl) peroxide and shake the tube until the catalyst has dissolved. Plug the tube with cotton wool and heat it in a water bath at about 100°C for 20 minutes, then examine the contents and compare with the original phenylethene.

4 What evidence is there that polymerisation is taking place?

5 Draw the structure of a section of the polymer chain.

Samples of polythene film, high and low density. To make comparison easier, the samples need to be of similar thickness. For example:

EYE PROTECTION MUST BE WORN

- Low density: polythene sheeting from a garden centre or hardware store.
- High density: cut from food containers such as large plastic milk bottles.

Time required 2–3 double periods

Polymerisation can be completed by heating the tube in an oven or water bath at about 50°C until a solid block is obtained. Of course, the glass tube would have to be broken to remove the polymer. Alternatively, the semi-polymerised material can be used as a casting or embedding resin by pouring it into a mould which has been lightly smeared with liquid detergent.

6 Classify polystyrene as

  a thermoplastic or thermosetting,

  b elastomer, plastic or fibre.

The preparation of a condensation polymer —nylon 6,10

Nylon 6,10 is prepared by a condensation reaction between decanedioyl dichloride (sebacoyl chloride) and 1,6-diaminohexane.

$$Cl-C-CH_2CH_2CH_2CH_2CH_2CH_2CH_2CH_2-C-Cl$$

decanedioyl dichloride

$$H_2NCH_2CH_2CH_2CH_2CH_2CH_2NH_2$$

1,6-diaminohexane

USE A FUME CUPBOARD

EYE PROTECTION MUST BE WORN

CORROSIVE
Decanedioyl dichloride

IRRITANT
1,6-Diaminohexane in 1,1,1-trichloroethane

HARMFUL
1,6-Diaminohexane in 1,1,1-trichloroethane
Decanedioyl dichloride

Working in a fume cupboard, put 10 cm³ of a 5% solution of decanedioyl dichloride in 1,1,1-trichloroethane into a 100 cm³ beaker.

CARE The vapour from this solution is harmful.

Very carefully, using a dropping pipette, add 10 cm³ of a 5% solution of 1,6-diaminohexane in water. Do **not** allow the two solutions to mix—try to float one layer on top of the other so that the nylon forms at the interface. Use tweezers to pull the interface film out of the liquid and wind it on to a glass rod. The glass rod can then be rotated, pulling a continuous filament of nylon from the interface and winding it on to the rod. **Do not touch this filament by hand, even after washing it.**

7 Draw the structure of a section of the nylon 6,10 chain.

8 What other product is formed in this reaction, apart from nylon?

9 What reagents would you use if you were making nylon 6,6?

10 Classify nylon as

  a thermoplastic or thermosetting,

  b elastomer, plastic or fibre.

The preparation of a thermosetting plastic —urea–methanal resin

Urea and methanal react together to form polymer chain as shown in figure 1. These chains can then cross-link with other chains via further molecules of methanal (figure 2). The extensive cross-linking in this polymer makes it set hard on formation and prevents it from softening on heating. (See part 2 of this practical.)

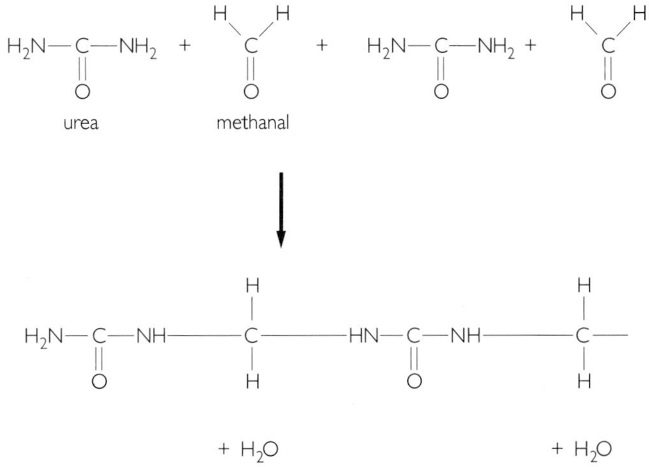

$$H_2N-\underset{\underset{O}{\|}}{C}-NH_2 \quad + \quad \underset{\underset{O}{\|}}{\overset{H}{\underset{}{}}C\overset{H}{} \quad + \quad H_2N-\underset{\underset{O}{\|}}{C}-NH_2 \quad + \quad \underset{\underset{O}{\|}}{\overset{H}{}C\overset{H}{}}$$

urea   methanal

$$H_2N-\underset{\underset{O}{\|}}{C}-NH\text{——}\underset{\underset{H}{|}}{\overset{H}{|}}C\text{——}HN-\underset{\underset{O}{\|}}{C}-NH\text{——}\underset{\underset{H}{|}}{\overset{H}{|}}C\text{——}$$

$$+ H_2O \qquad\qquad\qquad + H_2O$$

Figure 1

Polymerisation of urea and methanal.

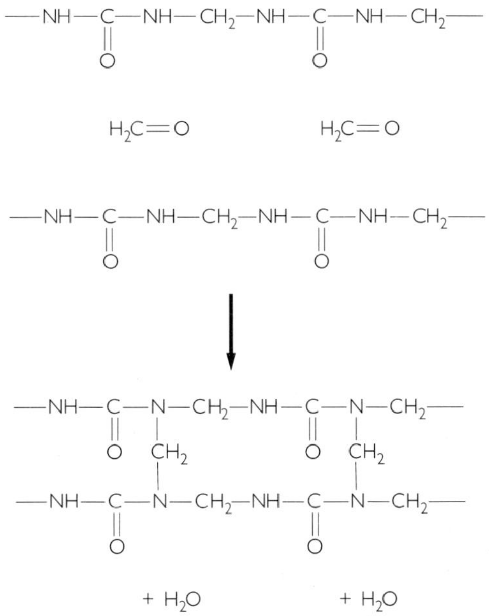

$$\text{——}NH-\underset{\underset{O}{\|}}{C}-NH-CH_2-NH-\underset{\underset{O}{\|}}{C}-NH-CH_2\text{——}$$

$$H_2C{=}O \qquad\qquad H_2C{=}O$$

$$\text{——}NH-\underset{\underset{O}{\|}}{C}-NH-CH_2-NH-\underset{\underset{O}{\|}}{C}-NH-CH_2\text{——}$$

$$\text{——}NH-\underset{\underset{O}{\|}}{C}-\underset{\underset{CH_2}{|}}{N}-CH_2-NH-\underset{\underset{O}{\|}}{C}-\underset{\underset{CH_2}{|}}{N}-CH_2\text{——}$$

$$\text{——}NH-\underset{\underset{O}{\|}}{C}-\underset{\underset{}{|}}{N}-CH_2-NH-\underset{\underset{O}{\|}}{C}-\underset{\underset{}{|}}{N}-CH_2\text{——}$$

$$+ H_2O \qquad\qquad + H_2O$$

Figure 2

Cross-linking between urea–methanal chains.

EYE PROTECTION
MUST BE WORN

USE A FUME
CUPBOARD

CORROSIVE
Concentrated
sulphuric acid

TOXIC
Methanal

CARE Methanal has toxic and irritant vapour.

Working in a fume cupboard put $20\,\text{cm}^3$ of a 40% solution of methanal in water into a disposable plastic cup. Add about $10\,\text{g}$ of urea and stir thoroughly. Add a few drops of concentrated sulphuric acid, stirring all the time.

When polymerisation is complete it should be possible to remove the solid mass of polymer intact from the container. Wash the polymer thoroughly before handling.

11 Describe the appearance of the polymer.

12 Is this a condensation polymer or an addition polymer?

13 What was the purpose of the concentrated sulphuric acid?

14 This polymer is often used to make electrical fittings such as plugs. How could this polymer be made into the shape of an electrical plug, bearing in mind that it is a thermosetting material?

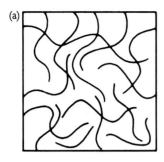

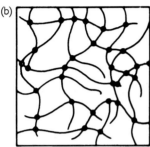

Figure 3
a Polymer with no cross-linking.
b Polymer with high degree of cross-linking.

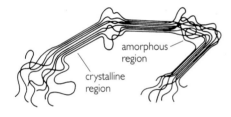

amorphous region

crystalline region

Figure 4
Crystalline and amorphous regions in a polymer.

USE A FUME CUPBOARD

TOXIC
Fumes from burning plastics

EYE PROTECTION MUST BE WORN

HARMFUL
1,1,1-Trichloroethane
Methylbenzene

HIGHLY FLAMMABLE
Methylbenzene

B The properties of some polymers

The properties of materials can usually be related to their molecular structure, and polymers are no exception. A number of molecular properties are particularly important in deciding the strength, elasticity, solubility and softening point of polymers.

(1) Chain length

In general, increasing the chain length increases the strength of a polymer.

(2) Cross-linking

A high degree of cross-linking reduces the extent to which the individual chains can move, reducing elasticity and increasing hardness and softening point (figure 3).

(3) Crystallinity

No polymer is completely crystalline—in some regions the chains are regularly arranged and in others they are at random (figure 4). A polymer will therefore have both crystalline and amorphous (non-crystalline) regions, although the proportion of one to the other will vary according to the polymer. A high degree of crystallinity increases the density, the softening point and the tensile strength of the polymer. Crystalline polymers are usually opaque, while non-crystalline ones are transparent and glassy. Fibres have very high crystallinity, but in elastomers crystallinity is very low.

Two factors are of major importance in determining the degree of crystallinity:

i Intermolecular forces between chains
A polymer carrying highly polar groups along its chain will have strong interactions between chains and this will tend to increase crystallinity.

ii Shape of the chains
Linear chains pack together well, giving high crystallinity. Chains carrying many branches, or with irregularly arranged side-groups, pack together less well, giving lower crystallinity.

Experiment 1: Effect of cross-linking on properties

In these tests, polystyrene will be used as an example of a linear polymer with no cross-linking, urea–methanal resin as an example of a highly cross-linked polymer, and vulcanised natural rubber as an example of a polymer with an intermediate degree of cross-linking.
CARE Molten plastics can cause severe burns, and the fumes from burning plastics are often poisonous.
Working in a fume cupboard, gently heat a small sample of each polymer in turn on a piece of broken porcelain.

15 Compare the effect of heating the three polymers, and relate it to the degree of cross-linking in the material. Bear in mind that the polymers may contain additives such as dyes or fillers, which may modify their properties.

   Investigate the effect of:

   a methylbenzene, an aromatic hydrocarbon solvent;

   b 1,1,1-trichloroethane, a chlorinated hydrocarbon solvent;

   on each polymer in turn.

   Look for signs of the polymer dissolving, softening or swelling.

16 Tabulate your results and try to explain them in terms of the nature of the solvent used and the degree of cross-linking in the polymer.

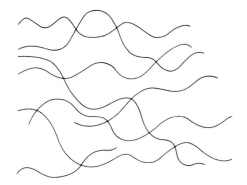

Figure 5
Polythene chains before cold drawing.

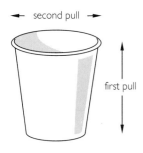

Figure 6
Tearing a polystyrene cup.

Experiment 2: The effect of 'cold drawing' on the crystallinity of a polymer—the effect of stretching polythene film

With a pair of sharp scissors or a sharp knife cut out a strip of low-density polythene film. Make sure the edges of the strip are clean-cut. Stretch the film lengthways by pulling it slowly and steadily—avoid sudden jerks. Record any changes that occur in the film as you stretch, particularly the width of the strip, its appearance, its elasticity and its strength, as indicated by the force required to stretch it.

17 What changes occur in the crystallinity of the polythene as it is stretched?

18 If the polymer chains are distributed as shown in figure 5 before stretching, indicate by means of a sketch how you think they may be arranged after stretching.

19 The operation you have just carried out is called 'cold drawing'. What industrial importance does this process have?

Repeat the experiment using a fresh strip of polythene, but this time stop pulling when you think the crystallinity of the sample has reached a maximum, but before it breaks. Now pull the strip across its width, that is at right angles to the original direction of stretching.

20 What happens? Suggest an explanation in terms of the arrangement of the polymer chains.

Take a polystyrene drinking cup (made of normal, not expanded polystyrene) and try to tear it, pulling in the first direction shown in figure 6. Now try to tear it at right angles, pulling in the second direction shown in figure 6.

21 Suggest a reason for any differences in the ease with which the polystyrene can be torn in the different directions.

Experiment 3: Comparing low- and high-density polythene

Low-density polythene contains chains which are branched and carry side chains. In high-density polythene the chains are unbranched. This means the chains can pack more closely together.

22 Use samples of high-density and low-density polythene film to compare the following properties:
  −transparency
  −flexibility
  −softening in hot water
  −texture
  −density

23 Try to relate the differences in properties to the different structures of the two forms.

1b INVESTIGATIONS

Some general guidance on Investigations

In an Investigation you have more control over what you do than in ordinary practical work. You are expected to plan and make decisions for yourself. This means that Investigations usually take longer than the kind of practical work where you follow instructions, but they are often more enjoyable because you are in control.

Finding references

The Investigations in this book give enough information to start you off, but leave a lot for you to do. You will need to find references to help you with the design of your Investigation, and to give you the chemical background. You may need to refer to your teacher for help with suggested references. Be sure to list all the references you use at the end of your report.

Planning your Investigation

You must have a clear plan of action before you start. Among other things, you will need to decide the following.

- What exactly are you going to investigate? The Investigations in this book are a starting point, but you will need to formulate the particular aspects you are going to investigate. It is always best to put the title of your Investigation in the form of a question, for example: 'What affects the activity of an enzyme?'

- What chemicals will you use? You will need to consider what is available, and what is safe to use.

- What apparatus will you use? Again, you will need to consider what is available.

- What are the safety considerations? (See the section entitled 'Checking safety'.)

- What observations and measurements will you make?

- How will you control variables? For example, if you are investigating the rate of a reaction which is affected by both temperature and pH, you will need to think about how you will keep the temperature constant while you vary pH, and vice-versa.

You may find that you need to modify your plans as you go along. Nevertheless, it is important to make careful plans before you start.

You MUST check your plans with your teacher before starting any practical work.

Checking safety

Your teacher will need to approve your plans from the point of view of safety, but it will help if you carry out your own Risk Assessment.

A Risk Assessment identifies all the hazards associated with the chemicals you will be using, and those you will be making, and seeks ways to reduce the risks from them, for example by giving the safety precautions that need to be taken.

The stages in carrying out a Risk Assessment

1 List all the chemicals you will be using, and those you will be making. Give the form in which they will be used (e.g. solution, concentration) and the quantities.

2 Identify any hazard associated with each substance listed in point 1. The types of hazards you are likely to meet are listed in table 1. Your teacher will advise you on where to look up the hazards. If you refer to older publications, remember that safety standards may have changed.

3 Now consider the *operations* you will be carrying out with the chemicals. What are the hazards associated with these operations? (For example, heating certain substances can give rise to a fire hazard; or you might estimate the likely concentration of hazardous gases and thus decide if you need to use the fume cupboard.)

4 Consider whether replacing a hazardous chemical by a less hazardous one would reduce the risk.

5 Finally, list all the safety precautions that you will need to take in view of the hazards you have identified in points **2** and **3**.

Include the Risk Assessment in your plans for the Investigation, and discuss it with your teacher. Remember—if you change your plans, you may have to change your Risk Assessment.

Table 1
Chemical hazards

Hazard	Symbol
Highly flammable	
Explosive	
Oxidising (assists combustion)	
Harmful	
Toxic (more serious than Harmful)	
Irritant	
Corrosive (more serious than Irritant)	
Radioactive	

Carrying out your Investigation

It is important to record all your results as you go along. You never know which may prove useful later!

Don't worry too much if you seem to be getting unexpected results. Many important scientific discoveries were made when scientists obtained unexpected results. If things really do seem to be going wrong, you may need to change your plans—but remember to discuss any changes with your teacher.

Writing up a report on your Investigation

Your teacher will advise you on how the Investigation should be written up.

A good report will include:

- a clear description of what you were investigating

- a Risk Assessment with a clear statement of any safety precautions

- a description of what you did, with clearly labelled diagrams of your apparatus and materials

- a list of the precautions which you took to obtain more accurate and more reliable results

- *all* your results and calculations

- tables, graphs and diagrams wherever they are appropriate

- your conclusions

- some comments on errors, if your investigation was a quantitative one

- suggestions for how your method could be improved

- a list of references

Investigations

Investigation 1
Do iron tablets deteriorate? (relates to Practical 2)

Iron(II) compounds are slowly oxidised in air to iron(III) compounds, usually iron(III) oxide, Fe_2O_3. This compound, which is a brown, rusty colour, is insoluble in water and poorly absorbed from the stomach into the bloodstream.

Investigate whether the iron(II) sulphate in iron tablets gets significantly oxidised under various conditions. You could investigate factors such as:

- whether the tablets are whole or crushed
- the presence of water
- pH
- temperature

Do your answers suggest that deterioration by oxidation is likely to be a significant problem for the manufacturers and users of iron tablets?

Discuss your plans with your teacher before starting any practical work.

Investigation 2
The salt content of different foods (relates to Practical 4)

Excess salt has been linked to high blood pressure. Because of this, many people follow 'low salt' diets.

You can use the titration method in Practical 4 to investigate the differences in salt content between normal and 'low salt' foods. Potato crisps might be a good example. Among other things, you will need to think about:

- how to separate the salt from the rest of the food
- whether there are any other substances present in the food that might interfere with the titration: for example, other ions as well as Cl^- can form a precipitate with silver ions
- the best concentration of silver nitrate to use in your titration

Discuss your plans with your teacher before starting any practical work.

Investigation 3
Investigating the effect of a charged rod on liquid jets
(relates to Practical 6)

You have probably found that a charged rod causes a jet of liquid to deflect. Polar liquids such as water tend to be deflected more than non-polar liquids such as hexane.

The explanation for this behaviour is that polar molecules become lined up as the liquid flows past the rod. The charge at one end of the molecules lines up with the opposite charge on the rod. The attraction between the opposite charges causes the jet to deflect.

However, *non-polar* liquids are also attracted to a charged rod to some extent, because the rod induces temporary dipoles in the molecules.

Investigate the factors which determine how much a liquid jet is deflected. For example, you might investigate:

- the effect of changing the polarity of the liquid: for example, you might investigate different members of the homologous series of alcohols
- the effect of mixing a polar liquid with a non-polar one
- the extent to which the density of a liquid affects its deflection

In making a Risk Assessment, you will need to bear in mind that some of the solvents you use may be flammable, and may have harmful vapours. It will probably be necessary to work in a fume cupboard.

Discuss your plans with your teacher before starting any practical work.

Investigation 4
Designing a thermochemical titration (relates to Practical 7)

Enthalpy changes of neutralisation can be used to find the concentration of a solution of an acid or alkali. The idea is similar to the titration of an acid with an alkali using an indicator. Instead of observing the colour change of an indicator, in thermochemical titrations the temperature change is measured as the acid reacts with the alkali.

Design a method for carrying out a thermochemical titration. Try it out, and compare its accuracy with a conventional titration using an indicator. Try to improve the accuracy of your method.

There is an opportunity to use datalogging if you have a suitable computer, interface and probe available.

When might this type of titration be particularly useful?

Discuss your plans with your teacher before starting any practical work.

Investigation 5
Using enthalpy changes for cooling (relates to Practical 9)

Campers and others without access to a refrigerator can keep food and drinks cool by lowering the temperature of an insulated container using chemical means.

A convenient method is to add a salt with an endothermic enthalpy change of solution to water in a plastic bag within the insulated container.

Devise a system that could be used to keep food cool. Here are some points which you might like to think about.

- What salts can be used? Cost and availability need to be borne in mind, as well as suitability of enthalpy change of solution.
- What temperature drop is required?
- What quantities of salt and water are needed to achieve the required temperature drop?
- Does the system work in practice?

Discuss your plans with your teacher before starting any practical work.

Investigation 6
Looking at indicators from plants (relates to Practical 10)

Many plants contain dyes which are acid–base indicators.

Red cabbage, beetroot and blackcurrant are examples. These indicators can be extracted by grinding the plant material with water or an organic solvent.

Investigate the indicators from a coloured plant of your choice. You could investigate:

- what colour each indicator is at different pH values
- whether the indicator is a single dye, or a mixture
- the acid–base strength of the indicator (see experiment 4 in Practical 10)
- whether different plants of the same colour contain the same indicator(s)
- whether different dyes can be combined to produce a type of universal indicator

Discuss your plans with your teacher before starting any practical work.

Investigation 7
Concentration cells (relates to Practical 11)

Figure 2 in Practical 11 shows an example of a concentration cell. Investigate this and other concentration cells. You might investigate:

- the maximum voltage obtainable
- the mathematical relationship between the concentrations in the two half-cells and the overall cell voltage
- whether the same relationship applies for cells based on other half-cells besides $Cu(s)/Cu^{2+}(aq)$. Another half-cell that you could investigate is $Fe(s)/Fe^{2+}(aq)$.

Discuss your plans with your teacher before starting any practical work.

Investigation 8
How soluble is calcium carbonate in water containing dissolved carbon dioxide? (relates to Practical 19)

Calcium carbonate, $CaCO_3$, is the major constituent of chalk, limestone and sea shells. Although calcium carbonate is insoluble in water, it is slightly soluble in water containing dissolved carbon dioxide. This is because $CaCO_3$ and CO_2 react together to form soluble calcium hydrogencarbonate, $Ca(HCO_3)_2$:

$$CaCO_3(s) + CO_2(g) + H_2O(l) \longrightarrow Ca(HCO_3)_2(aq)$$

This process is very important geologically, because it leads to the gradual dissolving of limestone rocks in rainwater containing dissolved CO_2. In the deep oceans, where under high pressure the concentration of dissolved CO_2 is high, the reaction leads to the dissolving of sea shells.

The reaction is however reversible, and calcium hydrogencarbonate solution gradually decomposes to reform calcium carbonate. This is how stalactites, stalagmites and the furry deposit in pipes and kettles are formed.

Investigate the solubility of calcium carbonate in solutions containing different concentrations of dissolved carbon dioxide. You could use marble chips or sea shells as a source of calcium carbonate. You can get solutions of carbon dioxide from a 'Sodastream' or other device for making fizzy water, or you could buy bottled soda water. Bear in mind that the reaction will be slow and the quantities involved will be small. You will need to devise an accurate way to measure the mass of calcium carbonate that has dissolved.

Discuss your plans with your teacher before starting any practical work.

Investigation 9
Do aluminium saucepans release aluminium ions? (relates to Practical 20)

There have been suggestions that aluminium ions in the diet may result in Alzheimer's Disease, or presenile dementia, which causes premature deterioration of mental faculties.

Aluminium ions in the diet can come from a number of sources, including:

- drinking water (aluminium compounds are sometimes added to water in the purification process)
- tea
- aluminium saucepans

In this investigation you should look at the last of these.

Investigate the extent to which aluminium ions are released from an aluminium saucepan under different conditions that might occur during the cooking of food. The conditions you investigate could be pH, temperature or the presence of ions such as Cl⁻ and citrate, which are commonly found in food.

You will need to find an effective way of estimating the concentration of aluminium ions, and you may need guidance from your teacher on this. Bear in mind that aluminium ions will only be released slowly, so you will need a sensitive method to detect them.

Discuss your plans with your teacher before starting any practical work.

Investigation 10
Chlorine in swimming pools (relates to Practical 21)

Chlorine is used to kill harmful bacteria in swimming pools. Chlorine reacts with water to form ClO^- ions, which are a powerful bleach and germicide.

$$Cl_2(g) + H_2O(l) \longrightarrow ClO^-(aq) + Cl^-(aq) + 2H^+(aq)$$

The chlorine is not usually added in the form of chlorine gas, but as compounds such as NaClO which have a similar effect to chlorine.

The chlorine gradually escapes from the pool and has to be replaced.

Investigate the variation in concentration of chlorine in swimming pools. You could compare the concentration:

- in different parts of the same pool
- at different times of day
- at different temperatures
- in different pools

You will need to find a way to measure the concentration of chlorine, bearing in mind that this concentration is quite low. Your teacher will be able to suggest some references.

Discuss your plans with your teacher before starting any practical work.

Investigation 11
Electrolysis of salt solution (relates to Practical 21)

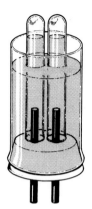

The electrolysis of sodium chloride solution is an important source of industrial chemicals (*Chemistry in Context*, Fourth Edition, section 17.3). When concentrated sodium chloride solution is electrolysed, hydrogen is formed at the cathode and chlorine at the anode, with a solution of sodium hydroxide remaining. However, when the sodium chloride solution is very dilute, *oxygen* is formed at the cathode instead of chlorine. What do you think happens with sodium chloride solution of intermediate concentration?

Investigate how the products at the anode are affected by the concentration of sodium chloride. Your investigation should be as quantitative as possible. You will need to think carefully about how you will collect and analyse the anode products: you may need some guidance from your teacher on this.

Discuss your plans with your teacher before starting any practical work.

Investigation 12
The photochemical reaction of bromine with alkanes
(relates to Practical 25)

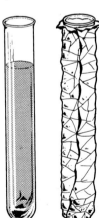

In the presence of light, alkanes undergo substitution reactions with bromine. Practical 25 gives a simple method for carrying out the reaction, using hexane as the alkane.

Investigate the rate of this reaction under different conditions. You might investigate factors such as:
- the colour (frequency) of the light
- the intensity of the light
- the nature of the alkane used

You will need to begin by thinking carefully about how you will measure the reaction rate.

In your Risk Assessment you need to think carefully about the hazards associated with both bromine and alkanes. It will probably be necessary to do much of the work in the fume cupboard.

Discuss your plans with your teacher before starting any practical work.

Investigation 13
The hydrolysis of bromobutane (relates to Practicals 28 and 29)

1-Bromobutane is slowly hydrolysed to form butan-1-ol.

$$CH_3CH_2CH_2CH_2Br(l) + H_2O(l) \longrightarrow CH_3CH_2CH_2CH_2OH(aq) + H^+(aq) + Br^-(aq)$$

1-bromobutane   butan-1-ol

Investigate the factors which might affect the rate at which this reaction occurs. You might investigate one or more of the following:

- temperature
- pH
- the extent to which the 1-bromobutane is mixed with the aqueous phase

Practical 28, experiment 1, might help you think of a way in which you can follow the rate of the reaction.

You could extend or modify this investigation in a number of ways.

- Look at different halogenoalkanes, containing different halogens and/or different alkanes.
- Look at different techniques for following the rate of the reaction, for example using conductivity measurements. Your teacher may be able to suggest references.

Discuss your plans with your teacher before starting any practical work.

Investigation 14
The esterification equilibrium (relates to Practical 14)

Practical 14 gives a method you can use to find the equilibrium constant for the esterification reaction

$$CH_3COOH + CH_3CH_2OH \longrightarrow CH_3COOCH_2CH_3 + H_2O$$

ethanoic acid   ethanol   ethyl ethanoate

Investigate this equilibrium further. You might investigate one or more of the following:

- the effect of temperature on the value of the equilibrium constant
- the effect on the equilibrium constant of varying the concentration of catalyst
- the rate at which equilibrium is reached

It will be important to distinguish between the *position* of equilibrium and the *rate of attainment* of equilibrium. For example, varying the temperature will affect not only the value of the equilibrium constant, but also the rate at which equilibrium is reached. You will need to be satisfied that the reaction has had time to reach equilibrium before you make any measurements.

Discuss your plans with your teacher before starting any practical work.

Investigation 15
The hydrolysis of oils (relates to Practical 40)

Fats and oils are esters of propane-1,2,3-triol and long-chain carboxylic acids called fatty acids. The structure of a typical oil is shown in figure 1. (See *Chemistry in Context*, Fourth Edition, section 33.6 for more on the chemistry of fats and oils.)

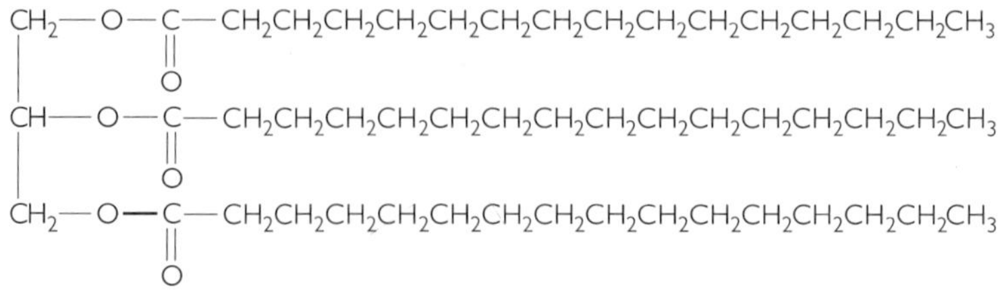

$$CH_2-O-\overset{\overset{\textstyle |}{\textstyle }}{C}-CH_2CH_2CH_2CH_2CH_2CH_2CH_2CH_2CH_2CH_2CH_2CH_2CH_2CH_2CH_3$$

$$CH-O-C-CH_2CH_2CH_2CH_2CH_2CH_2CH_2CH_2CH_2CH_2CH_2CH_2CH_2CH_2CH_3$$

$$CH_2-O-C-CH_2CH_2CH_2CH_2CH_2CH_2CH_2CH_2CH_2CH_2CH_2CH_2CH_2CH_2CH_3$$

Figure 1
A typical molecule found in an oil.

When fats and oils are stored, they slowly deteriorate. One of the reactions which causes deterioration is hydrolysis. The ester linkages are hydrolysed, and free carboxylic acids are formed. This makes the oil taste unpleasantly rancid.

Investigate the quantities of free carboxylic acids present in different oils. If necessary, ask your teacher for a reference for the basic experimental method for measuring the free carboxylic acid. You might investigate one or more of the following questions.

- Does oil that has been stored a long time contain a significantly higher proportion of free carboxylic acid than fresh oil?
- Does frying damp chips cause significant hydrolysis of oil?
- Do different types of oil (e.g. olive oil, sunflower oil) vary significantly in the proportion of free carboxylic acid they contain?
- The oils bought in shops usually contain preservatives to slow down deterioration. Does oil bought from a shop become hydrolysed more slowly than oil that has been freshly extracted from a plant? If necessary, ask your teacher for a method to extract fresh oil from a plant source such as sunflower seeds.

Discuss your plans with your teacher before starting any practical work.

Investigation 16
How fast does carbon dioxide escape from solution?

Fizzy drinks go 'flat' as the dissolved carbon dioxide escapes from solution. Investigate the factors affecting the rate at which the carbon dioxide escapes.

It is easier to follow the changes in concentration of carbon dioxide in the aqueous, rather than the gas phase. You can do this indirectly by measuring the pH of the solution. In solution, a small amount of carbon dioxide reacts with water to form a weakly acidic solution.

$$CO_2(aq) + H_2O(l) \longrightarrow HCO_3^-(aq) + H^+(aq)$$

A saturated solution of carbon dioxide has a pH of 3.9 at room temperature and pressure, compared with 7.0 for pure water.

The pH of the solution thus gives an indirect measure of the concentration of CO_2 in solution: it is a rough measure only, but good enough for the kind of comparisons you will be making. pH is a logarithmic scale, and if the concentration of CO_2 is halved, the pH rises by only 0.3. The pH changes you observe will therefore be small, and you will need to design your investigation to give the largest changes possible. If a computer and pH probe are available, you could use them to monitor the pH changes.

Begin by listing all the factors that you think will affect the rate at which CO_2 comes off, then decide which particular factor(s) you will investigate.

Discuss your plans with your teacher before starting any practical work.

Investigation 17
Investigating the activity of an enzyme

Diabetes can be detected by testing for glucose in a patient's urine.

A test that is often used involves test strips which contain the enzyme glucose oxidase. This enzyme oxidises glucose to gluconic acid and hydrogen peroxide:

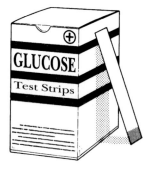

The test strips also contain a redox indicator, whose colour changes to blue when it is oxidised by hydrogen peroxide. The test strips thus provide a quick and simple test for glucose of the concentration typically found in the urine of diabetics. This concentration is about $0.02\,mol\,dm^{-3}$. They also provide you with a handy way of testing the activity of the enzyme glucose oxidase.

Investigate factors affecting the activity of glucose oxidase. You might investigate one or more of the following factors:

- specificity: the normal substrate for this enzyme is glucose, but does it work with other sugars?
- temperature
- pH

There are several brands of test strips. If necessary, ask your teacher for information about how to get them. Make sure you read the instructions on the packet.

Discuss your plans with your teacher before starting any practical work.

Investigation 18
Investigating rust control methods

Protecting iron and steel from rusting is vital. Some protection methods are more effective (and more expensive) than others. You can read about how these methods work in Activity 19 in this book. The activity also explains the chemistry of rusting.

The methods used include the following:
- painting
- covering in oil
- coating with zinc (galvanising)
- electrochemical protection involving a sacrificial anode
- special rust protection treatments—many examples can be found in hardware and car accessory shops

Choose one or more of these methods and investigate its effectiveness under different conditions. Your investigation should be as quantitative as possible.

You will need to find a method of monitoring the rusting of the iron. Here are two possibilities.

1 Measure the loss in mass of the iron as it rusts. Weigh the iron before rusting, allow it to rust, then remove the rust and weigh it again. The loss in mass will be quite small, unless you wait a long time.

2 Use 'ferroxyl indicator'. This is a corrosion indicator: it contains sodium chloride, phenolphthalein and potassium hexacyanoferrate(III) in solution. It produces a blue colour with Fe^{2+} ions and a pink colour with OH^- ions. If necessary, your teacher will be able to give you more details.

Discuss your plans with your teacher before starting any practical work.

Investigation 19
Investigating sunscreens

The Sun's radiation includes ultraviolet rays, which can damage the skin and sometimes cause skin cancer. Sunscreens protect the skin by absorbing ultraviolet radiation, especially the higher energy radiations, which are particularly damaging.

Sunscreens can be bought as lotions which are applied to the skin. Actually there are many chemical substances which absorb ultraviolet: they include glass, which explains why people do not get sunburnt when sitting behind a window on a sunny day.

Investigate the effectiveness of different substances as sunscreens. You could look at commercial sunscreen lotions, but also other materials that are relevant, such as glass, water and Perspex.

You will need a source of ultraviolet radiation, and a method for detecting it. The best source is the Sun. However, this may not always be practical, and you may need to use some kind of ultraviolet lamp. If you do, be sure to follow the safety instructions since some ultraviolet lamps can burn the skin and permanently damage the eyes.

There are several ways in which you could detect ultraviolet radiation.

1 Ultraviolet-sensitive paper, which turns blue when exposed to ultraviolet from the Sun. Your teacher will be able to tell you if this is available.

2 Most machine washing powders contain fluorescers. A piece of white cloth washed in such powder will give a bright fluorescent glow under ultraviolet radiation.

3 Some brands of photocopying paper fluoresce under ultraviolet radiation.

Discuss your plans with your teacher before starting any practical work.

Investigation 20
Investigating the formula of hydroxide precipitates
(relates to Practicals 23 and 24)

When sodium hydroxide solution is added to copper sulphate solution, a blue precipitate is formed. If, however, you do it the other way round and add the copper sulphate solution to the sodium hydroxide solution, you get a precipitate which is a different shade of blue and has a different formula.

Investigate the formulae of the precipitates. You might investigate one or more of the following questions.

- What is the formula of the precipitate formed when copper sulphate solution is added to sodium hydroxide solution, and vice-versa?
- Do solutions of other copper salts behave in the same way?
- Do the salts of other metals show similar behaviour?

You will need to plan a way to find the formula of the precipitate. One possibility is to monitor the change in pH or conductivity as the solutions are added to one another.

Discuss your plans with your teacher before starting any practical work.

SECTION TWO ACTIVITIES

I The vanilla counterfeiters

Vanilla extract, used to flavour many food products, comes from the fruit of the vanilla orchid (right). The dried pods (left) are often added to granulated sugar to give it a distinct taste and aroma.

The following passage by Professor C. H. Breedlove is taken from *Chem-Matters*, a magazine published by the American Chemical Society. It describes how government chemists have found ways to detect counterfeit vanilla flavouring, and how the counterfeiters have fought back.

One of the most common flavoring ingredients found in the kitchen is vanilla extract. In contrast, the label on many brands of ice cream, cookies, and cakes lists 'artificial vanilla flavor.' What is 'vanilla extract,' and how is it different from 'artificial vanilla?'

Technically, vanilla extract is a dilute solution containing the flavoring and aromatic essence of 100 grams of vanilla beans, dissolved in 1 litre of 45%, by volume, ethanol. Sugar is often added.

Vanilla extract comes from the fruit of the vanilla orchid, *Vanilla planifolia*, a tropical plant cultivated primarily in Mexico, Indonesia, and the Malagasy

Figure I
Vanillin.

Reprinted with permission from Breedlove, C. H. "Vanilla" *Chem-Matters* copyright American Chemical Society.

Republic (formerly Madagascar). Surprisingly, the unripe bean contains very little vanillin, the compound responsible for the unique flavor and fragrance we find so desirable in our desserts. It is in the ripening and fermenting that the beans generate vanillin, which may appear as white crystals on the surface of the bean. Vanillin ($C_8H_8O_3$) (figure 1) is classified chemically as a phenolic aldehyde. In its pure form, it is a white solid at room temperature.

Vanillin is not very soluble in water: only one gram of vanillin will dissolve in $100\,cm^3$ of water at room temperature. However, it is freely soluble in ethanol, which explains why the vanillin is extracted from the beans with alcohol and why the product sold in grocery stores has a minimum ethanol content of 35%. The use of alcohol to extract the vanillin has another effect. Vanillin is only one of hundreds of organic chemicals in the bean, and many of these compounds are also soluble in alcohol. Therefore the extract of the vanilla bean contains several hundred other components such as aromatic esters, alcohols, and other aldehydes. Although these other compounds affect the odor and flavor of the extract, it is vanillin that dominates.

If you look closely when you buy flavoring, you will see another type of vanilla: imitation vanilla extract. In the 1950s chemists discovered methods for oxidizing *lignin*, a waste product of the wood pulp industry, to make vanillin. This synthetic vanillin is identical to natural vanillin in all respects save one— lignin-derived vanillin is much cheaper. For example, in 1986, Madagascar beans cost $38 per pound and Indonesian beans were $30 per pound, but synthetic vanillin was only $3 per pound.

Smells like money

Because lignin-derived vanillin is so much cheaper than natural vanillin and is not subject to the fluctuations of supply and price that affect natural foods, it offers an inexpensive way for a food producer to impart a vanilla flavor to a food or beverage. Substituting synthetic vanillin for natural vanilla is safe, sensible, and legal—as long as the product is properly labelled as containing 'vanillin' or 'artificial vanilla flavoring.' Legal problems arise if a dishonest producer 'adulterates' the product by substituting synthetic vanillin for natural vanillin without properly identifying the flavoring on the label.

This presents a tempting situation for counterfeiters. One pound of Madagascar beans produces about 1 gallon (3.8 liters) of vanilla extract, which sells for about $150 retail. In comparison, one pound of synthetic vanillin combined with other botanical extracts yields about 60 gallons (227 liters) of artificial vanilla flavoring. When properly labelled 'synthetic vanillin,' the 60 gallons would retail for $3750. But if it is incorrectly labelled 'vanilla extract,' it would have a retail value of $7500! The possibility of cheating in the use of vanillin means that food chemists must devise a method to tell when a product contains natural or synthetic vanillin.

But vanillin is the same chemical compound, whether it originates in the bean or is synthesized from lignin. Standard chemical analysis indicates the identity and quantity of a compound, but usually gives no clues about its sources. In this case, the source can be determined by inspecting the carbon atoms in the vanillin with a technique called *stable isotope ratio analysis* (SIRA).

Carbon clues

SIRA is based on the fact that not all carbon atoms have the same mass. Of the carbon atoms found in nature, 98.9% have a mass number of 12, and 1.1% have a mass number of 13. Most organic compounds contain these percentages of carbon-12 (^{12}C) and carbon-13 (^{13}C) atoms. However, the ratio of these isotopes is slightly different for natural vanillin than for synthetic vanillin. The synthetic vanillin is enriched in ^{13}C. This happens because of differences in biochemistry of the vanilla orchid and trees, the source of the lignin.

The vanilla orchid carries on photosynthesis by the *Crassulacean pathway*. Most plants, however, including trees, use the *Calvin pathway*, which involves a greater number of chemical reactions. Because ^{13}C is heavier than ^{12}C, ^{13}C

reacts more slowly—not as much gets through each of the chemical reactions in photosynthesis. This results in a lower percentage of ^{13}C in lignin, hence in synthetic vanillin. By measuring the $^{13}C:^{12}C$ ratio, scientists at the Bureau of Alcohol, Tobacco, and Firearms have been able to identify counterfeit vanilla extract, and federal attorneys have prosecuted unscrupulous suppliers.

But the detective story does not end here. When the producers of the counterfeit extract discovered that government chemists could tell the difference between natural and synthetic vanillin by means of isotope ratios, the producers started searching for ways to adjust the $^{13}C:^{12}C$ ratio in the synthetic product to more closely match that of natural vanillin. The easiest way was to remove the methoxy group containing ^{12}C and replace it with another methoxy group containing ^{13}C (see figure 1). Fortunately, the government chemists were able to spot this ploy by removing the methoxy group and testing for the presence of ^{13}C. And so goes the competition between the organic chemist employed by an unscrupulous producer seeking to maximize profits and the regulatory government chemist charged with enforcing labelling laws.

References

Krueger, D.; Krueger, H. "Detection of Fraudulent Vanilla Labeled With ^{13}C? in the Carbonyl Carbon." *J. Argric. Food Chem.* **1985**, *33*(3).
Bricout, et al. "Detection of Synthetic Vanillin in Vanilla Extracts by Isotopic Analysis." *J. Assoc. Off. Anal. Chem.* **1974**, *57*(3).
Martin, et al. "Stable Isotope Ratio Determination of the Origin of Vanillin in Vanilla Extracts and its Relationship to Vanillin/Potassium Ratios." *J. Anal. Chem.* **1981**, *64*(5).
Martin, G.E. et al. "Determining the Authenticity of Vanilla Extracts." *J. Food Sci.* **1977**, *42*(6).
Figert, D., personal communication.
Burgraff, J., personal communication.

Questions

1   Use the data given to calculate the relative atomic mass of naturally occurring carbon to three decimal places.

2   Another isotope of carbon is known, carbon-14. Why is it not included in the isotopic composition figures given in the passage?

3   Why is there a lower percentage of ^{13}C in synthetic vanillin compared with natural vanillin?

4   Vanillin is extracted from vanilla beans using a solvent. Why does the choice of solvent have an important influence on the flavour of the extract?

5   Government scientists needed to measure the ratio between carbon-12 and carbon-13 in vanillin, in order to detect 'counterfeit' vanillin. What would be the best technique for making this measurement? Name the technique, and describe briefly how it would be used to measure this ratio.

6   According to this passage, the government scientists are now one step ahead of the counterfeiters. Other than admitting defeat, what might the counterfeiters' next move be?

7   Use your knowledge of organic chemistry to predict how vanillin would react with each of the following reagents. In each case, give the structural formula of the organic product and describe what you would see during the reaction.

   a warm acidified potassium dichromate

   b ethanoyl chloride

   c sodium hydroxide solution

   d 2,4-dinitrophenylhydrazine

2 Acid rain

The following passage concerns the problems of acid rain and some of the chemistry involved in its formation and possible control.

The term 'acid rain' is not new. It was first used over one hundred years ago. Nor is the term entirely correct. It should really be called **acid deposition**, because the acid may come to the earth in snow or hail as well as in rain. What is certainly true is that acid deposition has become a major environmental issue in the last thirty years. It has been blamed for the death of fish and other aquatic life, for damage to buildings and for the death of trees. Furthermore, it is a global problem because the acid gases produced in one country can be carried to another by the wind. Unfortunately, acid deposition involves complex chemistry, which makes it difficult to understand and even more difficult to solve.

What kind of acids?

Even in unpolluted areas, rainwater is slightly acidic, with a pH of about 5.6. This is caused by carbon dioxide in the atmosphere. Acid rain may have a pH between 5 and 2. Across central Europe, the average pH of rain is 4.1, but the rain in individual storms may have a pH of 3 or less. The main acids involved in acid deposition are sulphuric acid and nitric acid.

Sulphuric acid originates from atmospheric sulphur dioxide. In Europe about 90% of atmospheric sulphur dioxide comes from the burning of sulphur-containing fuels. When such fuels are burned, the sulphur they contain is converted to sulphur dioxide. Once it has entered the atmosphere, sulphur dioxide may be oxidised by air to sulphur trioxide. This oxidation normally occurs slowly, but it is catalysed by ozone, O_3, and oxides of nitrogen, which are common atmospheric pollutants. The oxidation of sulphur dioxide is also much more rapid in the presence of water than under dry conditions.

Once sulphur trioxide has formed, it dissolves in water to form sulphuric acid. The sulphuric acid may reach the ground in rain or snow, or it may combine with ammonia in the atmosphere to form solid ammonium sulphate. Ammonia is present in the atmosphere as a result of biological decay processes and agricultural activities, and the ammonium sulphate formed in this way makes a haze of suspended solid particles. Such hazes can often be seen on warm summer days.

Nitric acid in acid rain arises from oxides of nitrogen, NO and NO_2, sometimes jointly called 'NO_x'. These oxides are produced during combustion processes, particularly in car engines and in power stations. Nitrogen monoxide is oxidised by air to NO_2, and NO_2 undergoes reaction with water and further oxidation by air to form nitric acid.

What causes the damage?

Some of the damage from acid deposition is due to the acidity itself as all organisms are sensitive to variations in pH. Other effects are less direct. For example, acid water releases aluminium ions from rocks and soil. These ions are normally bound tightly as complexes, but the low pH causes the ions to be released. Aluminium ions are toxic: for example, they interfere with the operation of fishes' gills, so the fish cannot obtain enough oxygen.

Some of the damage ascribed to acid deposition may in fact be caused by other forms of pollution. For example, gaseous sulphur dioxide causes direct

These trees have been affected by acid rain.

damage even before it has been converted to sulphuric acid. Sulphur dioxide gas is believed to damage the leaves of trees and to be responsible for much of the acid damage to buildings. It also seems likely that **ozone** may be responsible for some of the damage attributed to acid deposition, particularly damage to trees. Ozone is a highly reactive gas which is produced by the action of sunlight on atmospheric oxygen. Its production is cataysed by air pollutants such as nitrogen oxides and unburnt hydrocarbons, both of which are released by vehicle exhausts.

Tackling the acid rain problem

There are several approaches to the control of acid deposition.

- **Neutralising the acid** after it has reached the earth is one possibility. This can be done using a cheap base such as limestone (calcium carbonate), which farmers have used for centuries to neutralise soil acidity. Acidified lakes can be treated in this way, though the treatment has to be repeated regularly. Twenty-five million pounds is spent each year on liming lakes in Sweden.

Adding limestone to an acidified lake.

- **Reducing the emission of sulphur dioxide** is a better approach, because it tackles the problem at its source. Two-thirds of the sulphur dioxide emitted in Britain comes from coal-burning power stations, so this is a good place to start. Ideally, the sulphur would be removed from the coal before it is burned, but this is difficult. An easier approach is to remove sulphur dioxide from the flue gases after the fuel has been burned. This is done by **flue gas desulphurisation (FGD)** illustrated in figure 1. The calcium sulphate produced by this process can be used to make plaster for the building industry. Unfortunately, FGD is expensive to install and run and could add 10% to electricity prices.

- **Reducing the emission of nitrogen oxides** can be effective because these oxides may be converted to nitric acid. They also play a catalytic role in the formation of sulphuric acid and ozone. The major producers of 'NO$_x$' are believed to be car engines and power station furnaces, hence one way of cutting down emission is by controlling combustion conditions. The combustion temperature and the ratio of fuel to air are particularly important in controlling the extent to which nitrogen and oxygen combine together to form oxides of nitrogen during

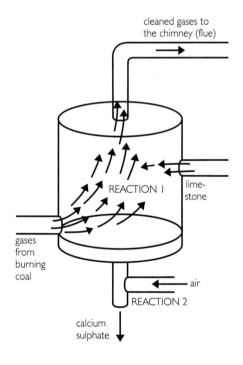

Reaction 1
$$CaCO_3 + SO_2 \longrightarrow CaSO_3 + CO_2$$

Reaction 2
$$CaSO_3 + \tfrac{1}{2}O_2 \longrightarrow CaSO_4$$

Figure 1
A simplified diagram to explain flue-gas desulphurisation.

combustion. New designs for power station furnaces take these factors into account and ensure they release less 'NO$_x$'.

In Britain, motor vehicles release about 40% of the oxides of nitrogen causing pollution. The simplest way of reducing 'NO$_x$' emission is by driving more slowly. The percentage of nitrogen oxides in car exhausts falls from 0.11% at 70 mph to 0.03% at 30 mph. New car engine designs, such as 'lean burn' engines which use a lower ratio of fuel to air, also help. Another approach is to fit catalytic converters to car exhaust systems which remove nitrogen oxides from the exhaust gases. However, these converters are expensive and only work if the car runs on lead-free petrol.

Questions

In these questions you may need the following relative atomic masses:

$$Ca = 40, \quad C = 12, \quad O = 16, \quad S = 32.$$

1 Consider the sequence of conversions:
sulphur → sulphur dioxide → sulphur trioxide → sulphuric acid.

   a What is the oxidation number of sulphur in each of these substances?

   b In which of the conversions is sulphur oxidised? What is the oxidising agent in each case?

   c **i** In what ways is this sequence of conversions similar to the sequence used in the 'Contact Process' for the manufacture of sulphuric acid?

     ii In what ways is it different?

2 Consider the sequence of conversions:
nitrogen → nitrogen monoxide → nitrogen dioxide → nitric acid.

   a What is the oxidation number of nitrogen in each of these substances?

   b In which of the conversions is nitrogen oxidised? What is the oxidising agent in each case?

   c Write equations for each of the reactions in this sequence.

3 It is believed that nitrogen oxides may catalyse the oxidation of sulphur dioxide to sulphur trioxide by the following reactions:

$$SO_2 + NO_2 \longrightarrow SO_3 + NO$$

$$2NO + O_2 \longrightarrow 2NO_2$$

Explain why the nitrogen oxides are acting catalytically in this reaction and write the overall equation for the reaction.

4 A lake contains 10^{10} dm^3 of water. Due to acid deposition, the pH of the water is 5.0. Environmental scientists have decided to add enough limestone (calcium carbonate) to the lake to bring the pH to 6.0.

   a What is the initial concentration of hydrogen ions in the lake, in mol dm^{-3}?

   b What is the total number of moles of hydrogen ions in the lake initially?

   c What will be the concentration of hydrogen ions in the lake after the pH has been raised to 6.0?

   d What will be the total number of moles of hydrogen ions in the lake after the pH had been raised to 6.0?

e Use your answers to **b** and **d** to calculate how many moles of hydrogen ions would have to be removed from the lake to raise the pH from 5.0 to 6.0.

f Using the equation

$$CaCO_3(s) + 2H^+(aq) \longrightarrow Ca^{2+}(aq) + H_2O(l) + CO_2(g)$$

together with your answer to **e**, calculate the number of moles of calcium carbonate that must be added to the lake to raise the pH from 5.0 to 6.0.

g Hence calculate the **mass** of calcium carbonate that must be added to the lake.

5   A large coal-fired power station is being planned. It will burn 5 million tonnes of coal per year. The average sulphur content of this coal is 1.5% by mass. The sulphur dioxide produced from the coal is to be removed by flue-gas desulphurisation using the equipment shown in figure 1.

a Calculate the mass of sulphur dioxide produced by this power station per year.

b Calculate the mass of limestone needed to react with the sulphur dioxide produced in one year. (Assume limestone is pure calcium carbonate.)

c Calculate the mass of calcium sulphate, $CaSO_4$, produced by the power station in one year.

d The total mass of calcium sulphate required by the British building industry for the manufacture of plaster is about 3 million tonnes per year.
Comment on your answer to **c** in the light of this information.

6   The following measures could each make a significant contribution to reducing acid deposition.

- Replacing coal-fired power stations with nuclear power stations

- Fitting flue-gas desulphurisation to all coal-fired power stations

- Imposing lower speed limits for road traffic

- Making catalytic converters compulsory on all cars.

Comment on the merits of these different courses of action. In each case, discuss the likely effectiveness of the measure, and how acceptable you think it would be to society.

3 Chromium plating

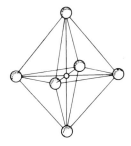

Figure 2
Cr^{3+} bound by water molecules as a stable complex ion.

The advertisement on the left originally appeared in *Scientific American*.

Humans have been plating chromium for over a century—even though puzzled by the electrochemistry involved.

For example, the normal process uses a bath containing Cr^{6+} ions. During plating, the Cr^{6+} ions reduce to Cr^{3+} and then to metallic Cr. Now you might wonder: If the process goes through the Cr^{3+} stage anyway, why not start with those ions? Well, strangely enough, if you try, the process won't work unless considerably modified.

Our scientists have long been intrigued by this enigma here at the General Motors Research Laboratories. And they now believe they've not only explained the Cr^{3+} mystery, but developed a correct theory of the entire chromium plating process as well.

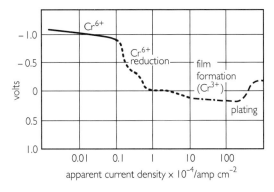

Figure 1
Typical polarization curve.

By analyzing polarization curves (figure 1) obtained from carefully designed experiments, they concluded that:

- Starting with Cr^{3+} fails because it immediately forms a stable complex with water molecules (figure 2) from which Cr cannot be deposited.

- Starting with Cr^{6+} succeeds because during reduction a chemical film forms around the cathode (the part being plated); and since Cr^{3+} is bound in that film, it does not react with water—but, instead, plates out as chromium metal.

Our researchers have, in fact, determined all 10 steps that take place as Cr^{6+} reduces to bright Cr, pinpointed the step at which catalysis begins, and identified the active catalyst. (It's not the sulfate ion, as commonly held, but the hydrogen sulfate ion.)

So have we merely solved a stubborn puzzle? No. More than that, we've gained important new insight to guide us toward a more efficient chromium electroplating process.

General Motors Research and Development Center,
Warren, Michigan

Questions

1   **a** Why are metals sometimes plated with other metals?

   b What properties make a metal suitable for plating onto others?

2   Name two metals, other than chromium, that are used for plating, and give the reason why they are used.

3   The passage mentions the use of Cr^{6+} ions for electroplating. In fact, simple Cr^{6+} ions do not exist in aqueous solution, but the ion used does contain Cr in the $6+$ oxidation state. Give the probable formula of this ion.

4   Explain briefly in your own words why Cr^{3+} cannot be used successfully in a plating bath, even though it is formed as an intermediate in the reduction of Cr^{6+}.

5   Give the name and formula of the stable complex ion formed by Cr^{3+} with water.

6   Draw a labelled diagram of the apparatus that could be used to chromium plate the whole surface of a door handle.

7   Write half-equations for the reduction of

   a the ion containing Cr in the $6+$ state, in acid solution, to Cr^{3+}

   b the Cr^{3+} ion to Cr.

8   It is required to plate a car bumper whose total surface area is $3500\,cm^2$ with a layer of chromium $0.0002\,cm$ thick. The plating bath used is designed to deposit chromium at a uniform rate over the whole surface of the bumper. The plating operation uses a current of $35\,A$.

   Assume that the density of chromium is $7.2\,g\,cm^{-3}$, its relative atomic mass is 52 and that the Faraday constant (the charge on one mole of electrons) is $96\,500\ C\ mol^{-1}$.

   a How many moles of chromium must be deposited on the bumper?

   b How much electrical charge would be required to deposit this amount of chromium from the type of plating bath described in the passage?

   c How long would the plating operation take?

4 Compounds of the noble gases

Until 1962, no-one had succeeded in making any chemical compounds of the noble gases. Attempts had been made to combine the gases with fluorine, but these had been unsuccessful. In any case, the octet rule proposed by Kossel and Lewis in 1916 led chemists to believe that the noble gases must be totally inert.

The breakthrough came in the early 1960s when Neil Bartlett was experimenting with platinum hexafluoride, PtF_6, a very powerful oxidising agent. Bartlett found that this compound was capable of oxidising oxygen molecules to form a stable compound:

$$O_2(g) + PtF_6(s) \longrightarrow O_2^+ PtF_6^-(s)$$

Bartlett predicted that a similar reaction might take place between xenon and platinum hexafluoride as the first ionisation energy of xenon $(1170 \, kJ \, mol^{-1})$ was very close to that of molecular oxygen $(1180 \, kJ \, mol^{-1})$. Furthermore, as the O_2^+ ion and the Xe^+ ion are approximately the same size, the lattice energies of the two compounds should be similar. When Bartlett mixed xenon with gaseous platinum hexafluoride there was an immediate reaction, forming an orange-yellow solid thought to be xenon hexafluoroplatinate, $Xe^+ PtF_6^-$. This discovery led to great experimental activity. Within a year, several other compounds of the noble gases had been prepared. These included three fluorides of xenon, made by direct combination under different conditions:

$$Xe(g) + 3F_2(g) \longrightarrow XeF_6(s)$$
$$Xe(g) + 2F_2(g) \longrightarrow XeF_4(s)$$
$$Xe(g) + F_2(g) \longrightarrow XeF_2(s)$$

Hydrolysis of XeF_6 gave two oxygen-containing compounds: XeO_3 and $XeOF_4$.

$$XeF_6(s) + 3H_2O(l) \longrightarrow 6HF(aq) + XeO_3(s)$$
$$XeF_6(s) + H_2O(l) \longrightarrow 2HF(aq) + XeOF_4(s)$$

Since these initial discoveries, many other thermally stable compounds of xenon have been prepared, all containing xenon bonded to the two most electronegative elements, fluorine and oxygen. Krypton difluoride, KrF_2, has

Xenon tetrafluoride crystals

also been made, though it is less stable than XeF_2, and radon difluoride has been prepared, despite the difficulties involved in working with a radioactive noble gas. No compounds of helium, neon and argon have yet been made.

Questions

1   Why did the discovery of the reaction between platinum hexafluoride and molecular oxygen open the way to the preparation of the first noble gas compound?

2   Why was it likely that 'the lattice energies of O_2PtF_6 and $XePtF_6$ would be similar'?

3   Why did the Kossel and Lewis octet rule lead chemists to believe that the noble gases were totally inert?

4   Draw 'dot/cross' diagrams to show the electronic structures of
    a XeF_2 **b** XeF_4 **c** XeF_6. Show outer-shell electrons only.

5   Use the electron pair repulsion theory to predict the shapes of XeF_2 and XeF_4.

6   Suggest reasons why all the known stable xenon compounds contain xenon bonded only to fluorine, oxygen or chlorine.

7   Suggest reasons why KrF_2 is less stable than XeF_2.

8   Suggest reasons why no compounds of helium, neon and argon have yet been prepared.

9   How did xenon become the first noble gas to be shown to form chemical compounds?

10 Why are there far more compounds known for xenon than for any other noble gas?

5 Energy levels of the electrons in atoms

Table 1 gives *some* of the energy levels available to electrons in atoms of hydrogen, lithium, sodium and beryllium. The **ground state** is printed in bold.

Transitions between the levels give rise to lines in the ultraviolet, visible and infra-red regions of the electromagnetic spectrum. Except in the case of hydrogen, transitions normally take place only between a level printed in upright type and a level printed in italic type.

In the case of elements, like beryllium, with two outer electrons, the energy levels occur in two sets marked S and T. Transitions do *not* normally take place between the levels in these two sets except between the lowest S and the lowest T levels.

The figures in table 1 show the difference in energy between an electron in the quantum level indicated and the electron at rest (i.e. with zero energy) well away from its ionised atom.

Table 1
Electronic energy levels for atoms of hydrogen, lithium, sodium and beryllium. Values in the table are in attojoules per electron. (1 joule (J) = 10^{18} attojoules (aJ).)

Hydrogen	Lithium	Sodium	Beryllium	
−0.022	−0.095	−0.088		
−0.027	−0.103	−0.101		
−0.034	−0.136	−0.127	S	T
−0.044	−0.139	−0.137	−0.127	−0.144
−0.061	−0.168	−0.164	−0.214	−0.212
−0.087	−0.242	−0.222	−0.407	−0.261
−0.136	−0.250	−0.244	−0.648	−0.459
−0.242	−0.323	−0.312	**−1.494**	−1.057
−0.545	−0.568	−0.487		
−2.180	**−0.864**	**−0.823**		

Questions

1 What is meant by the ground state of an atom?

2 Calculate the ionisation energy of hydrogen.

3 Calculate the first ionisation energy of lithium.

4 The emission spectra of elements which involve transitions down to level 2 are known as Balmer Series.
Calculate the frequencies of the first two lines (with the lowest frequencies) in the Balmer Series for hydrogen.

$$(E = h\nu, \quad \text{where } h, \text{ Planck's constant} = 6.626 \times 10^{-34} \text{ J s})$$

5 How many of the Balmer Series lines for hydrogen occur in the visible region of the electromagnetic spectrum? Assume that the visible region stretches from frequency 4.5×10^{14} Hz to 7.5×10^{14} Hz.

6 The frequency of the persistent yellow line in the emission spectrum for sodium is 5.1×10^{14} Hz. Which transition does this relate to?

7 Calculate the frequency of the line with the highest frequency in the beryllium spectrum. Which part of the electromagnetic spectrum would this line appear in?

8 How many lines are likely to be present in the emission spectrum for beryllium involving transitions only between the levels shown in table 1?

6 Solving the problems of Chernobyl

The accident at the Chernobyl nuclear power station in April 1986 caused a huge cloud of radioactive material to pass over Europe. Soils in the U.K. were contaminated with radioactive isotopes of caesium in areas such as Cumbria and North Wales where heavy rain fell when the cloud was overhead.

Soon afterwards, the Government set up a monitoring scheme to protect the public who might risk contamination by eating animal or plant products grown in these areas. Investigations showed that caesium levels in grass altered according to the concentration of other minerals in the soil. In a mineral-rich area, less caesium was taken up by plant roots. This suggested that other ions were competing with caesium for uptake. Also the rate of caesium uptake into plants varied with the seasons. Furthermore, there was a difference in uptake between clay and peaty soils. Clay seemed to bind the caesium ions, preventing them from being taken up by the roots of plants. This clay-like property was also found in non-toxic hexacyanoferrate compounds, such as Prussian Blue.

By studying the uptake of caesium and its prevention, scientists were able to put forward potential solutions to the problem.

Questions

1 Design a flow chart to show how caesium compounds can enter the body of humans from air.

2 Use table 1 to decide which ion is most likely to compete with caesium for uptake. (Roots have transporter molecules which only carry ions which have a complementary shape to them.)

Table 1

Ion	Hydrated ionic radius/nm
Cs^+	0.228
Mg^{2+}	0.196
Fe^{2+}	0.160
K^+	0.232

3 Draw a sketch graph to show how you think caesium uptake would vary with the seasons over the course of three years following the Chernobyl accident.
Explain the shape of your graph.

4 **a** Try to think of three possible solutions to the problem of caesium contamination using the information from the text above. (Hint: Use your flow diagram to remind yourself of all the stages at which caesium entry into humans could be blocked.)

b For each solution, say whether it might pose environmental or practical difficulties.

Sheep in the Lake District became contaminated by radioactive caesium from the explosion at Chernobyl in Russia in 1986.

7 Heavy water

The following passage concerns deuterium oxide, D_2O, often called 'heavy water'.

Isotopes of hydrogen

Three isotopes of hydrogen are known: protium (usually called 'hydrogen'), deuterium and tritium. Table 1 gives some details of their atomic structure and relative abundance.

Table 1
Isotopes of hydrogen

Name	Symbol	No. of protons	No. of neutrons	Abundance in natural hydrogen
Protium (hydrogen)	^1_1H or H	1	0	99.984%
Deuterium (heavy hydrogen)	^2_1H or D	1	1	0.015%
Tritium (radioactive, unstable)	^3_1H or T	1	2	1 part in 10^{17}

The electronic structure of these atoms is of course identical, so the isotopes are chemically very similar. Any differences in their chemical behaviour are due to the different masses of the atoms—deuterium atoms are twice as heavy as normal hydrogen atoms. As the ratio of the masses of the isotopes is large compared with the isotopes of other elements, differences in reactivity between deuterium and hydrogen are more marked than for other isotope pairs. In spite of this, chemical differences between the two isotopes are small, although biological systems, which are highly sensitive to changes in reaction conditions, sometimes show noticeably different behaviour when deuterium atoms are substituted for hydrogen atoms. In general, deuterium is slightly less reactive than hydrogen, probably because of the higher bond enthalpy of the D–D bond ($440 \, \text{kJ mol}^{-1}$ compared with $436 \, \text{kJ mol}^{-1}$ for the H–H bond).

Heavy water

Most of the hydrogen atoms in the Earth's crust occur combined as water. Ordinary water contains H_2O, HDO and D_2O molecules, the proportion of D atoms being about 0.015%, or about 1 in 6000. Although the chemical properties of H_2O and D_2O are very similar (D_2O can for example be drunk quite safely), some of their physical properties differ quite noticeably, as table 2 shows.

Table 2
A comparison of some physical properties of H_2O and D_2O

	H_2O	D_2O
Melting point/°C	0	3.82
Boiling point/°C	100	101.4
Density at 20°C/g cm^{-3}	0.9982	1.1059
Solubility of NaCl at 25°C/g per 100g	3.6	3.0
Viscosity/10^{-4} kg m^{-1} s^{-1}	10.9	12.6

Because of its higher density, D_2O is often called 'heavy water'. Heavy water has many important uses. It is employed as a source of deuterium atoms in the preparation of deuterated compounds (e.g. $NaOD$, C_2H_5OD) and in isotopic tracer experiments. Perhaps its best known use is as a moderator in nuclear reactors. The fissions of ^{235}U are triggered by neutrons, but only 'slow' neutrons are effective in causing the uranium nucleus to split. The function of a moderator is to slow down the neutrons, and D_2O is particularly effective for this purpose because it does not absorb neutrons but merely reduces their kinetic energy.

The manufacture of heavy water

The separation of isotopes is extremely difficult because of the very small differences in their physical and chemical properties. The isotopes of hydrogen are easier to separate than those of other elements, but their separation is nevertheless difficult and tedious. Deuterium is manufactured by first separating D_2O from natural water and then splitting up the D_2O by electrolysis. D_2O can itself be separated from natural water by electrolysis followed by fractional distillation. During the electrolysis of natural water, hydrogen is liberated at the cathode six times faster than deuterium, so the residual water becomes progressively richer in deuterium. Heavy water is therefore manufactured by a process involving the repeated electrolysis of an aqueous electrolyte. One cubic centimetre of 99% pure D_2O can be obtained from about $35\,dm^3$ of electrolyte from old electrolysis cells.

Questions

1   Assuming that naturally occurring hydrogen contains 1 deuterium atom in 6000, and that these proportions also apply to the hydrogen atoms in natural water, calculate the ratio of $D_2O : HDO : H_2O$ molecules in natural water.

2   Why are the isotopes of hydrogen 'easier to separate than those of any other element'?

3   Explain the differences in physical properties between H_2O and D_2O in table 2.

4   Starting with D_2O as your only source of deuterium atoms, how could you prepare

   a $NaOD$ **b** DCl **c** ND_3 **d** D_2SO_4 **e** CH_3COOD **f** C_2H_5OD?

5   Suggest an explanation for the fact that 'in the electrolysis of natural water, hydrogen is liberated at the cathode six times faster than deuterium' even when H_2O and D_2O are present in equal concentrations.

6   Why might biological experiments in which deuterium is used as a tracer give unreliable results?

8 The Heroes of Telemark

Well before the Second World War, both the Allies and the Germans knew there was the possibility of building an atomic bomb. By 1942, the Allies were still far from a solution and realised that German scientists were also involved in the development of an atomic bomb. Crucial to their work was the heavy water needed as a moderator for the fission reaction. For many years, the major world production of heavy water had been carried out at Rjukan, in the Telemark mountains of Norway. The site was near a large hydro-electric generating station. By 1942 the Nazis occupied Norway. To stop the Germans developing an atomic bomb, the Rjukan factory had to be destroyed.

The Vermork factory near Rjukan where heavy water was produced.

In March 1942 an attempt was made to parachute a British sabotage group into the area, but it failed when their gliders crashed. In February 1943, a new group was dropped into the area and this time they successfully linked up with Norwegian commandos and made their way to the Rjukan factory. Using wire clippers they entered the plant and placed explosives on the heavy water containers. In the explosion which followed, the containers were largely destroyed and the saboteurs escaped.

However, the Germans rebuilt the plant, and to counter any further threats the Americans decided to bomb the factory. In November 1943, 140 Flying Fortresses bombed the factory, and the Nazis abandoned all plans for heavy water production.

'The Heroes of Telemark' out to stop German production of heavy water in the film of the same name.

Questions

Before answering the following questions, it would be helpful to read the second and third sections in the text of Activity 7 entitled 'Heavy water'.

1 Why were the Allies anxious to prevent the Germans producing and stockpiling heavy water?

2 Why was the heavy water factory situated in the Telemark mountains?

3 Was it right for the Allies to prevent the production of a German atomic bomb? Explain and substantiate your views.

4 Was it right for the Allies to go ahead themselves in producing and then using an atomic bomb? Explain and substantiate your views.

9 Silicate rocks—the framework of the Earth

The following passage is taken from *Chemistry, Matter and the Universe* by R. E. Dickerson and I. Geis. It concerns silicate minerals.

In the centre of the third row of the periodic table sits silicon (electron structure 2,8,4), with four outer electrons like carbon (electron structure 2,4). The rocks of our planet are derived from silicon dioxide, SiO_2, and are surrounded by an atmosphere composed in part of carbon dioxide gas, CO_2. This does not seem remarkable until we recognise that silicon and carbon, which have the same outer electronic structure, should have similar chemical properties. Why then are their oxides so different?

The difference in properties arises because a silicon atom is larger than a carbon atom. Sharing two electron pairs with another atom in a double bond requires a closer approach of atoms than for a single bond. Silicon, with an inner core of ten electrons, cannot get close enough. Carbon, with a two electron inner core, is smaller and can make C=O bonds. Two such double bonds build a CO_2 molecule, O=C=O. Rather than making double bonds to two oxygen atoms, it is easier for silicon to make single bonds to four oxygens, arranged around the Si atom at the corners of a tetrahedron (figure 1). Each of these oxygen atoms can bridge two silicon atoms, and the result is an endless three-dimensional lattice of silicate tetrahedra as in **quartz**, shown in figure 1. Quartz is the main constituent in sand. If silicon were smaller and could make double bonds to oxygen, there would be no reason not to expect discrete molecules of O=Si=O. Quartz would be a gas instead of a very hard mineral, and the history of our planet would be vastly different.

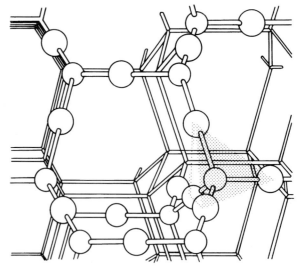

Figure 1
Silicate tetrahedra in quartz.

Pure quartz, with the overall composition of SiO_2, is an endless framework of Si and O atoms. Each Si is surrounded by four O atoms at the corners of a tetrahedron, and each O atom is shared between two adjacent tetrahedra (figure 2). One silicon atom has 'half a share' in each of four oxygen atoms around it, so the number of O atoms per Si atom is $\frac{1}{2}+\frac{1}{2}+\frac{1}{2}+\frac{1}{2}=2$, thereby accounting for the overall composition of SiO_2. In other types of silicates, one or more of the four oxygens around a silicon atom may not be shared with

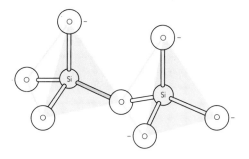

Figure 2
Silicate tetrahedra are linked by sharing corner oxygen atoms. Any unshared oxygens are left with a negative charge.

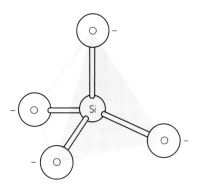

Figure 3
The free SiO_4^{4-} ion.

other silicons, and the unshared oxygen atoms each carry one negative charge.

The smallest freestanding unit of silicon and oxygen is the silicate ion, SiO_4^{4-}, with none of the four oxygen atoms shared, and with each of them negatively charged (figure 3). These silicate tetrahedra can exist separately in three-dimensional ionic structures, or they can be linked together by sharing oxygens to form one-dimensional chains, two-dimensional double chains (ladders) and sheets, and three-dimensional frameworks, such as quartz. These one-, two-, and three-dimensional structures are the basis for all silicate minerals. Any negative charges arising from unshared oxygen atoms are balanced by positive metal ions inserted alongside the chains or between the layers.

Minerals containing discrete SiO_4^{4-} ions have the general formula X_2SiO_4, where X is a metal ion carrying two positive charges, needed to balance the negative charges of the SiO_4^{4-} ions. The mantle of the earth, the 3000 km deep layer lying between the earth's crust and its core is made of minerals of this type, called **olivines**, in which X is Mg^{2+} or Fe^{2+}, in any proportions. Minerals like olivine are very dense and hard.

Less dense silicate minerals are produced if the SiO_4^{4-} tetrahedra are linked into long chains. Each Si then shares two of its O atoms with two other Si atoms, leaving it with a net of $1 + 1 + \frac{1}{2} + \frac{1}{2} = 3$ oxygens, and two negative charges on its two wholly owned oxygen atoms. The overall (empirical) composition of these chain silicates is SiO_3^{2-} (figure 4). These chains have only half the negative charge per Si atom that olivine has, and hence need fewer metal ions to counterbalance the charge. Because of this, and also because of the open way in which the chains are packed in the mineral, chain silicates are less dense than olivine. Many of them floated to the top of the mantle when the earth's interior was molten and helped build the crust, the outer layer of the planet, which is about 33 km thick under the continents but only 5 km thick beneath the ocean basins. **Pyroxenes** (figure 5a) are single-chain silicates, with the chains held together by positive ions. **Amphiboles** (figure 5b) are double-chain, or ladder, structures. All these minerals cleave easily along the chain direction, but the covalent Si–O bonds within a chain are not easily broken. This is why **asbestos** (an amphibole) is fibrous and stringy.

Silicate tetrahedra also can be linked into endless sheets, with three of the four oxygen atoms shared, and only one O atom per Si left with a negative charge (figure 5c). This negative O is fully owned by one Si, while the other three are shared; thus the overall ratio of O to Si is $1 + \frac{1}{2} + \frac{1}{2} + \frac{1}{2} = 2\frac{1}{2}$ to one. The silicate sheet has the composition $SiO_{5/2}^{-}$ or $Si_2O_5^{2-}$. Even fewer metal ions are required to balance the negative charges than in olivines or pyroxenes, so **micas** and **clays** with sheet structures are lighter yet. They are believed to be present only in the crust of the earth. The familiar flaking of

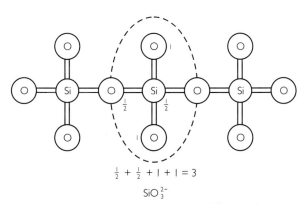

$\frac{1}{2} + \frac{1}{2} + 1 + 1 = 3$

SiO_3^{2-}

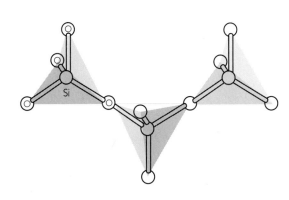

Figure 4
Chain silicates.

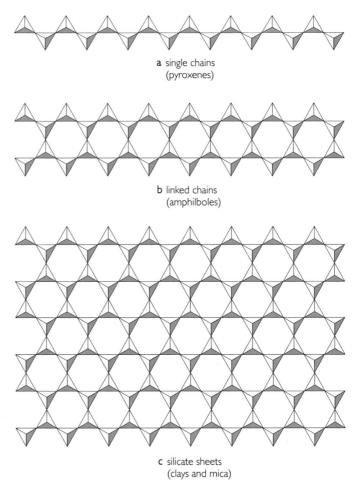

a single chains
(pyroxenes)

b linked chains
(amphilboles)

c silicate sheets
(clays and mica)

Figure 5

Chains and sheets of silicate tetrahedra.

mica arises because it is easy to separate silicate sheets, but much harder to break bonds within the sheets.

Kaolinite is a typical clay mineral. It has one Al^{3+} associated with the negative charge on each silicate tetrahedron in the sheet, and two OH^- ions balance the other two charges on Al^{3+}. It is a layer structure, with the negatively charged oxygen atoms all pointing out to one side of the sheet of tetrahedra, aluminium ions coordinated to these negative oxygens, and hydroxide ions on the other side of the Al^{3+}. This sandwich of silicate, Al^{3+}, and OH^- is stacked in layers to build up the three-dimensional structure. Water and other small molecules can get between the layers of kaolinite. Because the layers can slip past one another easily, wet clay is pliable and slippery. When clay is baked, or fired, in a kiln, water is driven out and the layers lock into a rigid structure. A primitive pottery maker is a true technologist, in the sense that he takes a natural material that is unsuitable for his purposes, fires it in a kiln, and transforms it into a material with quite different physical properties. Pottery making ranks with brewing as one of the oldest chemical technologies of mankind.

Dickerson, Richard E. and Geis, Irving. *Chemistry, Matter and the Universe*, Menlo Park, California: W. A. Benjamin, Inc. pp. 107–110. Illustrations copyright by I. Geis.

Questions

1   Explain in your own words why CO_2 is a gas, but SiO_2 is a solid with a high melting point.

2 Would you expect GeO_2 to be a gas or a solid with a high melting point? Explain your answer.

3 Draw 'dot/cross' diagrams showing the bonding in **a** SiO_4^{4-} **b** two SiO_4 tetrahedra linked by an oxygen bridge.

4 Figure 6 shows a portion of the structure of a pyroxene. Use a molecular modelling kit to make a model of this pyroxene structure.

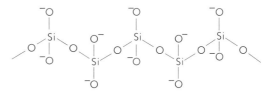

Figure 6

5 Draw the structure of an amphibole showing the bonds between atoms and any negative charges as in figure 6.

6 Use a molecular modelling kit to make a model of your drawing of your amphibole structure from question **5**.

7 How many negative charges are there per silicon atom in **a** pyroxenes **b** amphiboles?

8 Quartz and olivine are both very hard three-dimensional silicate minerals. What is the essential difference between them?

9 Explain in your own words why mica can be easily flaked into sheets.

10 Why do clay soils retain water well, and become heavy and waterlogged in wet weather, while sandy soils have poor water retention and remain relatively light and dry in wet weather?

11 Why are micas and clays found only in the earth's crust?

12 Use the information in the passage concerning kaolinite to work out the empirical formula of this mineral.

Asbestos, a fibrous silicate mineral.

10 Cameroon catastrophe: could it happen again?

The event

Late on the evening of Thursday, 21 August 1986, a deadly cloud of gas swept along the valleys north of Lake Nyos in western Cameroon. News rapidly spread of villages where every living animal had died—men, women, children, cows, chickens and even insects. The victims had been over-whelmed by a cloud of gas from Lake Nyos. As the lake lies in a volcanic crater, the first investigators had assumed that a dormant volcano had suddenly erupted, releasing a cloud of hot, toxic and acidic gases containing hydrogen sulphide and sulphur dioxide.

The evidence

The following evidence soon ruled out normal volcanic activity and pointed to a different explanation for the disaster.

Lake Nyos and the surrounding area.

- Water in Lake Nyos was tested after the disaster. It was not particularly acidic and contained no sulphurous gases.
- Vegetation around the lake had been flattened, but only to a height of about 25 metres.
- The lake water was a turbid yellowish brown due to a suspension of iron(III) oxide. A film of this yellow–brown iron oxide covered vegetation near Lake Nyos.
- Apart from the areas flattened by water, there was very little damage to vegetation near the lake.
- The leaves on some plants were blackened and shrivelled suggesting a similar effect to that of frost on tender plants.
- The damage caused to most vegetation suggested something in between the effects of wind and water.

Dead animals in the Lake Nyos area after the catastrophe.

- Almost all of the survivors who were admitted to hospital had lost consciousness for some hours after the disaster.

- Deep water from Lake Nyos contained an exceptionally high concentration of dissolved gas. This gas was 99.6% carbon dioxide, with a little methane and traces of helium.

- The dissolved gas from the water of Lake Nyos had no smell, but contained a higher than expected percentage of radioactive carbon and oxygen.

- Tests showed that dissolved carbon dioxide is being added to Lake Nyos at a rate of 5 million cubic metres per year.

- The water level of Lake Nyos fell by several centimetres immediately following the disaster.

- During the wet season, which reaches its peak in August, rain falls on the surrounding hills and then drains into Lake Nyos. This water forms a layer on the surface of the lake, but it is cooler and denser than the water below it. This stratification is removed as the surface water warms up at the end of the wet season.

The explanation

Late on the evening of Thursday, 21 August 1986, enormous volumes of slightly denser water accumulating on the surface of Lake Nyos became unstable and started to sink. This caused huge amounts of less dense deep water containing high concentrations of carbon dioxide to rise towards the surface of the lake and eventually erupt in a cold aerosol of water and carbon dioxide. The catastrophe had started.

Questions

1   Describe how the events of the catastrophe continued.

2   Explain the evidence given in each one of the twelve bulleted points.

(**Note**: the process $CO_2(aq) \longrightarrow CO_2(g) + (aq)$ is endothermic)

3   What could be done to prevent a repetition of the tragedy?

11 Carbon dioxide and the 'greenhouse effect'

What is the 'greenhouse effect'?

The Sun emits enormous amounts of electromagnetic radiation mainly in the infrared, visible and ultraviolet parts of the spectrum. Not all this radiation reaches the Earth. Most of the ultraviolet radiation is absorbed by gases, such as ozone, in the stratosphere (the upper atmosphere)—and this is just as well, because ultraviolet radiation can very harmful to living things.

The radiation that gets through to the surface of the Earth is mainly in the visible region, plus small amounts of infrared and ultraviolet. Our eyes have evolved to detect the visible part of the spectrum because it is the most intense radiation reaching the Earth.

The radiation that reaches the Earth keeps most of it at a temperature suitable for living things. Like the Sun, the warm Earth acts as a radiator. But because the Earth is cooler than the Sun, it radiates energy at a lower frequency—in the infrared region of the spectrum instead of the visible and ultraviolet regions (figures 1 and 2).

Most of the infrared radiation from the Earth passes through the atmosphere and escapes into space. Some of the infrared radiation is, however,

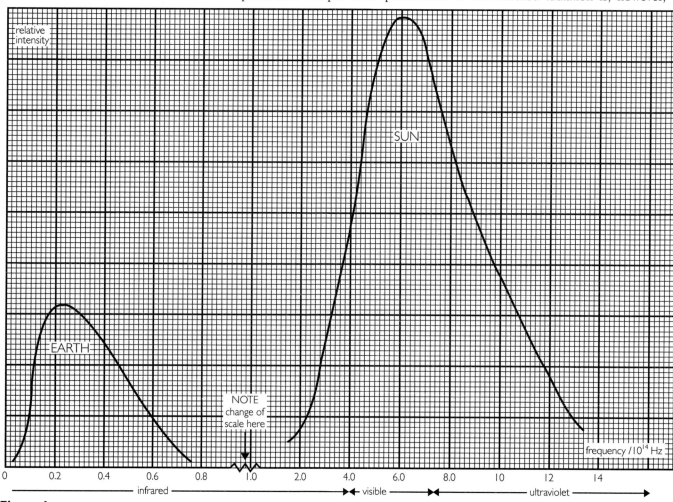

Figure 1
The frequency and intensity of radiation from the Earth and Sun.

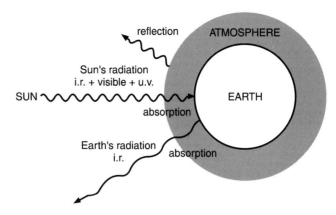

Figure 2
The Sun radiates in the infrared, visible and ultraviolet regions. The Earth's atmosphere absorbs and reflects some of this radiation, and some of it warms the Earth itself. The Earth in turn radiates in the infrared region.

absorbed by gases in the atmosphere. Instead of escaping, the infrared energy is trapped by the gases and warms them up. The atmosphere is therefore warmer than it otherwise would be. This in turn keeps the Earth warm. In effect, the atmosphere is acting as a kind of blanket for the Earth. This is just as well, because without its blanket the Earth would be very cold—a chilly −20°C or so, instead of a comfortable 15°C.

The effect of the atmosphere in keeping the Earth warm is called the '**greenhouse effect**'. Like the glass in a greenhouse, the atmosphere lets through the Sun's radiation, but stops the Earth radiating all of it back into space.

The 'greenhouse gases'

Different gases absorb radiation of different frequencies, depending on the bonds in their molecules. So, different gases have very different 'greenhouse effects'. Only those gases which absorb infrared radiation of the frequency radiated by the Earth can have a 'greenhouse effect'. These are the 'greenhouse gases' and some of them have a more powerful 'greenhouse effect' than others. Four important 'greenhouse gases' are carbon dioxide, water vapour, methane and chlorofluorocarbons.

Carbon dioxide
This is the most important because there are large amounts of it in the atmosphere and the frequencies of radiation absorbed by carbon dioxide correspond to those radiated most intensely by the Earth (figure 3).

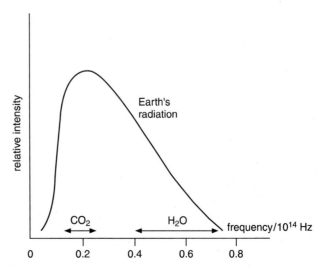

Figure 3
The Earth's radiation frequency curve showing the absorption ranges of CO_2 and H_2O.

Water vapour

This is also present in the atmosphere in significant amounts. Like CO_2, it has an important 'greenhouse effect'. Figure 3 shows the frequencies at which water absorbs. However, water vapour is of less concern than carbon dioxide because its concentration in the atmosphere is less directly affected by human activities.

Methane

This is present in the atmosphere in smaller quantities than carbon dioxide or water. However, molecule for molecule, it has a much more powerful 'greenhouse effect' than CO_2. Methane is produced as a result of various biological processes including the decomposition of decaying vegetation and the digestion of grass by ruminant animals.

Chlorofluorocarbons (CFCs)

These are better known for their damaging effect on the ozone layer, but they are also powerful 'greenhouse gases'. Molecule for molecule, they are around 10 000 times more effective than carbon dioxide. CFCs are released into the atmosphere from aerosols, refrigerators and other human activities.

So what's the problem?

For millions of years, the 'greenhouse effect' has kept the Earth at a comfortable temperature for living things. The Earth's average temperature has, of course, varied—there have been ice ages, for example—but on the whole it has stayed fairly steady. This is because the concentration of 'greenhouse gases' in the atmosphere has remained constant.

Since the mid-nineteenth century and the Industrial Revolution, human activities have caused the concentration of 'greenhouse gases' to increase. The Earth's 'blanket' is becoming thicker, and the result is that the Earth has become warmer. This has only been very slight, but enough to have an effect on the Earth's climate. Small changes in average temperature can, however, have big effects, such as more droughts, more violent winds, and a rise in sea level that could have a disastrous effect on low-lying countries such as the Netherlands and Bangladesh.

The carbon dioxide problem

Carbon dioxide is released into the atmosphere in enormous amounts by the burning of fossil fuels. Every year about 18 billion tonnes of *extra* carbon dioxide enter the atmosphere from burning fuels. Many scientists estimate that, by the year 2080, the concentration of carbon dioxide in the atmosphere will have doubled compared to its value before the Industrial Revolution. This could cause an average temperature rise of about 2°C—enough to make a big difference to the climate. If other 'greenhouse gases' such as methane are also taken into account, this temperature rise could occur much sooner.

Carbon dioxide is the most significant 'greenhouse gas'. So the most effective way of tackling the 'greenhouse' problem is to reduce the concentration of carbon dioxide in the atmosphere. This could be done by:

- reducing the consumption of fossil fuels

- using fossil fuels that produce relatively small amounts of carbon dioxide

- absorbing the carbon dioxide after it has been produced by combustion, but before it gets into the air

All three approaches have serious drawbacks, but none as serious as the possible consequences of failing to control the 'greenhouse effect'.

The Thames barrier was built to protect London from floods at high tide. However, if the Earth's climate becomes much warmer, as a result of the 'greenhouse effect', even the Thames barrier may not be able to cope with the resulting rise in sea level.

Questions

1   The 'greenhouse effect' depends on the fact that gases absorb infrared radiation. *Why* do they absorb this radiation? What changes does the radiation cause in molecules of the gas?

2   Oxygen and nitrogen are not 'greenhouse gases', but carbon dioxide and methane are. Suggest an explanation for the difference.

3   Water vapour is a 'greenhouse gas', and water is produced in large quantities when fossil fuels burn. Yet it is the carbon dioxide produced by burning fuels that is causing concern, not the water. Suggest a reason why.

4   Table 1 shows the distance from the Sun, the composition of the atmosphere and the surface temperature of three planets: Mercury, Venus and the Earth. Comment on the relative surface temperatures of the three planets. Suggest an explanation for the relative values.

Table 1

Planet	Distance from Sun/10^7 km	Atmosphere	Surface temperature/K
Mercury	6	hardly any	440
Venus	11	mainly CO_2	730
Earth	15	mainly N_2, O_2	288

5   Consider the three suggested approaches to the reduction of carbon dioxide emission at the end of the passage.

   a What problems are there in implementing the *first* approach—reducing the consumption of fossil fuels?

   b Now consider the *second* approach—using fuels that produce relatively small amounts of carbon dioxide.

Table 2 gives details of three possible fuels.

Table 2

Fuel	Typical constituent	Enthalpy change of combustion of typical constituent/kJ mol^{-1}
Coal	carbon	−394
Natural gas	methane, CH_4	−890
Gasoline	octane, C_8H_{18}	−5470

  i For each fuel, calculate the number of moles of carbon dioxide given out per kilojoule of energy released by the fuel. What are the implications of your answers?

  ii Are there any fuels that produce *no* carbon dioxide at all?

  c Now consider the *third* approach—absorption of the carbon dioxide after it has been produced by combustion but before it gets into the air.

  i How might this absorption be carried out?

  ii What problems can you foresee in the methods you have suggested?

  d What other approaches would help to reduce the concentration of carbon dioxide in the atmosphere?

12 Fuel and fuel cells

The following passage is modified from *Chemical Principles* by Dickerson, Gray and Haight. Read the passage, then answer the questions following it.

For thousands of years, we have known from experience that when you want energy, you burn something. The first fuel was wood, and then later came coal and some of the oils and gases that seep out of swampy places. We could also burn fats and tallow from animals to get energy, but only in the last two hundred years did we appreciate that this was what the animals were doing with them as well. The energy for the operation of almost all living creatures is obtained by combustion; that is, by the burning of energy-rich compounds in the presence of oxygen.

There are two main problems in extracting useful energy from chemical substances: finding the substances with the most energy, and finding ways to get the maximum energy out in a usable form. Both of these problems become important when the supply of possible fuels is short, when their use harms the environment with waste products, or when we have to transport the fuels far from their natural source, as in space exploration.

The most thoroughly tested fuel systems on earth are those of living organisms. The tests have been going on for three billion years or more, and the penalty for a bad experiment is extinction. If we look at table 1, we see that living organisms have not done too badly. The most efficient combustion energy source, in terms of kilojoules of heat per gram of fuel, is hydrogen gas. Floating gasbag organisms have never evolved. Aside from the logistics problem, natural sources of hydrogen gas are not that abundant. Hydrocarbons such as gasoline yield one third as much energy per gram, and have the advantage of being more compact as liquids. Animals store most of their energy in fats, which are esters of long, gasoline-like fatty acids such as stearic acid. As the table shows, these fats are very nearly as good energy-storage compounds as gasoline on a weight basis. The esterification helps to make them solids instead of liquids, an additional practical advantage for a creature that must move about.

Table 1
Energy obtained per gram from some fuels during combustion with oxygen

Fuel	Physical state	Relative molecular mass	Enthalpy change of combustion/ kJ mol	Enthalpy change of combustion per gram/kJ g^{-1}
H_2	g	2	−287	−144
C_8H_{18} (octane, a typical component of gasoline)	l	114	−5473	−48
$C_{17}H_{35}COOH$ (stearic acid, a typical fatty acid)	s	285	−11390	−40
$H_2NCH(CH_3)COOH$ (alanine, a typical amino acid)	s	89	−1630	−18
$C_6H_{12}O_6$ (glucose, a typical carbohydrate)	s	180	−2827	−16

Proteins (represented by the data for alanine, an amino acid) and carbohydrates (represented by glucose) are only half as efficient in storing energy. But for plants, which do not move about, the energy yield per gram of fuel is really not very important. A redwood tree does not need to be weight-conscious. It happens that the biochemistry required to store energy in fatty acid molecules and fats, and to retrieve it again when needed, is complicated. In contrast, carbohydrate synthesis and breakdown are simpler and faster. Plants give up the unimportant energy-per-gram advantage of fats, for the significant advantages of easier carbohydrate biochemistry. In green plants, energy is stored as starches rather than fats. Even animals use the fast-access advantage of carbohydrates. We store a limited amount of energy as glycogen, a starch-like molecule, as a buffer against sudden energy needs.

When we leave our own planet and begin exploring space, the energy-per-gram problem of all animals becomes even more serious. Gasoline then becomes too energy-poor, and we turn to direct combustion of hydrogen for the first stage of rockets. We also look for newer and better ways of generating electrical energy to operate the spacecraft systems. One approach is not to attempt to carry energy from our home planet on the mini-planet of a spacecraft, but to generate electricity directly from the energy of the sun by means of solar batteries. But if we have to use terrestrial fuel, then it should at least be the best fuel on a weight basis. The answer is the generation of electrical power from a fuel cell that uses the combustion of hydrogen as its energy source:

$$H_2(g) + \tfrac{1}{2}O_2(g) \longrightarrow H_2O(l) \qquad \Delta H = -287\,kJ$$

About the worst thing that we could do with hydrogen in our spacecraft would be to burn it like we do most fuels on earth, and use the heat to generate electricity. We would be lucky to convert as much as 25% of the energy available in the reaction into electricity.

There is a better way. Why convert chemical energy into heat energy and then into electrical energy, if the heat step can be omitted? A **fuel cell**, which makes a direct chemical–electrical conversion, is shown in figure 1. The overall reaction is combustion of hydrogen. As with any other electrical cell, the half-reactions have been separated at two electrodes, and the electrons made to flow through an external circuit from anode to cathode. This cell is

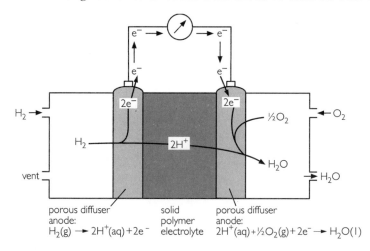

Figure 1

A hydrogen–oxygen fuel cell. Hydrogen gas introduced at the left dissociates in the porous, conducting barrier at the left side. Hydrogen ions migrate to the right through the electrolyte (for spacecraft applications, a solid polymer), and the electrons flow through the external circuit. At the right diffuser, these electrons, hydrogen ions from the electrolyte, and molecular oxygen combine to produce water. In a gravity field, the product water will run off into a storage tank; in free space, it can be drawn away from the diffuser cathode by a wick. In either event, the resulting water is available for human use. The standard e.m.f. of the hydrogen fuel cell is calculated to be 1.23 V.

no different in principle from more familiar electric cells. The innovation is that new reactants (H_2 and O_2) are fed constantly into the cell, and the product (H_2O) is drawn off so that the voltage of the cell remains constant and the power output is uninterrupted. The great advantage of all fuel cells is that they convert chemical energy directly into electrical energy without the intermediate conversion through heat energy.

Methods that are tolerable on board a spacecraft do not necessarily work economically on earth. Why do we persist with antiquated coal-burning power stations, which pollute our skies with smoke and our rivers with warm water? Why not react coal, or at least readily available methane gas, directly in a fuel cell? The problems are all practical, and not theoretical. There is no known reversible electrode suitable for the methane half-reaction,

$$CH_4(g) + 2H_2O(l) \longrightarrow CO_2(g) + 8H^+ + 8e^-$$

If there were, we immediately could set up a methane fuel cell similar to the one shown, and a revolution in energy production would be at hand. Many hundreds of man-years have been spent in seeking suitable reversible electrodes for hydrocarbon fuels or coal, but so far with only limited success.

So, in spite of all our knowledge about electrochemical cells, the one key answer that could transform our use of fuels eludes us. The old fuels are good, but what we do with them in the process.

$$\text{Bond energy} \longrightarrow \text{Heat} \longrightarrow \text{Electrical energy} \longrightarrow \text{Other uses}$$

is sloppy, inefficient and polluting. We cannot even escape this thermodynamic trap with atomic energy. For after developing this energy from nuclear reactions, what do we do with it as the first step in generating electricity? We use it to boil water! James Watt and Ernest Rutherford, wherever they are, must be laughing.

R. E. Dickerson, H. B. Gray and G. P. Haight Jr., *Chemical Principles*
Menlo Park, California, The Benjamin/Cummings Publishing Company, Inc.
pp. 756–760.

Questions

1 Explain in your own words why green plants store their energy in carbohydrates rather than fats, even though on a mass basis the latter are a more compact energy store.

2 Explain why hydrocarbons like octane release more energy per gram on combustion than carbohydrates like glucose.

3 It is not completely accurate to say that 'the energy for the operation of almost all living creatures is obtained by combustion'. Why not?

4 What are the principle differences between a fuel cell like the one described here and a conventional electrochemical cell like the Daniell cell?

5 What material might be used to construct the porous diffuser anode and cathode in the fuel cell shown in figure 1? Give a reason for your choice.

6 Write half-equations for the reactions that would occur at the anode and cathode in a fuel cell powered by methane. Use these half-equations to produce an overall equation showing the net reaction occurring in the cell.

7 Outline the advantages that would be gained by generating electricity in fuel cells rather than in the thermal power stations used at present.

8 If fuel cells could be developed to the point where they met industrial and domestic demands for electricity, they would depend on the availability of fossil fuel resources, which we know are limited. In view of this, is it worth spending money on the research and development of fuel cells?

13 Spontaneous human combustion

The passage in part 1 by John Heymer originally appeared in *New Scientist*. It concerns 'a rather unusual death by fire'. The letters in part 2 appeared in *New Scientist* shortly after the article and attempt to explain the case.

Read part 1 first, then answer questions 1 and 2. Then read the two letters in part 2, and answer questions 3–8.

Do not look at Part 2 until you have done questions 1 and 2.

Part 1

I am a retired Scenes of Crime Officer who served 25 years in the Gwent Police. My job involved attending the scenes of serious crimes and sudden deaths to gather evidence for forensic examination. As a result, I am both familiar with death and a trained witness.

On 6 January 1980, I was called to a council house in Gwent, to the scene of what I was told was a rather unusual death by fire.

The house was located on top of a hill and the weather was bitterly cold. On entering the house I was struck by the pleasant warmth. There was no sign of central heating or any other form of heating. The uniformed officers who had requested by presence told me that the fire had occurred in the living room.

I opened the door and stepped into a cooling oven. There was a steamy, sauna-like heat, and the room was bathed in a garish, orange radiance. The orange light emanated from a bare light bulb which was coated in a sticky, orange substance, as was the window. The temperature of the room had recently been extremely high. The walls were radiating heat. Condensation was running down the window. Heat had cracked one of the window panes.

The light bulb was bare because the plastic lampshade had melted, oozed down over the bulb and fallen to the floor. The walls, ceiling and all surfaces were coated with a greasy black soot.

There have been many reported cases of spontaneous human combustion in history and the subject has become a topic of interest to scientists and artists alike. The etching above shows an artist's impression of one such case in the 1800's.

In one wall as an open grate, which contained the dead ashes of a coal fire. The hearth was tidy; there were no signs of any coals having fallen from the fire.

On the floor, about one metre from the hearth, was a pile of ashes. On the perimeter of the ashes, furthest from the hearth, was a partially burnt armchair. Emerging from the ashes were a pair of human feet clothed in socks. The feet were attached to short lengths of lower leg, encased in trouser leg bottoms. The feet and socks were undamaged. Protruding from what was left of the trousers were calcined leg bones which merged into the ashes. The ashes were the incinerated remains of a man.

Of the torso and arms nothing remained but ash. Opposite the feet was a blackened skull. Though the rug and carpet below the ashes were charred, the damage did not extend more than a few centimetres beyond the perimeter of the ashes. Less than a metre away, a settee, fitted with loose covers, was not even scorched. Plastic tiles which covered the floor beneath the carpet were undamaged.

Although extremely high temperatures had developed in the room, nothing had burnt that had not been in contact with the body while it was being consumed. Reason told me that the scene I was viewing was impossible. Everyone at the scene experienced the same urge to deny the evidence of their senses.

I decided to call forensic scientists to the scene so they could examine the evidence *in situ*. I soon discovered that scientists, like policemen, are human, and consequently fallible.

When I suggested spontaneous combustion as the cause of the incineration, the scientists dismissed my proposal with knowing smiles and stated that the fire was entirely explicable. Their "reasoning" was as follows: the deceased had burnt to ashes in a room in which there was a coal fire: human bodies do not burn without the application of an external source of fire, *ergo*, the coal fire was the cause. In support of their supposition, they fixed on some burnt fibrous tissue adhering to the top bar of the grate. They deduced that the deceased had somehow fallen headfirst into the grate thereby setting himself on fire. They were certain that analysis would show the fibrous tissue to be burnt human skin.

Amazingly, the scientists saw nothing wrong in a man falling headfirst into a fire grate, igniting like a wax candle, then somehow picking himself out of the grate and sitting in his armchair to burn himself and most of his armchair to ash. As I said, the grate was tidy. It certainly did not indicate that anyone had fallen into the fire. However, they had their sample of "skin" and went away satisfied.

A week or so later, my superintendent called me to his office and showed me the report on the forensic analysis of the fibrous substance. It was revealed to be 'of bovine origin'. Despite this difficulty, there was no further investigation into the cause of the fire.

The human body consists of 70 to 80 per cent water, so it is not a readily flammable object. Modern gas-fired crematoria, starting from cold, use up to 30 cubic metres of gas, burnt with 600 cubic metres of air per hour, to incinerate one corpse. A crematorium, using forced draught, oxidises a corpse at 900°C. To achieve the same effect without the forced draught requires a temperature of 1600°C for many hours. How can such heat be achieved in a council-house living room without scorching loose cushion covers within a metre of the incinerated body? Both doors to the room were fitted with draught excluders, so the room was virtually hermetically sealed.

I have never seen a body, even in the fiercest of fires, where the torso burnt away. Even in the hottest of fires, the extremities may burn away but the torso remains. In this case, as in other reported cases of spontaneous human combustion, the opposite had happened. The torso had burnt and the extremities remained.

Scientists have tried to explain human combustion in terms of the 'candle effect'. This explanation derives its name from tests made about 20 years ago. A few ounces of human fat were wrapped around a test tube and covered with several layers of thin cloth. The test tube was used to provide a bone-like rigidity. The roll of fat was ignited by a bunsen burner after about a minute. The test piece was burnt in the draught of an extractor fan and took about an hour to burn completely.

Any substance requiring the application of a bunsen burner for more than a minute hardly constitutes a fire hazard. If the incineration of a large human body in an airless room can be explained by reference to the burning of a 'human fat candle' in a forced draught then you can expect to incinerate a bull by putting a match to its tail.

Human combustion of the kind I have witnessed demands an explanation beyond known laws. Suppose, by some as yet unknown biochemical action, water in the body were to break down into its constituent gases, hydrogen and oxygen. If conversion of the gases occurred at a suitable rate, then the resulting flames would be confined to the body. As it consumed the body, the burning hydrogen would use up all the oxygen, leaving none to support the combustion of other materials. Water can be broken down to its constituent gases with the application of electric current. The living human body can develop a considerable charge of static electricity.

As a layman propounding such a theory, I realise I shall bring down on my head, together with the wrath of 'experts', the comment 'A little learning is a dangerous thing...'. I have not submitted my 'theory' for expert consideration. I am of the same mind as Henry Ford '... an expert is a guy who will give me six reasons why it won't work'. If scientists are certain that human combustion is explicable by the 'candle effect' then let them incinerate to ashes a clothed corpse in an airless room without damaging the furnishings.

Questions

1   John Heymer is very sceptical of the scientists' explanation for the fire in terms of 'the candle effect'. What are the main reasons for this scepticism?

2   Do you think the theory of spontaneous human combustion given in the penultimate paragraph is possible? Explain your answer clearly, saying which parts are convincing and which are unconvincing.

3   Suggest an alternative explanation for the combustion, different from the theories in this passage.

Part 2

The passage you have just read stimulated people to write to the *New Scientist*. The following two letters appeared in the journal two weeks after John Heymer's original article. Read the letters, then answer the questions which follow.

Letter 2

Assuming the phenomenon of spontaneous human combustion to exist, it would require a combustible body, a zone of relatively high ignitability, and an ignition source.

Obesity and dehydration would tend to favour the first of these requirements, and the consumption of great quantities of liquid paraffin, which habit I believe still survives among the constipated elderly, would add to the overall fuel content of the body and, as is known in the case of overconsumption, of the underwear and cushion.

Anaerobic fermentation within the gut, as is perhaps favoured by paraffin encapsulation of its contents, produces sometimes prodigious quantities of inflammable gas; consumption of eggs, for example, which are especially rich in phospholipids, might well add, to the normal methane and hydrogen, significant amounts of phosphine, and, worse, phosphorus dihydride, thereby imparting to the gas the property of spontaneous inflammability—the dreaded phosphinic fart. (How many of your readers have attributed singed underpants and burning thighs to mere frustration or, while strolling on a warm summer night after a second *soufflé*, have observed their breath glowing?)

Autoxidation of lipids leads to the formation of peroxides, the decomposition of which is no doubt involved in the spontaneous combustion of oil-impregnated rags. Postmortem body temperatures as high as 43° Celsius have been reported within hours of death, possibly as a result of similar reactions. Were it to come about that morbid reservoirs of peroxidised short-chain lipid—or even of ketonic bodies generated by a disordered metabolism—accumulated, their endogenous oxygen might explain the precocious burning away of the torso which John Heymer describes.

Sidney Alford
Explosives Engineering Consultant
Corsham, Wiltshire

Letter 1

John Heymer's mistake is in trying to draw a parallel between the extensive burning to the body which he examined and the processes of cremation, when they can be distinguished by one critical factor. Cremation is intended to destroy a body in the shortest possible time and is therefore carried out under extreme conditions, but a relatively small fire can consume flesh and calcine bone if it is allowed to burn for a long time.

This process, which I prefer to call prolonged human combustion, is usually fuelled by fat rendered from the body by the fire. It is no coincidence that in many of the cases this unit has encountered the victim was obese, and there was always a long delay before the fire was discovered. Examples of prolonged human combustion are, admittedly, rare but this should not be taken as evidence that an unusual source of ignition is involved. Indeed, all cases investigated by this unit have been resolved to the satisfaction of the courts without recourse to the excuse of 'spontaneous' human combustion.

D. J. X. Halliday
Fire Investigation Unit
The Metropolitan Police Forensic
*   Science Labotatory*
London SE1

Questions

4   Summarise in your words the explanation of the fire in letter 1.

5   Letter 2 proposes that spontaneous human combustion would require:

    i a combustible body;

    ii a zone of relatively high ignitability;

    iii an ignition source.

    What does the letter propose each of these might be?

6   Letters 1 and 2 both mention obesity. Why is this important?

7   Letter 2 also mentions liquid paraffin. Why might this be significant?

8   Do you consider that these two letters satisfactorily explain the case described by John Heymer, or do you think some further explanation is needed? If so, what other explanation can you suggest?

14 Acids and bases in the home

Acids and bases have many applications in industry and the home. The following passage summarises a few of their important domestic uses.

Acids in the home

Cleaners

Acids react with bases and this makes them useful in a number of ways. Metals tarnish because they react with the air to form a layer of oxide or sulphide. Acids can be used to remove this layer. One of the most difficult oxide layers to remove is rust, Fe_2O_3. Rust removers usually contain a strong mineral acid such as hydrochloric or phosphoric(V) acid. The latter has the advantage that it also forms a protective phosphate layer to help prevent further corrosion. Such strong mineral acids can be hazardous, though, and for most domestic purposes weaker acids are used. Rust stains on cloth can be removed using ethanedioic (oxalic) acid (table 1), but this has the disadvantage of being toxic. The compound is probably effective because of the complexing of iron ions by ethanedioate ions.

Other metals can be cleaned using ethanoic or citric acid (table 1). Vinegar is a five per cent aqueous solution of ethanoic acid, and citric acid is present in lemons and other citrus fruit. An effective way of cleaning brass or copper is to rub it with a piece of lemon. Vinegar should be avoided with copper and its alloys because of the formation of poisonous copper ethanoate. In any case, metals should always be washed well with water or washing soda (see below)

Table 1
Some acids commonly encountered in the home

Systematic name	Common trivial name	Formula	Natural occurrence
Hydrochloric acid	—	HCl	in the stomach
Phosphoric(V) acid	—	H_3PO_4	—
Methanoic acid	formic acid	$H-\underset{\underset{O}{\|\|}}{C}-OH$	ants, nettles
Ethanoic acid	acetic acid	$CH_3-\underset{\underset{O}{\|\|}}{C}-OH$	vinegar
Ethanedioic acid	oxalic acid	$\underset{COOH}{\overset{COOH}{\|}}$	some plants e.g. rhubarb
2-Hydroxypropane-1,2,3-tricarboxylic acid	citric acid	CH_2-COOH $\|$ $HO-CH-COOH$ $\|$ CH_2-COOH	citrus fruit
2,3-Dihydroxy-butanedioic acid	tartaric acid	$HO-CH_2-COOH$ $\|$ $HO-CH_2-COOH$	grapes

after cleaning with acid, in order to remove possible toxic products and prevent the retarnishing which occurs if the metal is left in contact with acid.

Hard water often forms undesirable deposits in kettles, baths and lavatory pans. These deposits are usually carbonates of calcium and magnesium (white) or iron (brown) which can be removed with acid. A weak organic acid is usually sufficient—vinegar or a slice of lemon will 'de-fur' a kettle. Commercial preparations containing methanoic acid (table 1) can be bought which do the same job rather more quickly.

Food additives

Acids have been used as food preservatives for centuries. Food-spoilage bacteria are inhibited or killed by low pH, so pickling in vinegar is an effective way of increasing the life of, say beetroot or herrings. Nowadays, we have other methods of preserving food which affect its flavour and texture less than pickling. Nevertheless, we continue to pickle food and to add acids to it because we like the sharp flavour which acids produce. Vinegar and lemon juice are frequently used to flavour food.

It is sometimes necessary to generate carbon dioxide in food so that the mixture will 'rise'. For example, baking powder is added to cakes to generate carbon dioxide bubbles and make them lighter. Baking powder is usually a mixture of sodium hydrogencarbonate and 2,3-dihydroxybutanedioic acid (tartaric acid—see table 1). Some sweets contain 'sherbet'—a mixture of sodium hydrogencarbonate and citric acid which generates carbon dioxide and a pleasant fizzing sensation when moistened in the mouth.

Bases in the home

Cleaners

Many household cleaning problems involve grease-bound dirt. Fats, grease and oil bind dirt to a surface, making the dirt difficult to remove with water alone, because water and grease do not mix. The usual solution to this problem is to use a detergent, which helps grease and water to mix. For some very greasy surfaces, such as ovens and kitchen surfaces, detergent alone is not very effective. In such cases, an alkali cleaner can be used which reacts with the grease chemically.

The greases, fats and oils encountered in the kitchen are all of natural origin. They contain the triesters of long-chain carboxylic acids. Like all esters, they are hydrolysed (saponified) by alkalis.

Some acids and bases commonly found in the home.

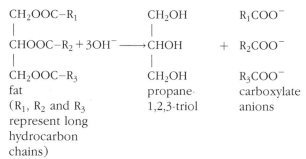

Long-chain carboxylate anions of the type formed here have detergent properties because the product of saponification of a fat is **soap**. Thus, alkalis not only break down fats, but they turn them into soap. They are therefore very effective in removing fatty, greasy deposits. Oven cleaners, for example, usually contain sodium hydroxide (caustic soda). They are applied to the warm oven surface and left for half an hour or so. During this time the grease is partly saponified so that it can be removed easily using warm water.

Some drain-cleaning preparations contain solid sodium hydroxide together with a little aluminium powder. When this mixture is poured down the drain it comes into contact with water and the following reaction occurs:

$$Al(s) + OH^-(aq) + 3H_2O(l) \longrightarrow Al(OH)_4^-(aq) + \tfrac{3}{2}H_2(g)$$

165

This reaction is very exothermic. At the high temperature reached, the grease blocking the drain melts and the cleaning action of the sodium hydroxide is much more effective.

Ammonia and sodium carbonate (washing soda) are two other alkaline cleaning agents. An aqueous solution of ammonia contains hydroxide ions because of the following equilibrium:

$$NH_3(aq) + H_2O(l) \rightleftharpoons NH_4^+(aq) + OH^-(aq)$$

Ammonia is present in many liquid cleaners. It has the advantage of being a weaker alkali than sodium hydroxide, so it is less caustic. Household ammonia was first manufactured from coal, and this gave an impure cloudy solution. With the discovery of the Haber process, ammonia could be made very pure and clean, but manufacturers continued to make household ammonia cloudy by adding soap because consumers had become used to a cloudy product.

Oven cleaning preparations usually contain sodium hydroxide.

Sodium carbonate is another weak alkali:

$$CO_3^{2-}(aq) + H_2O(l) \rightleftharpoons HCO_3^-(aq) + OH^-(aq)$$

It is often present in scouring powder.

Medicinal antacids

Acid indigestion is caused by an excess of hydrochloric acid in the stomach. Indigestion tablets contain weak bases, usually oxides, hydroxides or carbonates, which neutralise the excess acid. Table 2 gives a few examples. Carbonates have the advantage of being weak bases which act quickly, but they have the disadvantage that carbon dioxide is produced when the carbonate is neutralised by an acid, and this can have embarrassing consequences. Some indigestion tablets are effervescent. They usually contain citric acid and sodium hydrogencarbonate (sodium bicarbonate), with the latter in excess. When water is added, effervescence occurs, but the solution formed has an overall alkaline pH.

Table 2
Some bases present in indigestion tablets

Carbonates	Hydroxides	Oxides
$NaHCO_3$	$Al(OH)_3$	Al_2O_3
$MgCO_3$	$Mg(OH)_2$	MgO
$CaCO_3$		

Questions

Explain each of the following statements and write balanced equations for any reactions which occur.

1   Rust can be removed from the steel bodywork of a car using phosphoric(V) acid. This treatment also protects the steel from further corrosion.

2   Copper retarnishes rapidly when it is left with lemon juice on its surface after cleaning.

3   A badly stained aluminium saucepan is well cleaned if rhubarb is gently stewed in it.

4   Vinegar can be used to clean the surface oxide off copper, but it should not be used with copper cooking utensils.

5   Methanoic acid is sold commercially to 'defur' kettles in hard water areas of the country.

6   Sherbet does not fizz until water is added to it.

7   Oven cleaning operations usually contain sodium hydroxide.

8   A method once used to clean a greasy oven involved warming the oven, putting a dish of ammonia solution inside, closing the door and leaving overnight. Next day, the oven could be wiped clean with a damp cloth.

9   Indigestion tablets containing carbonate ion can have embarrassing consequences.

10 A greasy aluminium frying pan should never be cleaned with sodium carbonate (washing soda).

15 Water biotreatment

The following article concerns a new product for treating polluted water called 'Bio Aquafix'.

Introduction

As the regulations regarding water purity become more and more stringent, effective ways of combatting the problems of water pollution have to be sought. In this respect, non-chemical methods of treating effluents are particularly attractive. A French laboratory has patented a way to clean up polluted salt water or fresh water using naturally occurring bacteria and fungi. Their product, 'Bio Aquafix', can degrade hydrocarbons, break down leaves and other organic matter and reduce organic silt levels by 80% whilst increasing the flocculation of inorganic silt. In healthy rivers, natural bacteria and fungi inhabiting the mud keep the water in a stable condition by breaking down dead vegetation and nitrogenous waste products from fish and wildfowl. However, where oxygen levels are low due to pollution, these bacteria cannot flourish. This allows algae and unpleasant smelling anaerobic bacteria to take a hold.

'Bio Aquafix'

'Bio Aquafix' consists of a column, packed with a porous mineral matrix onto which the bacteria and fungi are fixed. The fixed bacteria feed and multiply using the pollutants as food. All the bacterial and fungal colonies are classified as safe by the European Community. A whole range of columns are available, suitable for different water systems. It is possible to select bacteria and fungi with differing appetites for hydrocarbons, animal and vegetable fats, phenols and other organic compounds.

The matrix itself protects the bacteria and fungi from extremes of pH, toxic chemicals, predators and ultraviolet radiation. Research shows that the support given by the matrix enables the bacteria and fungi to survive for longer periods than free-living indigenous micro-organisms used in other treatment systems.

Because of serious pollution such as that in this picture, the regulations concerning water pollution are becoming stricter.

Organic waste

'Bio Aquafix' can also flocculate organic particles in the water owing to aluminium, iron and magnesium ions in the mineral matrix. This flocculated material becomes food for the fixed bacteria and fungi.

Heavy metals

Heavy metals in polluted water are removed by ion exchange. The mineral matrix, containing potassium aluminosilicates, swaps potassium ions for heavy metal ions in the polluted water. As the concentration of heavy metal ions in the water decreases, so desirable microflora flourish. The increased bacterial activity leads to more efficient use of dissolved oxygen in the water and anaerobic bacteria find it harder to survive. At the same time, fish and frogs now have a more favourable environment in which to live.

Inorganic anions

'Bio Aquafix' can also control nitrate and phosphate levels. In the presence of oxygen, toxic nitrogen compounds like ammonia and nitrites are oxidised to nitrates. Acidification normally occurs during nitrification and inhibits this process, but the mineral matrix buffers the pH changes. The nitrates are then used by the bacteria and fungi whilst phosphates are precipitated by calcium ions in the matrix.

Sewage

'Bio Aquafix' is also useful in the treatment of sewage. It will accelerate the settling of suspended solids as sludge in the same way that it flocculates organic waste. As heavy metal ions are rendered harmless, the sludge is suitable for agricultural use.

Hydrocarbons

Hydrocarbons, usually detrimental to natural bacteria, are digested rapidly by bacteria and fungi on the matrix. This avoids the build up of hazardous intermediates formed by incomplete degradation.

Questions

1   Explain what the following mean in your own words.

   a effluents

   b degrade

   c flocculation

   d anaerobic

   e matrix

   f indigenous

   g toxic

   h heavy metals

   i ion exchange

   j microflora

   k buffers

2   Explain how 'Bio Aquafix' removes:

   a mercury ions, Hg^{2+}

   b nitrate ions, NO_3^-

   c phosphate ions, PO_4^{3-}

   d solid particles in sewage

   e octane from oil in polluted water

3   Design a two-page promotional leaflet to be sent to water authorities advertising 'Bio Aquafix'.

   a The front page of the leaflet should highlight the most important features of 'Bio Aquafix'.

   b The back page of the leaflet should explain its action in such a way that water authority managers, who are non-scientists, can understand how it works.

16 Anions of the alkali metals

The alkali metals in Group I of the Periodic Table are usually associated with high reactivity and the formation of ions with a single positive charge. However, compounds of these metals have been made which contain **negatively** charged alkali metal ions, as this extract from *Scientific American* explains.

The alkali metals are a group of elements whose most notable and most familiar chemical property is their eagerness to give up an electron. The alkali metal sodium, for example, readily donates an electron to chlorine, forming sodium chloride. Metallic sodium is so strongly disposed to get rid of an electron that it will even split a water molecule, displacing a hydrogen atom and forming sodium hydroxide; the reaction can be a violent one. Because the metallic form of sodium is so reactive it does not exist in nature; the element is found only as a positive ion, or cation, denoted Na^+. The cation forms when the atom surrenders one of its electrons to some other chemical species.

These properties of the alkali metals have been known since the beginning of chemistry, and it has therefore come as a surprise to learn that alkali metals can also accept an electron, acting in a way which is precisely the reverse of their usual one. The addition of an electron to the neutral sodium atom, for example, forms the negatively charged anion, Na^-. This anion has been known for some time as a stable species in gaseous sodium; what is more important, it has recently been discovered in solutions and even as a component of a crystalline salt. It appears that the anions of all the other alkali metals can also be prepared; those of potassium (K^-), rubidium (Rb^-) and cesium (Cs^-) have already been observed. It may even be possible to prepare salts containing the simplest possible anion: the immobilized electron.

The key to the preparation of the alkali metal anions, curiously, is the trapping of the alkali **cations** in an organic molecule with a cage-like structure. Ordinarily, any negative metal ions present in a solution would quickly react with positive ions to yield neutral atoms of the metal. When the cations are sequestered in an organic cage molecule, the resulting complex is so stable that the 'backsliding' reaction is prevented. The negative ions and the crystals containing them are nonetheless highly reactive. They cannot be exposed to air or moisture, and they are stable for long periods only when stored at low temperature.

. . .

The alkali metals comprise six elements: lithium, sodium, potassium, rubidium, cesium and francium. (The last is a rare, radioactive species.) In the usual arrangement of the periodic table of the elements they are listed in the first column. This grouping reflects similarities in the chemical properties of all the alkali metals and in their underlying electronic structures: each has a solitary electron in its outermost, or valence, shell of electrons.

The alkali metals can be regarded as noble gases with one extra electron (and, of course, one extra proton in the nucleus). Lithium, for example, has the filled 1s orbital of a helium atom, and one additional electron half filling the 2s orbital. Sodium has filled 1s, 2s and 2p orbitals, as in neon, and, in addition, one 3s electron. The remaining alkali metals are similar in structure; in each of them the outermost electron is alone in an s-type orbital.

The strong tendency of the alkali metals to lose an electron and form a cation can now be understood. With the removal of the valence electron, each of the alkali metals takes on the exceptionally stable structure of a noble gas.

Crystals of sea salt, sodium chloride (Na^+Cl^-).

Even though the resulting ion has an unbalanced positive charge, in the presence of an electron acceptor it is stabler than the neutral atom.

Adding one electron to an alkali metal results in a configuration that is much less strongly favoured than the noble-gas structure of the cation. Nevertheless, the extra electron does fill an *s*-type orbital, and a filled orbital is somewhat stabler than a half-filled one. Under certain carefully contrived circumstances that slight gain in stability is enough to favour the existence of alkali metal anions.

From *Anions of the Alkali Metals* by James L. Dye.
© Scientific American Inc. All rights reserved.

Questions

1   Why are cations of alkali metals, for example Na^+, more stable than their anions such as Na^-?

2   The anion Na^- was known for some time as a stable species in gaseous sodium before it was obtained in solution or as a component of a crystalline salt. Why is Na^- more likely to exist in the gas phase?

3   What would you expect to happen when Na^+ and Na^- ions are in solution together? Write an equation for the reaction which occurs.

4   What conditions have been employed to prevent this happening, thus allowing the existence of Na^-?

5   How would you attempt to prove experimentally that a solution actually contained alkali metal anions?

6   Which of the alkali metals Li or Cs will form anions most readily? Explain your answer.

7   Would the Group II elements be as likely to form anions as the Group I elements? Explain your answer.

8   The elements of Group VII, the halogens, normally form singly charged anions such as Cl^-. Is there any chance that compounds could be prepared containing halogen **cations**? Which of the halogens would be most likely to form cations? Explain your answer.

17 Castner's mercury cell

Hamilton Young Castner.

The following passage by Dr D. J. Adam is taken from *Education in Chemistry*. It concerns the development of an early mercury cell, whose modern equivalent is used in the manufacture of sodium hydroxide and chlorine by the electrolysis of brine. The cell was pioneered by an American called Hamilton Young Castner.

Castner, born in Brooklyn, New York in 1858, was a remarkably inventive chemist. At the age of 28, having already sold out a successful business, he came to Britain with a process he had perfected for making metallic sodium from caustic soda by fusing it with carbon. Lack of home interest caused him to set up a small factory in London to continue his work. The interest of the recently formed Webster Crown Metal Co. Ltd, of Solihull, Birmingham, was aroused since they required metallic sodium for the preparation of metallic aluminium by the reduction of aluminium chloride (Deville process). After investigation and validation of the excellence of Castner's method, it was decided to set up a new company, The Aluminium Company Ltd. based on Oldbury, Birmingham, to exploit the new process, with Castner as managing director. The Aluminium Co. bought Castner's patents for £140 000 and opened a new factory in 1888 with a potential annual ouptut of 50 tonnes. However, just as the business was beginning to develop, the Hall–Héroult electrolytic process for aluminium, patented in 1886, was coming into commercial being, causing the price of aluminium to fall rapidly yet again. So Castner, who was to achieve his greatest triumph in industrial electrolysis, was initially one of its victims.

Castner quickly realised that the company's only real asset was his process for making sodium metal cheaply and so, with characteristic determination, he endeavoured to look for an outlet for this product. He was very successful in developing processes for sodium peroxide (made by controlled oxidation of sodium in aluminium trays) and sodium cyanide (made in two stages by reaction between sodium, charcoal and ammonia.)

$$2Na(l) + O_2(g) \longrightarrow Na_2O_2(s)$$

$$2Na(l) + 2NH_3(g) \longrightarrow 2NaNH_2(s) + 2H_2(g)$$

$$2NaNH_2(s) + 2C(s) \longrightarrow 2NaCN(s) + 2H_2(g)$$

The latter was required by the gold mining industry which was accustomed to working with the potassium salt. To overcome the initial difficulty of getting the sodium salt accepted, it was marketed as 130 per cent potassium cyanide. In fact, so successful was the cyanide process that the Aluminium Co. (which now made no aluminium) was restored to financial health. Furthermore, the demand for sodium was such that Castner set out to improve on his original process for the manufacture of the metal. For this he returned to Sir Humphrey Davy's experiment on the electrolysis of molten sodium hydroxide.

He used an iron pot containing an iron cathode separated from the cylindrical nickel anode by a gauze diaphragm. In theory this process was continuous but impurities in even the best quality caustic soda available to him gave cathode deposits which caused difficulties. So with typical perseverance he embarked on the task of making the purer caustic soda needed for his electrolytic sodium process. It was well known that on the electrolysis of brine, sodium hydroxide and hydrogen were produced at the cathode and chlorine was evolved at the anode. The difficulty was in separating the caustic soda from the salt. Castner's ultimate solution, the rocking mercury cell

(British Patent 16046/1892, 10584/1893) depended on a property again known to Davy, that of the solubility of sodium in mercury to give sodium amalgam. This on reaction with water gave caustic soda solution.

$$2Na/Hg(l) + 2H_2O(l) \longrightarrow 2NaOH(aq) + H_2(g) + Hg(l) \text{ (re-used)}$$

The original cell consisted of a rectangular slate box divided into three compartments by slate partitions almost reaching to the bottom. A sufficient depth of mercury, acting as the cathode, sealed off the compartments. The two end sections, fitted with carbon anodes, contained brine and the centre compartment contained water. Electrolysis gave sodium amalgam in the outer sections. The rocking of the cell caused the mercury to circulate and the amalgam, coming into contact with the water in the centre compartment, formed caustic soda solution and hydrogen, regenerating the mercury. Drawing off the caustic soda and topping up with brine and water made the process continuous. Not only was caustic soda produced continuously but also hydrogen and chlorine, and it obviously had great commercial possibilities.

D. J. Adam, Early Industrial
Electrolysis, *Education in Chemistry*,
Vol. 17, No. 1.

Questions

1 Castner's original process for the production of sodium involved heating molten caustic soda (sodium hydroxide) with carbon. Suggest an equation for this reaction.

2 Write an equation for the production of aluminium by the Deville process.

3 Outline, with electrode equations, the modern electrolytic process for making aluminium (the Hall–Héroult process).

4 Why is this process substantially cheaper than the Deville process?

5 To overcome the initial difficulty of getting sodium cyanide accepted in place of potassium cyanide, Castner's company marketed NaCN as '130 per cent' KCN. Show how the figure 130 per cent is arrived at.

6 Why did Castner decide to look for a method of making purer caustic soda?

7 Draw a labelled diagram of Castner's rocking mercury cell for the electrolysis of brine. Show clearly what happens when the cell is in operation, and write equations for all the chemical reactions which occur.

8 Castner's mercury cell was developed by an Austrian called Carl Kellner. The modern cell is known as the **Castner–Kellner** cell. How does the modern version of the mercury cell differ from Castner's original rocking cell?

9 The Castner–Kellner process for the electrolysis of brine is of great importance to the chemical industry, producing three major industrial chemicals—sodium hydroxide, chlorine and hydrogen—from a cheap and abundant raw material. List five important uses of the products of the process.

10 Outline three social or environmental disadvantages/problems of the Castner–Kellner process.

18 Knocking and the search for anti-knock agents

Knocking

When the piston reaches the top of its cycle in the cylinder of an internal combustion engine, a spark is passed from the spark plug. An explosion occurs in the combustion chamber and the flame front is steadily propagated through the cylinder, accompanying the expansion of the hot gas. As the flame front advances, the unburned mixture or 'end-gas' is compressed and the resulting rise in temperature ordinarily causes it to burn smoothly. However, it may sometimes burn explosively and the sudden, violent ignition gives rise to a metallic rattling or 'knocking' in the cylinder. This causes power loss in the engine and in extreme circumstances can cause cracking of the cylinder head. This phenomenon is known as **knocking** or **knock**.

Knock in the internal combustion engine was first investigated in America by Thomas Midgley Jnr. It was Midgley who was the first to produce a commercial anti-knock gasoline additive.

Midgley's search

Midgley first encountered the problem of knock in 1916 while he was investigating the substitution of kerosine for gasoline in small, portable lighting units which consisted of an internal combustion engine attached to a d.c. generator. Kerosine worsened the problem of knock very considerably. In the earliest stages of his work Midgley thought that the knock arose from the slow vaporization of kerosine. A completely false theory (that the absorption of radiant energy by a dye would promote vaporization and hence eliminate knock) led him to the discovery that iodine, when dissolved in the gasoline or kerosine, inhibited knock. The discovery was tantalizing since his original theory proved incorrect (dyes had no effect) and the mode of action of iodine remained unknown.

In the following five years or so, Midgley developed a theory to explain knock, and searched through thousands of chemicals for other anti-knock agents. His search was unsuccessful until he changed his tactics from trial and error to a systematic search. Midgley explained:

'... in the search for a material with which to control knocking in an internal combustion engine, the following determinations were arrived at.

1 Iodine, dissolved in motor fuel in very small quantities, greatly enhanced the anti-knock characteristics of the fuel.

2 Oil-soluble iodine compounds had a similar, though modified, effect.

3 Aniline, its homologues, and some other nitrogenous compounds were effective, though their effectiveness varied over a wide range depending on the hydrocarbon radicals attached to the nitrogen atom.

4 Bromine, carbon tetrachloride, nitric acid, hydrochloric acid, nitrites, and nitro-compounds in general increased knocking when added to the fuel and air mixture.

5 Selenium oxychloride was extremely effective as an anti-knock material.

6 A large number of compounds of other elements had shown no effect.

With these facts before us, we adopted a correlation procedure based on the periodic table. What had seemed at times a hopeless quest, covering many years and costing a considerable amount of money, rapidly turned

IV	V	VI	VII
14 Si	15 P	16 S	17 Cl
32 Ge	33 As	34 Se	35 Br
50 Sn	51 Sb	52 Te	53 I
82 Pb	83 Bi	84 Po	85 At

Figure I
Groups IV, V, VI and VII of the periodic table.

Unleaded petrol is gradually being introduced in many countries, following concern about the medical and environmental problems caused by lead in petrol.

into a "fox hunt". Predictions began fulfilling themselves instead of fizzling out...'

The correlation of behaviour with chemical structure and the periodic table was the key to success. It was a simple, logical step to proceed through groups VII and VI to group IV and organic derivatives of tin and lead (figure 1), since anti-knock properties seemed to improve as a group was descended (iodine better than bromine, tellurium better than selenium) and as the table was traversed from right to left. Tetraethyl tin, although effective, caused pre-ignition but when, on 9 December 1921, in the General Motors research laboratories, Midgley started an engine fuelled with gasoline containing tetra-ethyl lead (TEL) he was rewarded by the sound of smoothly functioning combustion with no audible trace of knock. The anti-knock properties of TEL were so superior to those of any previously investigated substance (see table 1) and so evident at very low concentrations that it was clear that the search for an anti-knock gasoline additive was over.

Table I
Properties of some anti-knock agents
1 *Percentage by volume of agent that must be mixed with kerosine to produce a given anti-knock effect.*
2 *Number of molecules of the fuel–air mixture on which one molecule of the anti-knock agent can act.*

Compound	% by vol. (see 1)	Approx. no. of molecules (see 2)
C_2H_5I	1.6	2150
Xylidene	2.0	2600
$(C_2H_5)_4Sn$	1.2	7100
$(C_2H_5)_4Se$	0.4	11750
$(C_2H_5)_4Te$	0.1	50000
$(C_2H_5)_4Pb$	0.04	215000

TEL production

The elaboration of a laboratory bench discovery into commercial or industrial production is seldom just a scaling up job. TEL might be outstandingly effective but how was it to be manufactured? The newly formed Ethyl Gasoline Corporation eventually adopted a route to TEL involving the reaction of chloroethane with a lead/sodium alloy:

$$4CH_3CH_2Cl(g) + 4Pb/Na(s) \longrightarrow (CH_3CH_2)_4Pb(l) + 3Pb(s) + 4NaCl(s)$$

Since the combustion of gasoline containing TEL deposited metallic lead and lead(II) oxide in the engine cylinders, a lead 'scavenger', such as 1,2-dibromoethane, was incorporated into the gasoline. This ensured the removal of lead and lead(II) oxide as volatile lead bromide or oxybromide in the exhaust gases. The blend of TEL and scavenger became known as 'ethyl fluid'. This innovation involved a considerable expansion in the industrial output of bromine and, in collaboration with the Dow Chemical Company, Ethyl Gasoline Corporation established a new chemical plant, extracting bromine from sea water in which it is to be found at concentrations of about $0.07 \, g \, dm^{-3}$.

Gasoline containing TEL was sold for the first time on 2 February 1923, in Dayton, Ohio, and was introduced into the United Kingdom by the Anglo-American Oil Company in 1928. Since the 1980s, however, there has been increasing concern about the medical and environmental problems of lead. All new cars are now built to run on unleaded gasoline, which will eventually replace the leaded sort.

Adapted from C.B. Hunt, Knocking and the Search for Anti-knock Agents, *School Science Review.*

Questions

1 Explain in your own words the meaning of 'knock' in internal combustion engines.

2 Use your textbook to find out

   a What actually causes knocking.

   b How anti-knock agents help control knocking.

3 Why did the use of kerosine in place of gasoline increase the problem of knocking in internal combustion engines?

4 How did the periodic table help Midgley in his search for an effective anti-knock agent?

5 Why do you think $(C_2H_5)_4Pb$ has greater anti-knock properties than $(C_2H_5)_4Sn$?

6 **a** TEL is manufactured by reacting chloroethane with a sodium/lead alloy. How is chloroethane manufactured?

   b 1,2-Dibromoethane is added to gasoline in conjunction with TEL to act as a 'scavenger' for lead. How is 1,2-dibromoethane manufactured?

7 The disadvantage of adding anti-knock compounds to gasoline is that they put lead into the atmosphere.

   a In what form does the lead enter the atmosphere?

   b Explain why lead in the atmosphere is undesirable.

19 Rust

The problem of rust

Rust is hydrated iron(III) oxide, $Fe_2O_3 . xH_2O$. It has none of the characteristic physical properties of metallic iron, such as high tensile strength. Rusting is therefore an important factor determining the useful life of iron and steel articles. On the other hand, the major ore of iron is virtually identical to rust, and a material with a built-in tendency to revert slowly to the form in which it exists in nature has certain environmental advantages. Nevertheless, rusting is a major problem costing millions of pounds each year in the UK alone.

Most metals tend to corrode in air. Many metals, though, produce a protective oxide layer—aluminium is a good example. The dimensions of the unit cell in aluminium oxide are very similar to those in aluminium itself. Aluminium oxide therefore adheres tightly to the metal surface and protects it from further attack by oxygen. Unfortunately, rust and iron differ significantly in packing dimensions. This causes the rust to flake off as it forms and the rust layer is porous and non-protective.

What happens during rusting?

Rusting is an electrochemical process, requiring the presence of both air and water. Anodic (electron-releasing) and cathodic (electron-accepting) regions are set up in the iron (figure 1). In the anode regions, iron dissolves:

$$Fe(s) \longrightarrow Fe^{2+}(aq) + 2e^-$$

The electrons produced in this process flow through the iron to a cathodic region, where they are accepted in a reaction involving dissolved oxygen:

$$2H_2O(l) + O_2(aq) + 4e^- \longrightarrow 4OH^-(aq)$$

The Fe^{2+} and OH^- ions produced in these processes migrate outwards. Where they meet, iron(II) hydroxide is precipitated:

$$Fe^{2+}(aq) + 2OH^-(aq) \longrightarrow Fe(OH)_2(s)$$

This precipitate is then oxidised to rust, hydrated iron(III) oxide.

Notice that the iron dissolves and corrodes **only in the anodic regions.** At the anodes 'pits' are formed where the iron has dissolved away.

There are several factors which determine which regions of the iron become anodic and which cathodic.

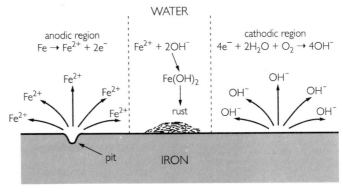

Figure 1
Cathodic and anodic regions in the corrosion of iron.

Oxygen supply

In regions where the oxygen supply is good, cathodes tend to be set up, because the cathodic reaction involves oxygen. It follows that regions of poor oxygen supply, such as crevices in a structure or areas covered with sediment or sand, are more likely to behave as anodes and become corroded.

The presence of other metals

If iron is in electrical contact with a more reactive metal, such as zinc, the more reactive metal will have a greater tendency than iron to lose electrons and will therefore act anodically and corrode in preference to the iron. If the iron is in contact with a less reactive metal, the opposite applies and the iron will rust more quickly.

The presence of impurities

Certain impurities in the iron may set up cathodic regions, causing other parts of the iron to become anodic.

Preventing rust

Several methods are used to prevent rusting.

Use of a protective layer

This prevents the surface of the iron coming into contact with air or water. Examples are painting, covering with oil or grease, coating with plastic and plating with another metal.

Cathodic protection

The iron is made cathodic by bringing it into electrical contact with a more reactive metal, such as zinc, which corrodes in preference to the iron. This is sometimes called **sacrificial protection**.

Alloying

By alloying iron with relatively unreactive metals, like nickel or chromium, stainless steels are produced. These alloys are protected from corrosion by thin non-porous films of oxide, such as chromium oxide and nickel oxide.

Use of inhibitors

Certain chemical substances inhibit rusting by producing insoluble layers in close contact with cathodic or anodic regions. Magnesium sulphate, for example, acts as an inhibitor in cathodic regions by forming insoluble magnesium hydroxide by interaction between magnesium ions and the hydroxide ions produced at the cathodes.

Zinc blocks bolted to a ship's hull to prevent corrosion.

Questions

1 Explain why iron rusts readily, while aluminium, which is generally more reactive, hardly corrodes at all under normal conditions.

2 When a piece of tin-plated iron is scratched, the exposed iron rusts rapidly. When zinc-plated (galvanised) iron is scratched, hardly any rusting of the exposed iron occurs. Explain this difference.

3 Why should copper rivets never be used to join two pieces of iron? Could aluminium rivets be used? Explain.

4 Why is corrosion particularly severe in the 'nooks and crannies' of a car body such as the door sills and box sections of the chassis? How can car manufacturers overcome this problem?

5 Rusting in car bodies could be largely overcome if cars were made from zinc-coated steel plate instead of ordinary mild steel plate. Why do you think car manufacturers have not adopted this practice, despite its advantages?

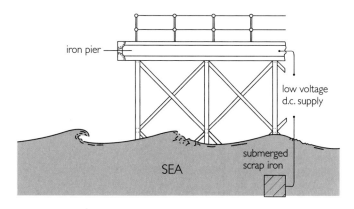

Figure 2
Electrical corrosion protection of an iron pier.

6   Iron structures are sometimes electrically protected from corrosion as
    in figure 2. To which terminal of the low-voltage d.c. supply should the
    iron pier in the figure be connected? Explain your answer.

7   Underwater steel pillars used to support piers often corrode more
    severely where they are sunk beneath the sea bed than where they are
    in contact with sea water. Suggest a reason for this.

8   Most corrosion protection is only temporary. Suppose chemists
    discovered a cheap way of permanently rust-proofing steel. Such a
    discovery would have enormous advantages. What disadvantages should
    chemists consider before marketing their discovery?

20 Biometallurgy—mining with microbes

The process of biometallurgy—using bacteria to extract metals—was first stumbled upon by Spanish engineers in 1752 as they investigated the possibility of reopening an old copper mine in Rio Tinto.

The Spaniards noticed streams of blue-green liquid running down the excavated rock. Where these streams flowed over old iron tools, it left a brown film of pure copper. They deduced that iron was reacting with the blue-green solution to form copper. In 1947, American microbiologists discovered that these streams of blue-green liquid contained the bacteria *Thiobacillus ferroxidans*. Research showed that these bacteria gain energy to live by oxidising the sulphide ions in copper, zinc, lead and uranium ores, forming sulphate ions. This process also releases ions of the different metals.

Since 1947, several mines have used biotechnology commercially. In 1970, uranium was extracted from a few mines in Canada and gold from two mines in South Africa. In the mid 1980s, mining engineers in the United States decided that biometallurgy was a viable alternative to traditional methods of extracting copper. Production costs in smelting copper ores had risen sharply as regulatory agencies enforced new rules about sulphur dioxide emission levels. The industry had to devise new methods for controlling sulphur dioxide and this brought extra expense. Consequently, biological extraction became attractive as it was more cost-effective and less polluting.

Nowadays, 30% of the copper produced in the USA is extracted by biometallurgy. The process used is fairly straightforward.

First, the low grade copper ore is piled on an impermeable surface. Then it is sprayed with an acidic solution containing *Thiobacillus ferroxidans*. The solution is acidified because the bacteria are acid-loving. The solution also contains iron(III) ions which act as oxidising agents. Copper(II) ions and iron(II) ions are released when the bacteria catalyse redox reactions and reduce sulphide ions to sulphate.

Because the ore sits on an impermeable surface, a solution containing copper(II) ions can be drained off and later electrolysed. During the electrolysis, pure copper collects at the cathode. The Fe^{2+} which remains in the leaching solution after electrolysis can be oxidised back to Fe^{3+} by *T. ferroxidans* in an open pond. This solution is then ready to be re-used as a leaching solution.

In a few years time, it may be possible to reduce costs even further by using absorption filters containing algae which reduce Cu^{2+} to copper rather than using electrolysis.

The main obstacle to biometallurgy is the slowness of the process. It takes decades rather than months or years to recover the metal. However, far less capital is required. For example, instead of the intensive drilling and excavation needed in conventional mining, a mine in Arizona used only five holes drilled into an ore deposit. The acidic leaching solution was then pumped down one hole and the resulting copper-rich solution was pumped up the other four holes. This technique is much less damaging to the environment, but it requires time for the process of leaching to work, so cashflow can become a problem for the operators.

At present, scientists are searching for ways to speed up the leaching process. They have had some success with a bacterium which feeds on carbohydrate and uses manganese as an oxidising agent. The more carbohydrate they add, the more bacteria reproduce and the faster the manganese can be mined. If other ways are found to speed up leaching times, then microbes could revolutionise mining throughout the world.

Questions

1   Write two half-equations to show how copper was formed when streams of blue-green liquid from the old copper mine in Rio Tinto flowed over iron tools.

2   Write two half-equations to show how *Thiobacillus ferroxidans* oxidises sulphide ions to sulphate ions with the help of iron(III) ions.

3   Write a half-equation for the process at the cathode when the leached solution containing copper ions is electrolysed.

4   Using the labels provided, annotate this flow diagram to show the extraction of copper using biometallurgy.

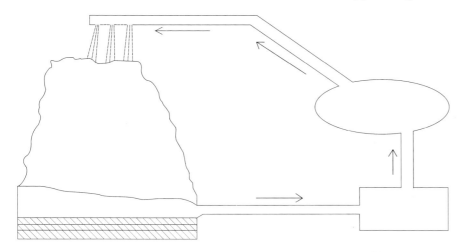

| pile of low grade ore |
| impermeable layer |
| $Cu^{2+}(aq)$ in solution plus $SO_4^{2-}(aq)$ and $Fe^{2+}(aq)$ |
| sprinklers |
| copper metal recovery plant |
| bacteria and $Fe^{3+}(aq)$ in acid solution |
| oxidation pond where *T. ferroxidans* converts $Fe^{2+} \longrightarrow Fe^{3+}$ |

5   Explain why the Fe^{2+}, which remains in the leached solution after electrolysis, is converted back to Fe^{3+} in an open pond.

6   Imagine that you are the Government Minister for Trade and Industry. Write a letter to the manager of a copper-producing company using traditional methods, explaining biometallurgy. Try to convince the manager that it is worth investing time and money in using this method. Think about the problems and extra costs involved in conventional extraction methods and show the advantages of mining with microbes.

21 Hydrogen—fuel for vehicles

The following passage by J. J. Reilly and Gary D. Sandrock is taken from *Scientific American*. It concerns the use of metal hydrides as a possible storage medium for hydrogen fuel in hydrogen-powered vehicles of the future.

What fuel will power the motor vehicles of the world when petroleum is no longer an economic source? Hydrogen is high on the list of candidates, but the problem of storing it safely and compactly has seemed to stand in the way. Now a solution to that problem is at hand in the form of metal hydrides: chemical compounds of hydrogen and metals. Already hydrogen stored in this way has served as a fuel for buses operated experimentally in the U.S. and West Germany, and for an experimental automobile. Metal hydrides have also served on an experimental basis as energy-storage compounds for levelling peak demands on an electric-power system. In addition they hold promise for such applications as refrigeration, heat pumps and heat engines.

Hydrogen is by far the most abundant element in the universe. It is the raw material from which all the other elements have been made in the interior of stars. Moreover, it is chemically unique in that it can behave either like an alkali metal or like a halogen, that is, in forming a chemical bond it can either donate an electron (as an alkali metal does) or accept one (as a halogen does). This property is useful in processes that make chemical compounds by combining hydrogen with one or more elements.

Since hydrogen on the earth is almost always combined with another element or elements in a compound such as water, it must be separated in order to serve human purposes. The annual worldwide production of pure hydrogen is about 10 trillion cubic feet. The main consumer is the chemical industry, which utilizes hydrogen as a raw material in the manufacture of a large number of products ranging from plastics to fertilizers.

Hydrogen powered vehicles.

Hydrogen is attractive as a fuel because it has the highest density of energy per unit of weight of any chemical fuel, is essentially non-polluting (the main by-product of burning it is water) and can serve in a variety of energy converters ranging from internal-combustion engines to fuel cells. In the near future hydrogen could be extracted relatively cheaply from coal. In the more distant future, when fossil fuels are no longer economic, hydrogen could be separated from water by the process of electrolysis, driven by nuclear, solar or other forms of energy.

The present methods of storing hydrogen are suitable and safe for the present industrial uses of hydrogen, but they would never do for moving vehicles or for special applications where compactness is required. For example, hydrogen stored as a compressed gas calls for large and heavy vessels. At a typical pressure of 136 atmospheres hydrogen gas in a steel container weighs about 30 times more than an equivalent amount of gasoline, and 99 per cent of the weight is in the container. The same container takes up about 24 times more space than a container holding the equivalent amount of gasoline. Hydrogen as a liquid is useful in certain circumstances, but the energy consumed in the liquefaction process is a major fraction of what could be generated by burning the hydrogen. Moreover, liquid hydrogen would present a serious and probably insoluble safety problem if it were to be considered as a common fuel for use in motor vehicles. Liquid hydrogen is extremely cold (it boils at 20 K, $-253°C$), and it is highly volatile if it is spilled. Metal hydrides, in contrast, store hydrogen compactly and safely at ambient temperatures.

Most elemental metals will form metal hydrides. In many cases the reaction is simple and direct, consisting merely of bringing gaseous hydrogen (H_2) in contact with the metal (M). In chemical shorthand a typical reaction can be written $M + H_2 \rightleftharpoons MH_2$. The arrows point in two directions, which means that the reaction is reversible. Its direction is determined by the pressure of the hydrogen gas. If the pressure is above a certain level (termed the equilibrium pressure), the reaction proceeds to the right to form the metal hydride; if it is below that level, the metal hydride decomposes into the metal and gaseous hydrogen. The metal is in the form of particles in order to provide a large surface area for reaction with the gas.

The primary reason metal hydrides have been proposed for the storage of hydrogen as an energy carrier is that they accommodate an extremely high density of hydrogen. Indeed, it is possible to pack more hydrogen into a metal hydride than into the same volume of liquid hydrogen. A consideration of the mechanism by which a metal hydride is formed reveals why such a high packing density is possible.

When gaseous hydrogen is brought in contact with a metal that forms a hydride, hydrogen molecules (H_2) are adsorbed onto the surface of the metal. Some of the molecules dissociate into hydrogen atoms (H), which then enter the crystal lattice of the metal and occupy specific sites among the metal atoms. Such locations are called interstitial sites. They must have a certain minimum volume in order to easily accommodate the hydrogen atom. (See figure 1.)

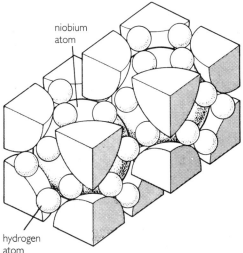

niobium atom

hydrogen atom

Figure 1

Interstitial sites in the body-centred cubic structure of the metal niobium. Two unit cells are shown, each with a niobium atom at the centre. Interstitial sites are shown fully occupied by hydrogen atoms.

As the pressure of the gas is increased a limited number of hydrogen atoms are forced into the crystal. Usually at some critical concentration and pressure the metal becomes saturated with hydrogen and goes into a new phase: the metal-hydride phase. If the hydrogen pressure is now slightly increased further, much greater amounts of hydrogen are absorbed. Ultimately all the original hydrogen-saturated metal phase will be converted into the metal-hydride phase. Since metal crystals have many interstitial sites, it is possible for them to accommodate large amounts of hydrogen in a highly compact manner. In many hydrides the number of hydrogen atoms in the crystal will be two or three times the number of metal atoms.

Although the density of hydrogen by volume in a hydride is high, the density by weight is less satisfactory (compared with pure hydrogen) because of the weight of the associated metal. It is only the high density of energy by weight of hydrogen as a fuel that makes metal hydrides feasible for the storage of energy. Table 1 compares the energy density of some hydride storage systems with the energy densities of other power sources.

Table I

Energy densities characteristic of various automotive power sources either already in existence or proposed are indicated in this table. As the figures in the column at the right show, metal hydrides lag far behind gasoline in terms of energy density, but they are competitive with electric batteries in this respect. (No allowance has been made in these calculations for the weight of the container holding either the metal hydrides or the gasoline.) The figures for the metal hydrides are based only on the available hydrogen in each case. The particular magnesium hydride tested contained an additive of nickel amounting to about 10 per cent by weight.

Power source	Energy density/ watt-hours per kilogram	Conversion efficiency/%	Net energy density/watt-hours per kilogram
Lead–acid battery	30–50	70	21–35
Lithium–metal sulphide battery	150	70	105
Iron–titanium hydride ($FeTiH_{1.7}$)	510	30	153
Magnesium–nickel hydride (Mg_2NiH_4)	1110	30	333
Magnesium hydride (MgH_2)	2332	30	700
Gasoline	12 880	23	2962

Another fundamental property of metal hydrides is their heat of formation, the heat given off when the hydride is formed by the reaction of hydrogen with the metal. In order to decompose the hydride back into its original constituents, metal and hydrogen gas, the same amount of heat must be added to the system; it is termed the heat of decomposition. The heat effect can be quite large. It is roughly proportional to the stability of the hydride, that is to the ease or difficulty of taking hydrogen out of the system. The stabler the hydride is, the higher the temperature and heat of decomposition will be. The fact that heat is evolved when hydrogen is stored in a metal hydride and is required when hydrogen is released is of great practical consequence. It is a primary consideration in the design of systems for storing hydrogen in metal hydrides. (Figure 2 shows one way a hydride storage system can be coupled with an internal combustion engine.)

Text from *Hydrogen Storage in Metal Hydrides* by J. J. Reilly and Gary D. Sandrock. © *Scientific American*, Inc.

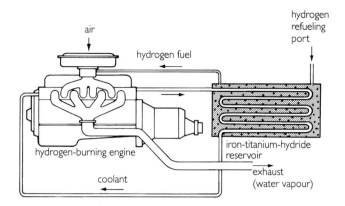

Figure 2

Hydrogen storage system based on the use of a metal hydride is shown in this schematic diagram, coupled with a standard internal-combustion engine that has been adapted to burn hydrogen gas.

Questions

1 List the advantages and disadvantages of hydrogen as a fuel for internal combustion engines.

2 Explain why 'hydrogen has the highest density of energy per unit weight of any chemical fuel' (Paragraph 4).

3 The passage gives the annual worldwide consumption of hydrogen as about 10 trillion cubic feet. Convert this figure to kg. State any assumptions you make. (1 foot = 0.304 m; 1 trillion = 10^{12})

4 Explain briefly why metal hydrides allow such a high packing density of hydrogen to be achieved.

5 Use the data below to calculate the mass of hydrogen stored in $1.0 \, cm^3$ of magnesium hydride, MgH_2, assuming no volume change occurs when magnesium is converted to the hydride. Compare this value with the mass of hydrogen in $1.0 \, cm^3$ of liquid hydrogen, and discuss the significance of your answer in relation to the use of magnesium hydride as a hydrogen storage medium.
$Mg = 24$, $H = 1$
Density of magnesium = $1.74 \, g \, cm^{-3}$
Density of liquid hydrogen = $0.07 \, g \, cm^{-3}$ (at 20 K)

6 Interstitial metal hydrides of the type described in this article have variable composition. For example, iron titanium hydride is often represented as $FeTiH_x$ where x can have a value up to about two. Explain why such hydrides have variable composition, in contrast to most chemical compounds.

7 Consider the equation $M + H_2 \rightleftharpoons MH_2$ referred to in the passage.

   a Rewrite the equation showing state symbols and a conventional sign to indicate an equilibrium reaction.

   b Write an expression for the equilibrium constant of this reaction.

   c Use your answer to **b** to explain why 'If the pressure is above a certain level (termed the equilibrium pressure), the reaction proceeds to the right to form the metal hydride; if it is below that level, the metal hydride decomposes into the metal and gaseous hydrogen'.

8 Study figure 2 carefully.

   a Why does the engine coolant circulate through the iron–titanium hydride reservoir?

   b What procedure would be used to recharge the iron–titanium hydride reservoir?

22 Fizzy drinks

Equilibria in fizzy drinks

Fizzy drinks are sometimes called sparkling drinks or carbonated drinks. They contain carbon dioxide dissolved under pressure. When carbon dioxide dissolves in water (and the bulk of any drink is water), several equilibria are established. Carbon dioxide molecules in the gaseous phase (the space above the surface of the drink) are in equilibrium with hydrated molecules in the aqueous phase:

$$CO_2(g) \rightleftharpoons CO_2(aq) \quad \Delta H \text{ negative} \qquad \ldots (1)$$

Carbon dioxide may also react with water to form carbonic acid:

$$CO_2(aq) + H_2O(l) \rightleftharpoons H_2CO_3(aq) \qquad \ldots (2)$$

Carbonic acid is a fairly weak acid, dissociating to give hydrogencarbonate and carbonate ions:

$$H_2CO_3(aq) \rightleftharpoons HCO_3^-(aq) + H^+(aq) \qquad \ldots (3)$$

$$HCO_3^-(aq) \rightleftharpoons CO_3^{2-}(aq) + H^+(aq) \qquad \ldots (4)$$

In aqueous solution, carbon dioxide exists mainly as hydrated molecules, $CO_2(aq)$; less than one per cent of the carbon dioxide reacts with water to form carbonic acid.

Most fizzy drinks are made by dissolving carbon dioxide gas in the still drink under pressure, the liquid usually being cooled beforehand. This method is used for soft drinks such as lemonade and Coca-Cola, for keg beer and most bottled beers, and for some cheap sparkling wines.

Some alcoholic drinks are made fizzy by fermentation. After the initial fermentation process, the drink is put in a closed container (usually a bottle) along with a small amount of sugar. Yeast remaining in the drink from the initial fermentation causes a brief second fermentation to occur with the added sugar. This produces a small amount of carbon dioxide, which can only dissolve in the drink because the container is closed.

Champagne is produced in this way. It is claimed that drinks made fizzy by this method retain their fizziness for longer than drinks that have merely had carbon dioxide forced in under pressure.

Bubble formation

When a fizzy drink is in a closed container, at a fixed temperature, it is in a state of equilibrium. When the top is taken off the bottle, gaseous carbon dioxide escapes and the equilibrium

$$CO_2(g) \rightleftharpoons CO_2(aq)$$

moves to the left in accordance with Le Chatelier's principle. Gaseous carbon dioxide is released from the aqueous phase and forms bubbles which rise to the surface. The equilibrium position adjusts fairly slowly, however, and gas is evolved from the solution for some time before the new equilibrium position is reached, whereupon the drink is said to be 'flat'. One reason for the slowness of the system to adjust to a new equilibrium position is the difficulty of forming bubbles of gas in the body of a liquid. Bubbles form fastest when there is a nucleus or 'seed' around which they can start to grow. When the drink enters the mouth, bubbles start to form round nuclei such as taste buds on the tongue, aided by the higher temperature of the mouth. The formation of bubbles in this way is responsible for the slight prickling sensation which is felt when a fizzy drink enters the mouth and which gives these drinks much of their appeal.

Aqueous carbon dioxide escapes into the gaseous phase.

Questions

1   Use the equilibria listed above to decide how the pH of a fizzy drink differs from that of the same drink without added carbon dioxide.

2   How would the addition of a little sodium hydrogencarbonate (sodium bicarbonate) affect the fizziness of a drink? Explain your answer in terms of the equilibrium reactions.

3   How would the addition of a slice of lemon affect the fizziness of a drink? Explain your answer in terms of the equilibrium reactions.

4   Refer to equilibrium (1) to explain why a fizzy drink goes flat more quickly if it is warm.

5   When the top is taken off a fizzy drink, a slight hiss of escaping gas can be heard. If a drink is taken straight from the refrigerator and opened, the hiss is much less noticeable. Explain why.

6   If a fizzy drink is poured into a glass, the bubbles rise to the surface in a stream, the stream originating from a particular point on the surface of the glass. Suggest an explanation for this.

7   If a bottle or can of fizzy drink is shaken vigorously before opening, carbon dioxide is released very rapidly when the bottle is opened and the drink often froths right out. A similar effect occurs if sugar is added to fizzy drink in a glass. Suggest an explanation for these observations.

8   Can you see any theoretical justification for the claim that drinks made fizzy by fermentation (e.g. champagne) stay fizzy longer than those produced by forcing in carbon dioxide under pressure? Explain your answer.

23 The physical chemistry of ammonia synthesis

The following passage by J. H. J. Peet, taken from the *School Science Review*, discusses some of the factors affecting the yield of ammonia in the Haber Process.

Figure 1 indicates the variation in the equilibrium constant, K_p, for the reaction

$$\tfrac{1}{2}N_2(g) + \tfrac{3}{2}H_2(g) \rightleftharpoons NH_3(g)$$

with temperature. Clearly, the highest yields are favoured by low temperatures and high pressures, as predicted by Le Chatelier's principle. If an initial reaction mixture containing 3 moles of hydrogen to each mole of nitrogen is used, then the equilibrium yield of ammonia is as shown in figure 2.

The reaction between nitrogen and hydrogen is slow at the temperatures preferred for maximum yield and so a catalyst is required. The rate-controlling step is the chemisorption of nitrogen onto the catalyst surface. There has been a lack of consistency in the value quoted for the activation energy for this step, reports varying between 70 and $220\,\mathrm{kJ\,mol^{-1}}$.

While the process of selecting a catalyst for a reaction seems to be more of an art than a science, certain clear principles have emerged. Figure 3 illustrates the strength of adsorption, in terms of enthalpy change, of nitrogen on transition metals of different groups. Experimental studies on the catalysts show that the rate of ammonia synthesis reaches a maximum with the iron group metals (d^6 structure), rapidly falling off to either the left or right of iron in the transition series (table 1). This can be related qualitatively to bonding between the nitrogen and metal being either too strong (and so slowing the rate) or too weak (so preventing activation of the nitrogen). Iron catalysts are poisoned irreversibly by such elements as sulphur, selenium, phosphorus, arsenic and also by carbon monoxide. Water, oxygen and carbon dioxide have reversible poisoning effects. Most of the catalysts (except Ni, Mo, W) can be promoted by basic oxides and all show an enhanced effect with certain metals. One commercial combination is usually

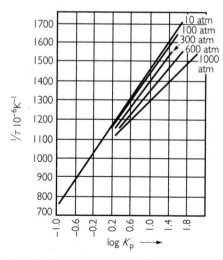

Figure 1

Variation of log K_p with $1/T$ at different pressures.

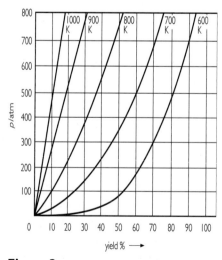

Figure 2

Variation of yield with pressure at different temperatures.

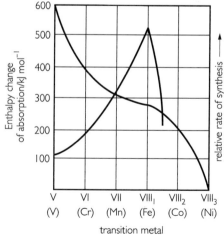

Figure 3

Effectiveness as catalysts of different transition metals. The left-hand axis refers to the broken line, the right-hand axis to the full line.

Table 1

Efficiency of metal catalysts in ammonia synthesis. (Equilibrium concentration of NH_3 under test conditions was 5%.)

Metal	Electronic structure	Yields of NH_3/%
Manganese	d^5s^2	0.8
Iron	d^6s^2	2.0
Cobalt	d^7s^2	0.2
Nickel	d^8s^2	> 0.1
Molybdenum	d^5s^1	1.5
Ruthenium	d^6s^2	~ 1.0
Tungsten	d^4s^2	0.4
Osmium	d^6s^2	2.0

produced from the fusion of iron oxide, alumina and potassium oxide, followed by reduction with synthesis gas.

In fact, the mixture is not allowed to react to equilibrium, the reactants being passed over the heated catalyst as a continuous flow. The rate of flow ('space velocity') determines the time of contact and so the yield (figure 4).

J. H. J. Peet, The Physical Chemistry of Ammonia Synthesis,
School Science Review

Questions

1 What are the usual sources of the nitrogen and hydrogen required for the Haber process?

2 Write an expression for K_p for the synthesis of ammonia as given in the equation at the beginning of the passage. What are the units of K_p?

3 A typical conversion plant might use a pressure of 300 atm and a temperature of 700 K. Use figures 1 and 2 respectively to obtain values for **a** K_p and **b** the percentage yield of ammonia using a 1 : 3 nitrogen : hydrogen mixture under these conditions.

4 What would be the new yield in each case if **a** the temperature were reduced from 700 K to 600 K without altering the pressure, and **b** the pressure were increased from 300 atm to 400 atm without altering the temperature?

5 Explain why temperatures below 700 K are seldom used even though this would result in a higher yield.

6 Explain why pressures above 300 atm are seldom used even though this would result in a greater yield.

7 What do you understand to be the mechanism of catalysis in this process?

8 Explain *in your own words* why the most effective catalysts for this process are to be found near the centre of the transition series.

9 What is a catalyst poison? What is meant by referring to some poisons as 'reversible' and others as 'irreversible'?

10 What is a catalyst promoter?

11 Study figure 4, then try to explain:

a why the percentage yield of ammonia decreases with increasing rate of flow ('space velocity').

b why for a given 'space velocity', the percentage yield of ammonia increases to a maximum then decreases with increasing temperature.

12 The Haber process has been described as the most important piece of chemistry on earth. Why is it of such importance to society?

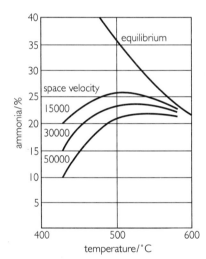

Figure 4
Variation of yield with temperature for different 'space velocities'.

24 The kinetics of enzyme-catalysed reactions

The first passage below is a summary of the lock-and-key theory of enzyme action. The second passage describes and gives the results of an experiment involving enzyme kinetics.

1 The lock-and-key hypothesis of enzyme action

Enzymes are extremely powerful biological catalysts, far more powerful than inorganic catalysts. They are also far more specific. Most enzymes catalyse only one reaction or one type of reaction. Catalase, for example, an enzyme widely found in living tissue, decomposes hydrogen peroxide extremely fast, yet it has no effect on any other naturally occurring compound. One molecule of catalase can decompose 6 million molecules of hydrogen peroxide every minute.

Any theory of enzyme action must explain this great efficiency and specificity. The lock-and-key hypothesis provides a relatively simple explanation of enzyme action derived from a study of the kinetics of enzyme-catalysed reactions.

Enzymes are proteins, and like all proteins they have a precise molecular shape which is destroyed by high temperatures and adverse pH conditions. The lock-and-key hypothesis suggests that the enzyme molecule has a particular location on its surface, called the **active site**, into which molecules of the reactant (called the substrate) fit and become attached. It is proposed that the active site is shaped specifically to fit the particular shape of the substrate molecule but no other. Figure 1 represents this diagrammatically.

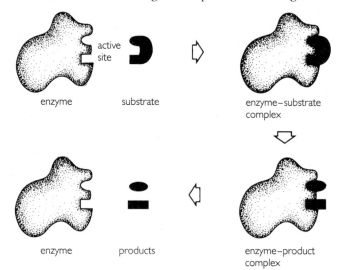

Figure 1

A diagrammatic representation of the lock-and-key model of enzyme action.

In reality, the active site is a cleft in the enzyme molecule formed by folding of the protein chain. The substrate becomes attached to the active site by intermolecular attractions such as hydrogen bonds. The attachment of the substrate to the enzyme facilitates the chemical reaction by weakening bonds or by bringing atoms into the correct configuration for reaction. The substrate

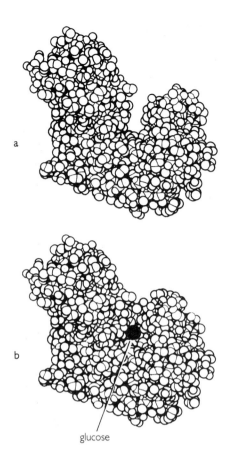

is converted to the products at the active site and these products then leave the enzyme which is now free to accept another substrate molecule. All this can be summarised as:

$$\text{enzyme} + \text{substrate} \rightleftharpoons \text{enzyme–substrate complex} \rightleftharpoons \text{enzyme–product complex} \rightleftharpoons \text{enzyme} + \text{product}$$

The enzyme and substrate combine for a very brief, but finite period. The substrate concentration is usually in great excess of the enzyme concentration (typically the ratio of substrate molecules to enzyme molecules might be $10^5 : 1$). Above a certain substrate concentration, all the enzyme molecules will be combined with substrate at any given time and the rate of the reaction will then be determined by the concentration of the enzyme and the time taken for the enzyme–substrate complex to form, rearrange and then release the products.

2 The kinetics of the enzyme-catalysed hydrolysis of urea

The following account describes two experiments which were performed to investigate the effect of varying enzyme concentration and varying substrate concentration on the rate of the enzyme-catalysed hydrolysis of urea:

$$\underset{\text{urea}}{NH_2CONH_2(aq)} + H_2O(l) \xrightarrow{\text{urease}} 2NH_3(aq) + CO_2(aq)$$

The reaction was followed by measuring the volume of hydrochloric acid of known concentration needed to react with the ammonia liberated in the reaction.

Experiment 1

In the first experiment, a fixed quantity of the enzyme, urease, was used, and the concentration of the substrate, urea, was varied. For each concentration, the average rate of reaction over the first three minutes was measured. The results are given in table 1.

Experiment 2

In the second experiment, the urea concentration was fixed and the concentration of urease was varied by adding different volumes of urease solution, keeping the total volume of the reaction mixture constant. Once again, the average rate of reaction was measured over the first three minutes. The results of this experiment are given in table 2.

Questions

1   Use the lock-and-key hypothesis to explain why enzymes are highly specific.

2   Why are enzymes made inactive by small changes in temperature or pH?

3   Enzymes can be rendered inactive by certain chemical substances, called inhibitors. Suggest an explanation for enzyme inhibition using the lock-and-key model.

4   Plot the results of experiment 1 on a graph, with concentration of urea on the horizontal axis. What does the graph tell you about the way in which reaction rate changes as the substrate concentration is increased?

5   Suggest an explanation in terms of the lock-and-key hypothesis for the behaviour you have described in question 4.

Figure 2
a A molecule of the enzyme hexokinase which catalyses the conversion of glucose to glucose-6-phosphate.
b The same enzyme with a molecule of the substrate, glucose, fitting neatly into the active site.

Table 1
Results for experiment 1

Concentration of urea/mol dm^{-3}	Rate/mol min^{-1}
0	0
0.005	1.7×10^{-6}
0.01	2.3×10^{-6}
0.02	3.2×10^{-6}
0.05	4.4×10^{-6}
0.1	5.9×10^{-6}
0.2	7.2×10^{-6}
0.3	7.7×10^{-6}
0.4	8.0×10^{-6}
0.5	8.1×10^{-6}

Table 2

Results for experiment 2

Volume of urease solution/cm³	Rate/mol min⁻¹
0	0
0.005	0.6×10^{-6}
0.1	0.8×10^{-6}
0.2	1.8×10^{-6}
0.3	3.2×10^{-6}
0.5	4.8×10^{-6}
1.0	10.4×10^{-6}
1.5	14.9×10^{-6}
2.0	19.5×10^{-6}

6 Plot the results of experiment 2 on a graph, with volume of urease (which is proportional to its concentration) on the horizontal axis. What does the graph tell you about the way in which the reaction rate changes as the enzyme concentration is increased?

A bioreactor, used to carry out biotechnological processes.

7 Explain why the shape of the second graph differs from that of the first.

8 Sketch on your first graph the line you would expect to obtain under the same conditions but with the concentration of urease halved.

9 Summarise the ways in which enzymes differ from inorganic catalysts.

10 The enormous efficiency of enzymes as catalysts is made use of in **biotechnology** to produce substances that might otherwise be difficult or expensive to produce.

    a Give one example of such a process.

    b What are the advantages of enzyme-catalysed processes over processes using ordinary catalysts?

25 Designing a medicine

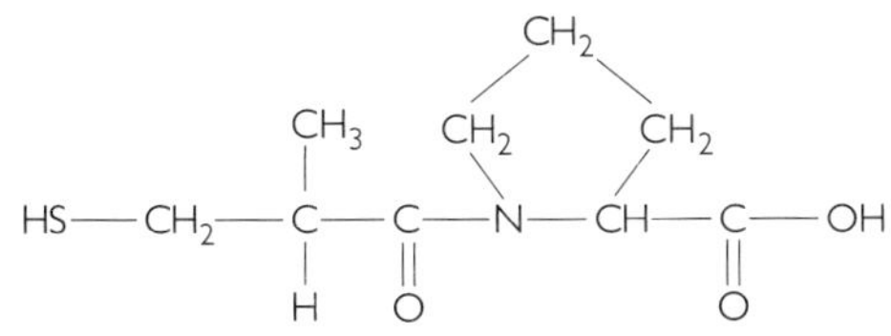

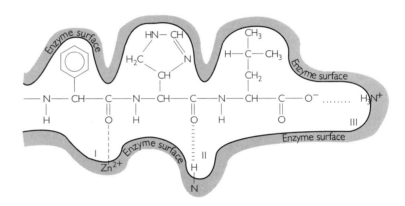

Figure 1
Captopril

Some medicines work by inhibiting the action of enzymes. An important example of this is captopril (figure 1) which was synthesised by chemists in the 1970s as a treatment to control high blood pressure (hypertension).

The first clue in the development of captopril was the discovery that venom from the Brazilian Arrowhead Viper caused a rapid fall in blood pressure when a person received a bite. Analysis of the venom showed that it inhibited an enzyme called 'angiotensin converting enzyme' or ACE. ACE catalyses a reaction to form a product which causes high blood pressure.

Further research showed that the snake venom contained a small protein which binds with the active site of the ACE to render it inactive. The key parts of this small protein which bind to the active site of the enzyme are shown in figure 2. Notice that the cleft which forms the active site of the enzyme has a precise shape into which groups on the small protein fit neatly.

Figure 2

Binding of the small molecule on the enzyme surface involved three separate interactions labelled I, II and III in figure 2.

Interaction I is a co-ordinate bond between a Zn^{2+} ion on the enzyme surface and an atom with a partial negative charge on the small protein.

Interaction II is a hydrogen bond between an N–H group on the enzyme and a C=O group on the small protein.

Interaction III is an ionic attraction between the $-C-O^-$ group at one end of
$$\quad\quad\quad\quad\quad\quad\quad\quad\quad\quad\;\;\overset{\|}{O}$$
the small molecule and a positive $-NH_3^+$ group on the enzyme.

Unfortunately, the protein in the snake venom could not be used to treat high blood pressure because it contains peptide bonds (CO–NH) which are readily split (hydrolysed) by digestive enzymes in a reaction with water.

This means that the protein could not be taken orally in tablet or in liquid form. However, an understanding of the structure of the small protein at the active site led to the synthesis of captopril, which could be taken orally.

Questions

1   Redraw the active site of ACE from figure 2. Leave out the portion of protein and instead include captopril in your diagram, showing how it binds at the active site.

2 Explain why captopril can bind strongly to the enzyme's active site.

3 Why does captopril bind more strongly and therefore reduce blood pressure most effectively in slightly alkaline conditions?

4 The proteins in snake venom cannot be taken orally as treatment for high blood pressure, but captopril can. Explain why this is so.

5 Captopril has three stereoisomers, all of which are much less active in reducing blood pressure than captopril.

    a Explain why captopril has three stereoisomers.

    b Suggest why these are less active than captopril.

This activity is based on information from the *Medicines by Design* unit in the Salters Advanced Chemistry Course.

26 Ozone depletion

Ozone, O_3, is found throughout the atmosphere. It is harmful when it occurs near ground level, but is valuable high up in the atmosphere because it absorbs ultraviolet radiation.

Most ozone occurs in the stratosphere (upper atmosphere) in a layer between 10 and 50 km above sea level. It tends to concentrate at about 30 km above the Earth and this region has been called the 'ozone layer'.

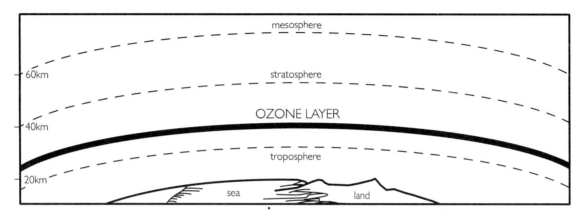

Figure 1
A profile of the Earth's atmosphere.

The first signs of damage to the ozone layer were reported in the 1970s. The British Antarctic survey team had been measuring ozone levels over the Antarctic since 1957. In the spring of 1985, they reported that ozone had been almost completely destroyed over the Antarctic in an area as large as the United States of America. There is now increasing evidence that the ozone layer is thinning all over the world. Analysis of data from the Nimbus satellite indicates that over the last twelve years there has been a 6–8% decrease in ozone every spring in northern latitudes. The ozone layer protects us from the harmful effects of ultraviolet radiation from the Sun. Any significant decrease of ozone in the stratosphere would result in an increase of UV radiation reaching the Earth's surface.

Research has shown that even short exposure to UV radiation can cause considerable harm. It damages the genetic material, DNA, and is related to some types of skin cancer.

The natural formation and breakdown of ozone

Ozone is continually being formed and broken down naturally in the upper atmosphere.

(i) Ultraviolet rays in sunlight split apart oxygen molecules (O_2) forming two oxygen atoms.

(ii) These oxygen atoms then combine with oxygen molecules to form ozone (O_3).

(iii) In turn, ozone molecules are broken down to oxygen by natural reactions with other molecules such as nitrogen monoxide, NO, in the upper atmosphere.

These processes, continually forming and breaking down ozone, would keep the level of ozone fairly constant under normal conditions. The rate of ozone

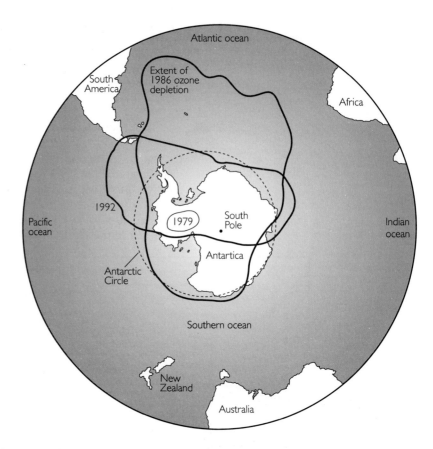

Figure 2
The discovery of a 'hole' in the ozone layer in Antarctica in 1985 showed the extent to which human activities affect the ozone layer. The 'hole' is shaded and superimposed on the map of Antarctica.

formation depends upon the action of sunlight so the concentration of ozone is about 25% more in summer than in winter.

The depletion of ozone

The effect of chlorofluorocarbons, CFCs, such as dichlorodifluoromethane, CCl_2F_2, on ozone depletion was first explained in 1974.

(iv) In the upper atmosphere, UV radiation breaks up CCl_2F_2 molecules forming chlorine atoms and $CClF_2$ radicals.

(v) These chlorine atoms react rapidly with ozone, forming O_2 and ClO.

(vi) The ClO reacts with oxygen atoms produced by the reaction in stage (i) above. This releases a chlorine atom which can undergo a **chain reaction** with more ozone molecules. The overall effect is that the chlorine atom acts like a catalyst before the chain is terminated.

(vii) The chain can be terminated by chlorine atoms reacting with each other or with radicals such as $CClF_2$.

Questions

1 Why is ozone important in the upper atmosphere?

2 What problems will result if the concentration of ozone in the upper atmosphere continues to fall?

3 Write equations to summarise:

a the natural formation of ozone in stages (i) and (ii) above;

b the natural breakdown of ozone in stage (iii);

c the depletion of ozone in stages (iv), (v) and (vi);

d termination of the chain reaction in stage (vii).

4 Why is there more concern over ozone levels in winter than in summer?

5 Use a molecular model kit to make models for the structure of oxygen and ozone. (Remember that oxygen atoms have two bonds when they are combined in molecules.)
Use your models of oxygen and ozone to make models for (i) and (ii).

6 **a** Use a molecular model kit to make dichlorodifluoromethane, CCl_2F_2.

b What happens in terms of bonds when UV light breaks up a CCl_2F_2 molecule?

7 Dichlorodifluoromethane, CCl_2F_2, is one of the simplest CFCs. One of the more complicated CFCs is dichlorotetrafluoroethane, $C_2Cl_2F_4$. Draw the possible structures for dichlorotetrafluoroethane.

8 At one time, very high flying aircraft were thought to be a major danger to the ozone layer. Why was this?

9 CFCs are very stable substances. Why does this make them such a threat?

10 Oxygen molecules, O_2, are broken apart by ultraviolet rays with a wavelength of 242 nm or less.

a Calculate the frequency of radiation with a wavelength of 242 nm. (Velocity of light $= 3 \times 10^8 \, m \, s^{-1}$.)

b Use the equation, $E = h \times \nu$ to calculate the energy of one photon of this radiation. (h = Planck's constant $= 6.63 \times 10^{-34} \, J \, s$.)

c Use your result in **b** to calculate the energy of one mole of bonds between oxygen atoms in oxygen molecules.
Compare your result with the data book value.

d Why will radiation with wavelengths above 242 nm *not* break O_2 molecules apart?

e Ozone is broken apart by radiation with a longer wavelength than 242 nm. What does this suggest about the bonding in ozone?

11 Ozone can be prepared by passing an electrical discharge through oxygen gas. Suggest an explanation for this reaction.

Ozone is formed when an electrical discharge is passed through oxygen gas. A very small amount of the oxygen around this drill will be changed to ozone each time the motor sparks.

27 Chaim Weizmann—the father of biotechnology

The following passage by Tony Travis describes the work of Chaim Weizmann, the Jewish scientist and politician. Weizmann's discovery of a biotechnological process for producing propanone made a crucial contribution to Britain's effort in the First World War. Weizmann later played a major role in establishing the state of Israel.

Chaim Weizmann was born in 1874 in Russia and at an early age decided on a career in chemistry. At this time, Germany was the centre for chemical studies and for six years after 1892 Weizmann worked in Berlin. Later, he moved to Geneva, Switzerland, and then to Manchester (1903) where he was employed by William Perkin Junior. Perkin was Professor of Organic Chemistry at Manchester University and son of the founder of the synthetic dyestuffs industry.

Weizmann worked with a group of scientists who were attempting to make synthetic rubber. They hoped to prepare materials which might show more useful properties than natural rubber, especially for the new electrical engineering and motor industries.

Chaim Weizmann at work in his laboratory.

The search begins

In 1910, the Manchester group teamed up with members of the Fermentation Laboratory at the Pasteur Institute in Paris. Weizmann's job was to find a viable route to 2-methylbuta-1,3-diene (isoprene), the basic building block for rubber. For this, he investigated methods of fermentation, which for thousands of years had provided useful substances like wine and vinegar.

During 1911, a mixture of bacteria was found to ferment the starch in potatoes, producing an isomer of the five-carbon alcohol pentanol which was considered a good starting point for making isoprene.

Shortly afterwards, experiments in Manchester and Paris were found to give the four-carbon alcohol butan-1-ol. It was proposed to convert the butanol into buta-1,3-diene, a molecule very similar to isoprene, and also useful for making synthetic rubber.

The Anglo-French group then attempted to find a bacillus (a type of bacteria) that might effectively convert starch into sugar and then ferment the sugar into butanol.

Several cultures of bacteria were sent from Paris to the Manchester research group, and one of them used sugar to produce butanol, together with ethanol, propanone (acetone), carbon dioxide and hydrogen.

Propanone—a strategic solvent

Propanone was a vital solvent in the manufacture of cordite, also called smokeless powder. This is a propellant for shells which burns with very little smoke. Some of Weizmann's colleagues realised that the process would offer a new route to the strategically important solvent. This was about two years before the outbreak of the First World War.

At that time Weizmann was not aware of the great importance of propanone and continued with his study of bacteria that might produce butanol in higher yields. He combed the relevant literature and undertook many experiments, but with only limited success.

Suddenly, in 1914, his brilliant inductive powers led to a novel idea. He decided that a likely source of a fermenting organism which would act most efficiently on a cereal such as maize was probably the cereal itself or some part of the plant. There were several failures before he was finally proved correct.

The experimental method involved inoculation of several test tubes containing sterilised maize mash with small amounts of maize meal, incubation of the tubes at 37°C for two or three days, and then a search for signs of gas formation. Weizmann then looked for a tube which gave an odour of the alcohol, butanol. From this tube he isolated a pure culture of bacillus.

Weizmann was fortunate in that his bacillus performed two necessary functions. It broke down starch to sugar, and then caused fermentation of sugar to butanol and propanone. Other organisms only acted upon the sugars, which had first to be obtained by breakdown (hydrolysis) of starch.

Weizmann found that his process gave three organic products, the major components being butan-1-ol and propanone (see table 1). Carbon dioxide and hydrogen were also produced.

Table 1
Approximate proportions of organic fermentation products

Product	butan-1-ol	propanone	ethanol
Approximate proportions	1	1	minor
Boiling point/°C	117	56	78

Scaling up the process

At the time of Weizmann's discovery, he was mainly concerned with production of butanol. However, with the outbreak of war in 1914, the demand for propanone soon became enormous. Until that time, it had been obtained from the distillation of wood and was mainly imported. Early in 1915, the head of research at the Nobel's Explosives Company saw a 2 litre scale demonstration of the fermentation process and advised Weizmann to take out a patent on the method.

Weizmann then offered his research as a contribution towards the British war effort. This was to be the first time that modern bacteriological knowledge was applied in the bulk production of chemicals.

The adviser to the Admiralty on cordite supply was sufficiently impressed to order the construction of a pilot plant. Weizmann was then presented to the First Lord of the Admiralty, Winston Churchill, who requested 30 000 tonnes of propanone from the fermentation process. The pilot plant was installed in a gin factory. The fermenter worked on a 250 litre scale and with its success a 9000 litre fermenter was ordered. In September 1915, a 70 000 litre fermenter was commissioned for use at the Royal Naval Cordite Factory, near Poole in Dorset.

After the war, the co-product butanol took on great importance as a quick-drying solvent for paints used in the car industry.

Weizmann's services to the British government during the First World War helped him make influential contacts which later came in useful for his Zionist cause. They helped to bring about the Balfour Declaration of 2 November 1917, which was the first major step in the establishment of a Jewish national home in Palestine. Thirty one years later, Weizmann was to become president of the new state of Israel. Weizmann died in 1952.

Questions

1 Weizmann originally looked for a method of making 2-methylbuta-1,3-diene (isoprene), the monomer for rubber.

  a Write the structural formula of 2-methylbuta-1,3-diene (isoprene).

  b Rubber is poly(2-methylbuta-1,3-diene). Write the structural formula of a section of rubber made up of three monomer units.

2 Use molecular models to make the structure of 2-methylbuta-1,3-diene. Note what happens to this structure when it polymerises to form rubber.

3 In 1911 Weizmann's group produced an isomer of pentanol which was considered a good starting point for making 2-methylbuta-1,3-diene (isoprene).

  a Write the structural formula of this isomer of pentanol.

  b Use molecular models to make this isomer of pentanol.

  c Suggest a method by which this isomer could be converted to 2-methylbuta-1,3-diene (isoprene).

4 Weizmann's most important discovery was the butanol–propanone fermentation. For each of butan-1-ol and propanone

  a write the structural formula,

  b make a molecular model.

5 At first, Weizmann was mainly interested in this fermentation as a source of butanol. Why was he interested in making butanol?

6 Why did the First World War lead to an enormous rise in demand for propanone?

7 Suggest a reason why the pilot plant for the butanol–propanone fermentation was set up in a gin factory.

8 What problem would have to be solved when the fermentation process was scaled up first from the laboratory scale, producing a few cubic centimetres of products, and then to full production scale producing tens of thousands of litres?

9 Fermentation processes like the one described here use very different conditions from the non-biological processes more commonly employed in the chemical industry. Compare the conditions of

  a temperature and

  b pressure,

  used in a fermentation process with those used in a non-biological process such as the Haber process. What advantages do the fermentation processes have?

28 Making molecules the right shape

The enzymes that digest your food and control all reactions in living things are catalysts. They catalyse chemical reactions by allowing reacting molecules to come close together onto their surface. Enzymes are proteins with special molecular shapes. The correct reacting molecules have a complementary shape to grooves on the enzyme's surface (figure 1).

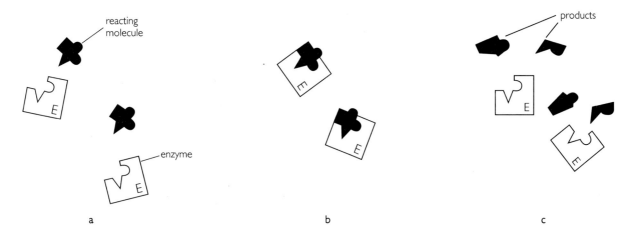

Figure 1

Just as your right hand will only fit into a right glove, and your left hand into a left glove, so the molecules that fit into enzymes must have the correct shape or 'handedness'.

Asymmetry of molecules

Louis Pasteur was the first to discover the 'handedness' or **asymmetry** of organic molecules. In 1848 he discovered two sorts of tartaric acid crystals. In fact, he separated them into two piles of slightly different-shaped crystals from crystallised grape juice using tweezers!

Later, in 1901, Van't Hoff won the first Nobel Prize for Chemistry when he realised that asymmetric compounds could be formed if the four bonds radiating from a carbon atom pointed towards the corners of a tetrahedron.

A tetrahedron with four different groups at its corners is different from its mirror image (figure 2). Modern chemists use rules to describe these mirror images. In the right-handed (or R) molecule, the attached groups increase in size as you travel clockwise looking down from the top vertex. In the left-handed (or S) molecule, the groups increase in size as you travel anticlockwise.

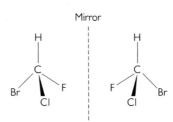

Figure 2
Asymmetric molecules of bromochlorofluoromethane.

At one time, chemists used the terms D (dextro) and L (laevo) to describe these asymmetric forms. Usually these were equivalent to the modern R and S but they were not defined so precisely.

In some cases, industrial and pharmaceutical chemists want to synthesise or isolate only one of the two forms of an asymmetric compound. For example, when Parkinson's disease was first treated, a 50:50 mixture of L-DOPA and D-DOPA was prescribed. Later, D-DOPA was found to cause serious side-effects, so only pure L-DOPA is used nowadays.

The drug thalidomide, prescribed for pregnant women suffering from morning sickness, proved to be disastrous, causing thousands of babies to be born with grossly malformed limbs. In the 1950s, thalidomide was first marketed as a 50:50 mixture of asymmetric compounds. At that time, chemists did not know how to make the separate forms. Now we know that it was only the S form which caused this ghastly side-effect.

Synthesising asymmetric compounds

In 1961, the American chemist Herbert Brown successfully synthesised right-handed butanol from butene. In doing this, he pioneered a general technique for the synthesis of asymmetric compounds.

Most asymmetric syntheses start with either a C=C bond or a C=O bond. In each case, the double bond holds the surrounding atoms in a plane and an attacking molecule can approach from either 'above' or 'below' this plane. If the chemist can devise a system (or **template**) which allows attack on the double bond from only one side, an asymmetric synthesis will result.

Brown used pinene (a naturally occurring asymmetric compound in turpentine from pine trees) as the template to cause attack preferentially from above. He used boron as a linking atom to connect the pinene template to a carbon atom in *cis*-but-2-ene. This method converted *cis*-but-2-ene to an asymmetric right-handed R-butan-2-ol with only 1% of its left-handed image, S-butan-2-ol. The reaction involved a borane intermediate which was treated with hydrogen peroxide.

Since Brown discovered this technique, other research groups have found important applications for it. For example, scientists have used it to make pheromones, compounds which act as sexual attractants for some species. They noticed that the only differences between a particular South-East Asian ant pheromone and the pheromone which attracts the beetles spreading Dutch elm disease were the configurations at two asymmetric carbon atoms in the compound. By using boron connected to a bulky asymmetric template, very pure samples of the two pheromones were obtained. One of these has been used to coax beetles away from elm trees.

Asymmetric synthesis has enormous potential in the manufacture of drugs. Many drugs work by inhibiting enzymes. The drug molecules slot into grooves on the enzyme surface and prevent it from catalysing and controlling a reaction. Most enzymes catalyse reactions involving proteins and peptides containing left-handed amino acids. Therefore, it has been suggested that if compounds were made similar to these left-handed amino acids but containing boron in place of carbon, these boron imitations could 'clog up' all the enzyme grooves and stop the reaction.

Scientists hope that this technique could lead to the production of new drugs. As yet it is too early to know whether the manufactured compounds will act safely and treat medical conditions specifically and efficiently.

Questions

1   What does the word asymmetric mean?

2   Look at figure 2. Which molecule is the R form?

3   How do you think the different spatial arrangements of asymmetric molecules might alter the way they react?

4   Using your knowledge of electrophilic addition and substitution reactions, draw the structure of the borane intermediate and R-butan-2-ol in this synthesis pathway.

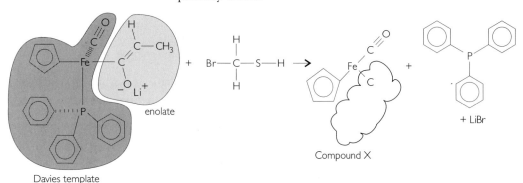

5 Compounds called enolates are often used in organic syntheses to add carbon atoms to molecules to as to control the 'handedness' of the final product. Using your knowledge of nucleophilic substitution reactions complete the missing compound formed in this synthesis.

6 The drug captopril, used to treat high blood pressure, is synthesised using an asymmetric template manufactured by Steven Davies of Oxford University. This template contains iron which holds the reactive enolate rigidly in one position so that a sulphur-containing group can attach itself from only one direction.

   a What do you think might prevent attack by the sulphur-containing group from the other direction?

   b Using your knowledge of nucleophilic substitution reactions, draw the complete structures of compounds X and Y and Captopril in the pathway below.

Davies template

7 Put a red circle around any asymmetric carbon atoms in the structures in the pathway.

Compound X

Compound Y

29 Bucky balls!

In 1985, chemists working at the University of Sussex, England in collaboration with colleagues at Rice University in Texas, U.S.A. succeeded in creating a new allotrope of carbon.

They irradiated graphite with a laser beam in a helium atmosphere. The initial evidence for a new allotrope came from the mass spectrum of the products shown in figure 1.

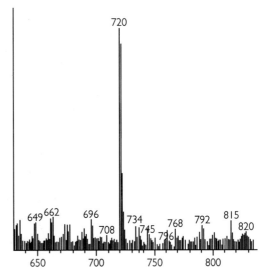

Figure 1
Mass spectrum of laser-irradiated graphite.

Soon after this, chemists deduced that the structure of the new allotrope was an icosahedral cage with 60 vertices and 32 faces (figure 2). Twelve of the faces are pentagons and the other 20 are hexagons. Because of this shape, the molecule was named **buckminsterfullerene** after the American engineer R. Buckminster Fuller who had designed icosahedral domes. This shape is

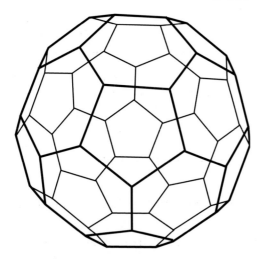

Figure 2
The overall shape of buckminsterfullerene.

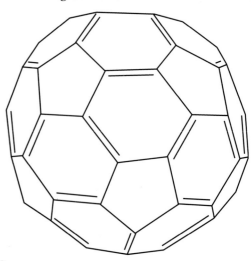

Figure 3
The bonding in a molecule of buckminsterfullerene.

also commonly used in the construction of modern footballs—hence the colloquial name 'bucky balls'.

The bonding in a molecule of buckminsterfullerene is shown in figure 3. Buckminsterfullerene is now known to be the archetypal member of a large class of trigonally connected carbon cages, known as **fullerenes**. Each of the fullerenes contains twelve five-membered rings and a variable number of six-membered rings.

Physical properties

Buckminsterfullerene is a mustard-coloured solid which appears black in larger quantities. It is moderately stable in air, but is degraded by ultraviolet light and attacked by ozone. Freshly prepared samples dissolve in benzene.

Chemical properties

Although the icosahedral structure confers physical resilience on buckminsterfullerene, the molecule is chemically reactive. It possesses only modest aromatic character due to poor orbital overlap. The electron density is substantially localised on the carbon atoms and the carbon–carbon double bonds react like those of alkenes rather than those in arenes, such as benzene.

Soon after buckminsterfullerene was discovered, chemists predicted that its fully fluorinated derivative, $C_{60}F_{60}$ would be a super-lubricant similar to PTFE (polytetrafluoroethene). Unfortunately, $C_{60}F_{60}$ is difficult to prepare and is unstable.

When potassium is added to a film of buckminsterfullerene and cooled to $18\,K$, a superconducting, stable product K_3C_{60} (crudely termed 'potassium buckide') is produced.

K_3C_{60} is described as a stable metallic crystal consisting of a face-centred cubic arrangement of C_{60} molecules with potassium atoms occupying the intermolecular cavities.

The ideas in this activity are based on an article in the *School Science Review* by Christopher Talbot

Questions

1 What do you understand by the term **allotrope**?

2 Why do you think the carbon was irradiated by a laser beam in these experiments?

3 Why were the experiments carried out in a helium atmosphere?

4 What is:

   a the relative molecular mass,

   b the formula of the dominant particle in the mass spectrum in figure 1?

5 Natural carbon contains 99% carbon-12 and 1% carbon-13.

   a Using this information, explain why the large peak at 720 a.m.u. is followed immediately by peaks at 721, 722, 723, etc.

   b Calculate the relative probabilities of the particles at peaks 720, 721 and 722 in a sample of buckminsterfullerene.

   Note: The vertical scale on the mass spectrum trace is *not* linear.

6 Look closely at figure 3.

   a What conclusions can you make about the bonding at each carbon atom?

   b What substance does buckminsterfullerene resemble in terms of its bonding?

   c Figure 4 shows the carbon-13 nuclear magnetic resonance (n.m.r.)

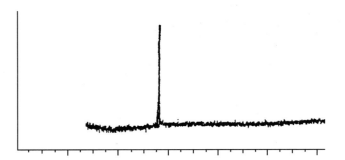

Figure 4
The n.m.r. spectrum of buckminsterfullerene.

spectrum of buckminsterfullerene. Note that there is a single absorption frequency. What does this confirm about its structure?

7 Explain why buckminsterfullerene is:

a degraded by ultraviolet light;

b attacked by ozone;

c soluble in benzene.

8 How and under what conditions do you think buckminsterfullerene will react with bromine?

9 Why was the fully fluorinated derivative of buckminsterfullerene compared to PTFE as a possible super-lubricant?

10 Why do you think $C_{60}F_{60}$ is difficult to prepare and is unstable?

11 Suggest a reason why 'potassium buckide', K_3C_{60} is superconducting.

12 Describe the face-centred cubic structure and use this to explain why the formula of potassium buckide can be written as K_3C_{60}.

30 The Seveso story

The following account of an accident at a chemical factory near Seveso in Northern Italy is taken from an article by George Burton which appeared in the *School Science Review*.

The formation of dioxin

2,4,5-Trichlorophenol (figure 1) has been manufactured for many years. It is used principally as an intermediate in the manufacture of two other chemicals, hexachlorophene (figure 2)—a bactericide, and 2,4,5-T—a herbicide whose structure and systematic name are shown in figure 3.

Hexachlorophene was once widely used in toothpaste, soaps, baby lotions and antiseptic washes. However, there is some evidence that hexachlorophene can cause brain damage and its use is being restricted. In 1967, the United States Defence department bought up all the US-manufactured 2,4,5-T for defoliation spraying on Vietnam. Evidence from Vietnam showed that the population exposed to the spraying developed many abnormalities, principally a severe skin rash called chloracne and a high incidence of babies born with severe deformities.

Although these two chemicals are dangerous in their own right, they contain an even more dangerous contaminant which is produced in a side reaction during the manufacture of trichlorophenol. This contaminant is known as 2,3,7,8-tetrachlorodibenzo-*p*-dioxin (TCDD or **dioxin** for short). Its structure is shown in figure 4.

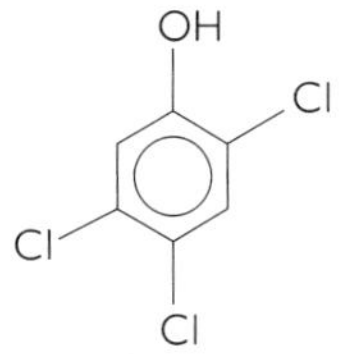

Figure I
The structure of 2,4,5-trichlorophenol.

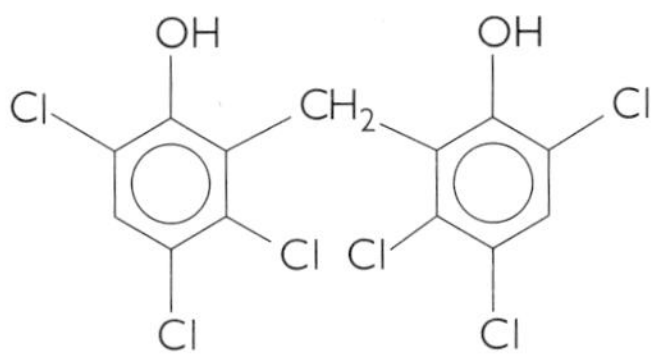

Figure 2
The structure of hexachlorophene.

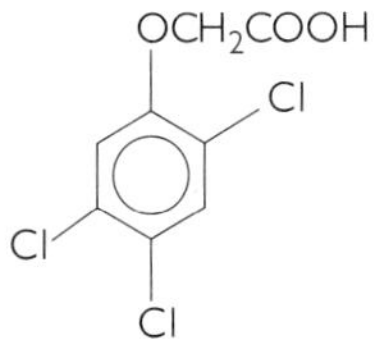

Figure 3
The structure of 2,4,5-trichlorophenoxy ethanoic acid (2,4,5-T).

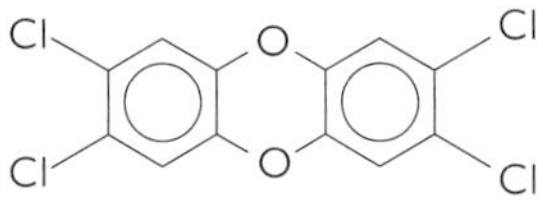

Figure 4
The structure of dioxin (TCDD).

This chemical has been recognized as a major hazard in the chemical industry for almost thirty years. It is extremely stable, being very resistant to heating and to attack by other chemicals. Once spilled it is almost impossible to remove from land, buildings or machinery. It has been tentatively linked with liver and kidney damage, cancer and brain damage. It is one of the most powerful teratogens (foetus deformers) known and it is probably the minute traces of dioxin impurity which give rise to this hazard in the use of 2,4,5-T.

The Seveso incident

Despite this accumulation of knowledge, an accident (on 10 July 1976) at Hoffman La Roche's Icmesa plant near Seveso in northern Italy caused the discharge of 1500 kg of trichlorophenol containing 2.5 kg of dioxin directly into the atmosphere. No warning was given to the local population for five days, during which time pets and poultry died and children fell ill. Only after that time were people warned not to eat contaminated food or plants. Evacuation of the area followed and guarded barbed wire barricades were erected. However, people were still allowed into and out of the contaminated area having paid the guards a small fee.

By summer 1979, over 400 children suffered from the severe skin rash

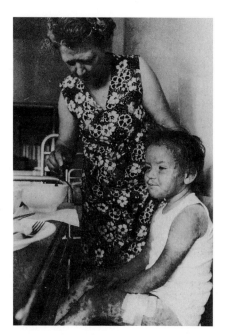

A victim of Seveso. Note the severe skin rash—chloracne.

chloracne, some had skin grafts, others almost permanently wear bandages to hide their disfigurement. The incidence of miscarriages rose from an average 12 per cent to 22 per cent. Presumably many of these foetuses were badly deformed. Of fifty babies born in the area since the accident, five have shown hideous abnormalities. Many women sought abortions but this is not easy in such a strongly Catholic community, and many women were afraid to ask.

The Italian government set aside £27 000 000 for the relief and rehabilitation of the area and the people, but a satisfactory decontamination plan has not yet been proposed. The incident was seized upon by the local political parties, the governing Christian Democrats denouncing it as a left-wing fabrication and the Communists accusing the local authorities of a 'cover-up'.

Following this incident, a factory in Derbyshire producing the same chemicals, which had been very carefully safeguarded by installation of computer-controlled operations, was forced to close by pressure from the local inhabitants.

W.G. Burton, The Seveso Story,
from Acceptability Equations
School Science Review.

Questions

1 An isomer of 2,4,5-trichlorophenol can be made simply by reacting phenol with chlorine water. This isomer is the major component of the antiseptic TCP. Give the structure of this isomer.

2 2,4,5-Trichlorophenol is itself made by reacting 1,2,4,5-tetrachlorobenzene with sodium hydroxide. Write an equation for this reaction.

3 Dioxin (TCDD) is produced in a side reaction during the manufacture of 2,4,5-trichlorophenol.

 a How do you think the production of dioxin occurs?

 b Write an equation for the reaction.

4 Hexachlorophene, once widely used as a bactericide, is made by a condensation reaction between two molecules of 2,4,5-trichlorophenol and one molecule of methanal, using concentrated sulphuric acid as a catalyst. Show by means of an equation how this reaction occurs.

5 What property of dioxin, apart from its extreme toxicity, makes the discharge of this chemical into the environment a major disaster?

6 2,4,5-T was used as a herbicide during the Vietnam War. It was sprayed on to forests in order to remove the leaf cover in which communist Viet Cong rebels took refuge. Were the US forces justified in using this tactic in an attempt to win the war? What are your views?

7 The major use of herbicides in peacetime is in agriculture, to kill weeds and thus increase the yield of food crops. In view of the risk involved in the manufacture of at least one herbicide, is the use of these agents justified? What are your views?

31 Beer

Beer was brewed by the ancient Egyptians. It is known to have been among the rations of the builders of the pyramids. From its origins, as fermented porridge, beer has developed into the wide range of brews that we drink today—bitters, milds, stouts, pales, browns, lagers and many others. All beers, though, are made by fermentation with four basic ingredients—malt, hops, yeast and water.

Fermentation

Yeast can metabolise a number of carbohydrate substrates, but fermentation occurs fastest with monosaccharides, particularly glucose (figure 1a). In the case of malt, most of the fermentable carbohydrate is in the form of the disaccharide maltose (figure 1b) which is broken down by the yeast to give glucose. Yeast can ferment glucose aerobically (in the presence of air) or anaerobically if there is no air (oxygen) present.

Aerobic fermentation:

$$C_6H_{12}O_6(aq) + 6O_2(aq) \xrightarrow{\text{yeast}} 6CO_2(g) + 6H_2O(l)$$
$$\text{glucose}$$

Anaerobic fermentation:

$$C_6H_{12}O_6(aq) \xrightarrow{\text{yeast}} 2CH_3CH_2OH(aq) + 2CO_2(g)$$
$$\text{glucose}$$

Both these reactions are far more complex than the above equations suggest. They involve several enzyme-catalysed stages.

In practice, the unfermented beer (called **wort**) contains much dissolved oxygen, so aerobic fermentation occurs when the yeast is first added. During this stage the yeast multiplies rapidly and fermentation accelerates. When the dissolved oxygen has been used up, anaerobic fermentation takes over and the yeast cells cease rapid division. Fermentation continues until all the fermentable carbohydrate is consumed, or until the concentration of ethanol is high enough to inhibit yeast activity.

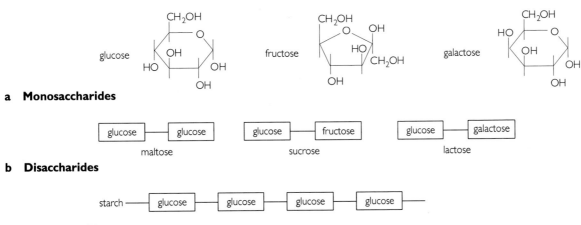

a **Monosaccharides**

b **Disaccharides**

c **Polysaccharide**

Figure 1
Structures of some carbohydrates involved in brewing.

Ingredients

Malt

Malt is the major source of fermentable carbohydrate. It is made by allowing barley to germinate and then killing it. Barley is first steeped in water, then removed and allowed to stand in warm air for a few days. The barley grains begin to germinate and produce enzymes which start to break down the reserves of starch into maltose (figure 1). After a few days, most of the starch has been converted to maltose and the process is stopped by heating the grains, thus killing the enzymes. Gentle heating produces a light malt, used in light ale, bitter and lagers. Further roasting gives progressively darker malt, used for brown ale and stouts.

Hops

Hops came relatively late to English beer. The original English brews were flavoured with nettles and other herbs, and called **ale**. The custom of adding hops spread from the continent. Originally they were used as much as a preservative as for their flavour because the pungent oils present in hops have a mild antibacterial action. Gradually the flavour of hops became established and the English began to call their ale by the Teutonic name 'bier'. However, the name 'ale' is still used today, though now there is little difference between ale and beer.

Yeast

Saccharomyces cerevisiae is a spherical single-celled yeast organism used in both brewing and baking. Different brewers use different yeast strains. The yeast multiplies during fermentation and a small quantity is retained for the next brew, the excess often being sold to yeast extract manufacturers. Some breweries have used the same yeast strain for hundreds of years.

Water

Fermentation needs an aqueous medium and the quality of the water itself affects the quality of the beer. Dissolved salts are very important. Hard water, containing a lot of calcium and magnesium salts, is good for making pale, fresh bitters. Burton-on-Trent water is particularly suited to making such beers. London water, on the other hand, is only temporarily hard, and becomes softened by boiling during the brewing process. London water is therefore better for making brown beers and stouts than bitters.

Sugar

The best beers contain only malt, hops, yeast and water. Sometimes, though, sugar is added to increase the fermentable material. Generally 'invert sugar' (sucrose which has been hydrolysed to glucose and fructose) is used.

Additives

Starchy additives such as wheat, rice or maize flour are sometimes used to increase body and give extra fermentable material. Chemical additives may also be added to improved the beer's 'head' or make it clearer.

The brewing process

The malt grains are ground into a fine powder called **grist** and soaked in hot water. This extracts soluble materials, mainly maltose and proteins. The malty liquor is then boiled with hops for two hours, which extracts the aromatic oils from the hops and kills off bacteria. The liquor is strained and cooled before yeast is added.

Fermentation is complete in about five days, after which time the beer is run into conditioning tanks to allow it to clear and to permit further biochemical changes which improve the flavour. Before fermentation the liquor contains many dissolved solids, particularly sugars, so it is denser than water. A typical value for its specific gravity (the density of the beer relative to that of water) might be 1.03. Brewers call this the 'original gravity' and often write the figure without the decimal point: 1030 in this case. After fermentation, some dissolved solids remain but the specific gravity of the beer is very

Tasting draught beer at the brewery.

close to that of water, that is 1.00. From the difference between the initial and final specific gravity values, the amount of sugar fermented and hence the percentage of alcohol in the beer can be calculated. In this example it would be about 4 per cent.

Dispensing beer

There are two ways of serving beer—from barrels (draught beer) or from bottles and cans.

Draught beer

Traditional draught beer is run into metal or wooden casks direct from the conditioning tank and receives no further treatment except for the addition of finings to help it clear. At the pub the cask is usually stored in a cellar and connected via pipes to hand pumps on the bar. Once the cask is opened the beer is in contact with the air. Initially this improves the quality of the beer due to certain oxidation reactions, but after a week or so the beer begins to deteriorate, mainly due to the action of airborne bacteria. Traditional cask beer must therefore be sold quickly to avoid deterioration, and to get over this problem many breweries produce **keg** beer. This beer is pasteurised and filtered before running into metal kegs which are sealed and injected with carbon dioxide. At the pub, the beer is forced out of the keg using carbon dioxide pressure. As the beer is 'killed' before leaving the brewery and because the carbon dioxide prevents it from coming into contact with air, keg beer lasts much longer than traditional beer. Many people, however, feel that it is too fizzy and lacks flavour.

Bottled beer

Most bottled and canned beer is treated in the same way as keg beer, that is pasteurised and pressurised with carbon dioxide. It therefore keeps for a long time.

The food value of beer

The composition of a typical bitter beer is given in the table below.

Total volume	$1 \, dm^3$ (1 litre)
Ethanol	30 g
Carbohydrate	20 g
Protein	3 g

Malt contains a substantial quantity of protein as well as carbohydrate, so the protein content of beer is quite high, particularly in the case of certain stouts and strong bitters which have a high malt content. The protein is responsible for the foamy 'head' on a glass of beer. Protein molecules lower the surface tension of the liquid, thus stabilizing the bubbles that make up the 'head'. Beer always contains some carbohydrate, usually in the form of unfermented maltose, though the quantity varies according to the type of beer. The sweetness of some stouts is increased by adding lactose, a disaccharide whose structure is shown in figure 1b.

Ethanol is a food as well as a drug—it is in fact a more concentrated energy source than carbohydrate, so beer can be very fattening if drunk in quantity. It can also be very intoxicating: in general a pint of beer contains the same amount of alcohol as a double whisky. The effect of a pint or so can be stimulating, but after two or three pints, confusion and loss of co-ordination begin, often with unpleasant and dangerous consequences.

Questions

1 Why must barley be malted before it can be used to make beer?

2 Give two reasons why it is important to exclude air once fermentation has started.

3 Why is 'invert sugar' added to beer when extra sugar is required, rather than ordinary sucrose?

4 The 'original gravity' of a beer gives an indication of its alcoholic strength. Explain why.

5 Government Customs and Excise Officers visit breweries regularly and measure the specific gravity of each brew before and after fermentation. Why?

6 Why does keg beer keep longer than traditional draught beer?

7 Suggest a reason why lactose is used to sweeten stout, rather than a more common sugar such as sucrose.

8 Why does a glass of beer often have a large frothy 'head', while a glass of lemonade never has?

9 The enthalpy change of combustion of ethanol is about $-1370\,\mathrm{kJ\,mol^{-1}}$, and the enthalpy change of combustion of glucose is about $-3000\,\mathrm{kJ\,mol^{-1}}$.

   a Calculate the energy value in kJ of the ethanol in $1\,\mathrm{dm^3}$ of bitter of composition given in the composition table above.

   b Assuming all the carbohydrate in the beer is present as glucose, calculate the energy value in kJ of the carbohydrate in $1\,\mathrm{dm^3}$ of bitter of composition given in the table.

   c Assuming $1\,\mathrm{dm^3}$ (1 litre) $= 1.8$ pints, and ignoring other components in the beer, calculate the total energy value of 1 pint of this beer.

   d Comment on your value. (For comparison the energy value of a slice of bread is about $300\,\mathrm{kJ}$.)

10 Alcohol is a dangerous drug. It is addictive, it can cause damage to the liver, brain and other organs, and it is responsible for many deaths each year through accidents on the road and elsewhere. Why do you think society accepts alcohol, while banning other dangerous drugs?

32 Fibres

Fibres are polymeric materials, either naturally occurring or synthetically manufactured. They possess certain properties which distinguish them from other polymers such as plastics and rubbers. These include high tensile strength, toughness and low extensibility. The high strength of fibre polymers derives from two properties. First, they have regular molecular structures, so their chains are able to pack closely together in an ordered way. This gives them a high degree of **crystallinity**. Second, they tend to have polar groups in their chain structures, and these give rise to strong interactions between adjoining chains. Synthetic fibres are usually formed by forcing the molten or dissolved polymer through a small hole called a spinnaret, then allowing it to solidify. The fibre formed in this way is then stretched or **drawn**. This process helps align the chains, increasing the fibre's crystallinity and hence its strength.

Until the First World War, all fibres in common use were of natural origin. Semi-synthetic fibres began to make an impression on the textile market in the 1920s. The development of fully synthetic fibres began before the Second World War, but these fibres did not make a serious impact until the 1950s, when the development of the petrochemical industry brought down the price of the raw materials needed for their manufacture.

Natural fibres

Animal fibres, such as wool and silk, are long-chain proteins. The monomers are therefore amino acids, which undergo condensation polymerisation under the influence of enzymes to form peptide links:

MONOMERS
[amino acids]

$+ H_2O$ $+ H_2O$

POLYMER
[protein]

(The small side groups R_1, R_2, R_3 etc. may themselves carry functional groups such as NH_2, COOH and OH which can form hydrogen bonds with water and other protein chains.)

The raw materials for the production of animal fibres are plants: sheep feed on grass, silk-worms feed on mulberry leaves. Animal fibres tend to be expensive, but they have many desirable properties—for example they feel pleasant and are comfortable to wear.

Plant fibres, such as cotton and linen, are cellulose polymers. The monomer is glucose, and the cellulose is formed by condensation polymerisation.

The raw materials for the production of plant fibres are carbon dioxide and water. Cotton comes from the cotton plant, linen from the flax plant.

MONOMER
[glucose]

POLYMER
cellulose

Cotton is relatively cheap and has a number of attractive features, including being comfortable to wear.

Semi-synthetic fibres

All semi-synthetic fibres are regenerated forms of natural cellulose. Cheap, abundant sources of cellulose such as wood pulp or straw are treated with chemicals to convert the cellulose into a soluble form which can then be extruded through a spinnaret to form fibres:

Viscose rayon is made by treating cellulose with sodium hydroxide and carbon disulphide. This causes partial cross-linking between chains.

Cellulose acetate and **triacetate** are made by treating cellulose with ethanoic acid and ethanoic anhydride so that some of the −OH groups on the cellulose chain are esterified with ethanoate (acetate) groups. 'Tricel' is an example of a cellulose triacetate fibre.

Semi-synthetic fibres are cheap but do not usually have the same quality as natural cellulose fibres. Rayon is often blended with natural fibres, particularly cotton, and it has a number of uses outside the clothing industry, for example in carpets and in tyre reinforcement cord.

Synthetic fibres

There are many synthetic fibres in use today, but the three major ones are nylon, polyester and acrylic.

Nylons are polyamides, formed by condensation reactions between −NH_2 and −COOH or −COCl groups. For example, nylon 6,6 is made from 1,6-diaminohexane and hexanedioic acid:

1,6-diaminohexane   [hexanedioic acid]

MONOMERS

POLYMER
nylon

The linkage is similar to the peptide link in proteins.

Which synthetic fibres might be used for the cardigan, blouse and skirt worn here?

Nylons are named according to the number of carbon atoms in the monomer molecules. Nylon 6,10, for example, is made from 1,6-diaminohexane and decanedioic acid. Nylon 6,6 is the dominant polyamide in the UK and the USA. The raw materials for its manufacture are phenol or cyclohexane, both of which can be obtained from coal or oil. Nylon is moderately priced relative to other fibres. It is hard wearing and makes good 'drip-dry' materials and stretch textiles. It is not as comfortable to wear as natural fibre because it lacks moisture absorbency.

Polyesters are condensation polymers formed from di-basic carboxylic acids and diols. The most common polyester is made from benzene-1,4-dicarboxylic acid and ethane-1,2-diol:

$$H \vdots OOC - \langle \bigcirc \rangle - COO \vdots H \qquad HO \vdots CH_2CH_2 \vdots OH$$

benzene-1,4-dicarboxylic acid ethane-1,2-diol

MONOMERS

$$\downarrow$$

$$- CO - \langle \bigcirc \rangle - COOCH_2CH_2O - \; + \; H_2O$$

POLYMER
[polyester]

The raw materials for polyester manufacture are 1,4-dimethylbenzene (xylene) and ethene, both of which are made from oil.

Polyesters are moderately priced relative to other fibres and have the advantage of great tensile strength and resistance to wear. They have good 'wash-and-wear' characteristics and can be permanently creased by ironing. Like nylons, they lack the moisture absorbency of natural fibres, so are often blended with cotton or wool.

Acrylic fibres are addition polymers of propenenitrile, commonly called acrylonitrile.

Monomer
propenenitrile $\qquad CH_2{=}CH_2{-}CN$

Polymer
$$\qquad \overset{CN}{\underset{|}{}} \quad \downarrow \quad \overset{CN}{\underset{|}{}} \qquad \overset{CN}{\underset{|}{}}$$
acrylic $\qquad -CH_2-CH-CH_2-CH-CH_2-CH-$

In some acrylic polymers small amounts of chloroethene (vinyl chloride) are copolymerised with the propenenitrile.

Nowadays, the raw material for the manufacture of propenitrile is propene, obtained from oil, but in the past it was made from ethyne, obtained from coal. Acrylic fibres are fairly low priced. Textiles based on them have a 'woolly' feel and are used as a substitute for wool, having the advantages of being machine-washable and non-shrinking.

Questions

1   For each of the fibres mentioned in the passage, give one example of an article of clothing you know to be made from that fibre. In each case, identify the property of the fibre that makes it suitable for the use you mention.

2   For a polymer to show fibre properties it needs to have strong attractive forces between adjacent chains. For each of the fibres mentioned above, identify the groups responsible for the attraction, and name the type of interaction involved.

3   Why does polythene (poly(ethene)) not have fibre properties?

4 One of the main advantages of wool over nylon is the greater ability of the wool to absorb moisture. This makes it more comfortable to wear because it does not make you feel 'sweaty' like nylon. Why does wool have greater moisture absorbency than nylon, even though the two polymers are formed by similar peptide condensation linkages?

5 The major polyamide fibre used in France and Germany is nylon 6. Nylon 6 has a structure very similar to nylon 6,6 but it is derived from only a single monomer molecule, known as caprolactam (left).

Indicate how caprolactam polymerises to form nylon 6, and draw a representative section of the polymer chain.

6 Suggest a reason why woollen garments often shrink when washed, but acrylic garments do not.

7 Why has the use of synthetic and semisynthetic fibres increased so much during the past forty years or so?

8 What is likely to be the future pattern of fibre use? Will synthetic fibres continue to replace natural ones or will natural fibres make a comeback? Explain your answer.

caprolactam

Synthetic fibres, such as polyesters, are spun out on machines called spinnarets.

33 Bread

A recipe for making bread is outlined below. This is followed by notes explaining some of the chemical principles behind breadmaking. Read the two passages and then answer the questions which follow.

A recipe for bread

1 Mix 25 g of fresh yeast with one teaspoonful of sugar. Add 600 cm³ of tepid water and stir.

2 Mix together 1 kg strong flour and two teaspoonfuls of salt. Sift into a bowl.

3 Make a depression in the centre of the flour, pour in the yeasty water and mix well.

4 Knead until the sticky dough becomes elastic and leaves the sides of the bowl clean.

5 Leave the dough in a warm place until it has risen enough to double its original volume.

6 Knead the risen dough well for five minutes.

7 Shape this into an oblong loaf or loaves and put into greased tins.

8 Leave the tins in a warm place until the dough has risen to the top.

9 Cook in a hot oven until the crust is brown and the loaf sounds hollow when tapped.

The principles behind breadmaking

Bread can be regarded as a solid foam with a network of gas bubbles trapped in a matrix of solidified starch and protein. The gas bubbles result from the carbon dioxide produced during the fermentation of sugars by yeast:

$$C_6H_{12}O_6(aq) \longrightarrow 2C_2H_5OH(aq) + 2CO_2(g)$$

Almost all bread eaten in the United Kingdom is made from wheat flour. Wheat differs from other cereals in that wheat flour contains certain proteins which, when mixed with water, form an elastic protein material called **gluten**. It is the gluten which makes the dough strong and elastic enough to trap and hold bubbles of carbon dioxide. Without gluten, the starch on its own would be unable to make a foam and the dough would not rise. Consequently it is important that the flour for breadmaking contains enough gluten. Flour with a high gluten content is called **strong** flour. Flour made from wheat grown in Britain and north-west Europe is fairly weak, with a total protein content averaging only 9 per cent. Flour from North American wheat is strong with a total protein content averaging about 14 per cent.

The elasticity of gluten is improved by mechanically stretching the dough. It is thought that this breaks bonds between adjacent protein molecules, allowing them to reform and produce an elastic three-dimensional network. This mechanical stretching occurs when the dough is kneaded, and during the rising caused by the fermentation processes.

When the dough is baked, many complex changes occur. The gas bubbles expand and the dough rises further. The starch grains absorb water and

Kneading dough. Note the cooked loaf alongside, cut open to show the bubbles formed by carbon dioxide gas when the dough rises.

burst, forming a rigid network. The gluten loses its elasticity and coagulates. Complex chemical changes occur on the surface of the loaf where the temperature is high, resulting in a crisp brown crust.

Questions

1 Apart from its function as a flavouring agent, why is sugar included in the recipe?

2 Why are bread recipes still successful even when sugar is not used?

3 Why does English bread normally contain a substantial proportion of North American wheat?

4 Suggest a reason why the French, who use little imported wheat, traditionally bake long, low loaves rather than the typical high English loaf.

5 Explain in your own words why it is necessary to knead dough.

6 Suppose a piece of dough initially $1000 \, cm^3$ in volume is allowed to rise until its volume has doubled. It is then kneaded for five minutes, after which time its volume has returned to $1000 \, cm^3$. It is then allowed to rise a second time until its volume has again doubled. What total volume of carbon dioxide must then have been evolved during both risings?

7 Use your answer to question 6 to calculate the mass of ethanol formed at the same time as this carbon dioxide. State any assumptions you make.

8 Question 7 suggests that bread contains ethanol, but bread is not normally considered to be intoxicating. Explain.

9 Why does dough stop rising fairly soon after being placed in a hot oven?

10 What structural properties of the protein gluten give it elasticity?

11 What changes are likely to be responsible for the coagulation (denaturation) of the gluten during baking? Bear in mind that the temperature of the interior of the loaf never exceeds 100°C.

12 Why do you think bread becomes dry and hard if left in the open, while biscuits, which are also made from flour, become soft and damp?

34 Chemicals in chocolate

Every year, each person in Britain eats an average of 7 to 8 kg of chocolate. So, what is it about chocolate that entices so many of us to consume it in such large quantities?

Much debate and mythology surrounds the obsession for chocolate. Some scientists believe it is a sex substitute, because every 100 g contains up to 660 mg of phenylethylamine ($C_6H_5(CH_2)_2NH_2$), a stimulant closely related to the body's own dopamine and adrenaline. It raises blood pressure and heart rate, and heightens sensation and blood glucose levels. In short, it induces a high similar in kind—if not in intensity—to a sexual climax.

Others believe that chocolate is a stimulant, rather like tea or coffee. Every 100 g also contains 5 mg of methylxanthine ($C_5N_4O_4H_4$) and 160 mg of theobromine ($C_5N_4O_2(CH_3)_2H$). Both are caffeine-like substances, though it would take a massive binge to achieve the same effect as caffeine.

Yet others believe that much of the pleasure of chocolate comes because it acts as a comforter. Chocolate melts in your mouth. It is solid at room temperature, gradually softens in the mouth and melts just below body temperature. As it melts, heat is absorbed from the lining of the mouth, giving the eater a pleasant, smooth sensation. It is the cocoa butter—the vegetable fat squeezed out of cocoa beans during production—that gives chocolate this unusual quality. Despite being one of the most saturated fats known, it seems to have little or no effect on serum cholesterol levels.

Questions

1   Our obsession for chocolate may be due to phenylethylamine.

   a Draw two possible structural formulas for phenylethylamine.

   b How would you modify the name phenylethylamine to distinguish between the two structures?

2   Describe an experiment that you could carry out to compare the effects on humans of the two different phenylethylamines.

3   Look at the structures of dopamine and adrenaline below.

adrenaline
(epinephrine)

dopamine

   a What structural features do the two molecules have in common?

   b Which of your structures for phenylethylamine do you think is the one found in chocolate? Give your reasoning.

4   Look at the structures of methylxanthine, theobromine and caffeine on the next page. What structural features do they have in common?

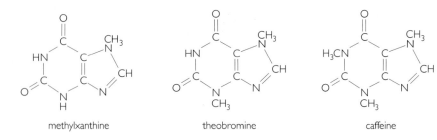

methylxanthine   theobromine   caffeine

5 Suppose you had the job of Marketing Manager for a chocolate company. Which three points in the above article would you consider using in a TV advert for your chocolate? Explain why.

35 Disaster at Bhopal

Casualties in Bhopal.

In December, 1984, a tragic accident occurred at a pesticide factory in Bhopal, India. Thirty tonnes of methyl isocyanate, a highly toxic chemical, escaped into the atmosphere in the world's worst industrial accident. The factory was owned by the American chemical company, Union Carbide, with the Indian government a minority shareholder.

Near to the factory was a slum area housing 200 000 people. Two thousand five hundred people living in this area were killed by the chemical, and many more were temporarily blinded or choked by the gaseous methyl isocyanate that escaped. Thousands of people fled from the area in panic, many having no idea of what had happened.

Methyl isocyanate and pesticides

Methyl isocyanate is a liquid which boils at 60°C. It has the formula $CH_3-N=C=O$. It is an intermediate in the manufacture of plastics, drugs and pesticides. The Bhopal plant used methyl isocyanate to produce an insecticide called 'Carbaryl', which is one of the most popular insecticides in the world.

Methyl isocyanate is itself made by reacting methylamine with carbonyl chloride, $COCl_2$ (phosgene).

Methyl isocyanate is a fairly reactive chemical. It is hydrolysed by sodium hydroxide solution, and on heating it polymerises to a plastic mass.

Methyl isocyanate was stored under pressure at the Bhopal plant in a stainless steel tank and kept at 15°C by refrigeration. The tank was underground and surrounded by a concrete shield. The tank was fitted with safety valves designed to open when the pressure exceeded a certain level. Once opened, these valves should allow the gaseous methyl isocyanate to leak into a holding tank, and from there into 'scrubbing towers' which were intended to remove chemically the methyl isocyanate as fast as it escaped. Methyl isocyanate should pass up the scrubbing towers, while a stream of sodium hydroxide solution passes downwards.

How did the accident happen?

An explanation of how the accident happened was given a month later by an Indian Government scientist. The following extract is from a report in *The Guardian* newspaper which appeared shortly after his statement.

The aftermath

Following the accident there were extended lawsuits in India and the USA, in order to establish who was to blame and how much compensation should be paid. Union Carbide denied all responsibility for the tragedy, blaming it on sabotage. The lawsuits continued for four years until the Indian Government and Union Carbide finally agreed on compensation of $470 million.

Water leak caused fatal chain reaction says Bhopal expert

Water entering an underground storage tank probably caused the Bhopal gas disaster in which 2500 people died, India's senior government scientist said yesterday.

Dr S. Varadarajan, scientific adviser to the government, told a meeting of the Indian Science Congress in Lucknow, the Press Trust of India reported, that the water set off a violent runaway reaction in liquid methyl isocyanate (MIC) stored in the tank at a pesticides factory owned by the American Union Carbide company.

"Just half a kilogramme (about 1.1 pints) of water entered the underground methyl isocyanate tank ... triggering a runaway reaction that probably pulled the entire tank from the ground causing cracks on its concrete shield." PTI quoted Dr Varadarajan as saying.

Clouds of poison gas escaped from the tank on December 3 and spread over Bhopal in the world's worst industrial accident.

The lecture by Dr Varadarajan, who led the government team which investigated the tragedy, was the first official account of the causes of the disaster.

He said 30 of the 45 tonnes of the MIC stored in the stainless steel tank escaped into the atmosphere, while the rest was turned into a plastic-like mass by the reaction. The tremendous heat generated by the reaction had ruptured valves, allowing the gas to escape.

Dr Varadarajan said phosgene, the basis for mustard gas, is added to MIC to stop it turning into plastic. The reaction between the water and phosgene probably triggered the initial process generating the heat which caused the methyl isocyanate to vaporise.

He gave no indication of how water could have entered the tank.

Questions

Note You are probably unfamiliar with the chemistry of isocyanates. In the following questions, you are *not* expected to know details of the chemistry of the isocyanate group: you should be able to answer the questions by using your understanding of general chemical principles.

1 Draw a 'dot/cross' diagram to show the electron structure of methyl-isocyanate, $CH_3-N=C=O$.

2 Methyl isocyanate is made by a reaction between methylamine, CH_3NH_2, and carbonyl chloride, $COCl_2$. What kind of reaction is this? Explain what you think happens during the reaction and write an equation.

3 Dr Varadarajan suggested that the initial reaction which led to the accident was between water and carbonyl chloride. What would be the products of this reaction? Write an equation.

4 The scrubbing towers designed to trap escaping methyl isocyanate used sodium hydroxide solution to hydrolyse the chemical. What would be the products of this hydrolysis? Write an equation.

5 Make a list of the safety precautions that were used in the storage of methyl isocyanate.

6 Which of the various safety precautions appear to have failed in the Bhopal accident?

7 What further information, beyond what is given here, would you want before forming an opinion on who was to blame for the accident?

8 Suppose you are the Chairman and Chief Executive of Union Carbide in India. What criteria would you set for any plant to replace the one destroyed at Bhopal?

SECTION 3
OBJECTIVE QUESTIONS

Each of the following thirty-five tests is based on the corresponding chapter in the textbook *Chemistry in Context*, Fourth Edition. Thus, Test 1, entitled 'Atoms, Atomic Masses and Moles' relates to the ideas, concepts and information presented in Chapter 1 of *Chemistry in Context* which is also entitled 'Atoms, Atomic Masses and Moles'. Each test contains between fourteen and twenty-five questions.

TEST I
Atoms, atomic masses and moles

This test is composed of fourteen questions. For each question, five possible answers are suggested. These answers are labelled **A**, **B**, **C**, **D** and **E**. Select the most appropriate *one* of the answers and write its corresponding letter on a separate answer sheet.

1 The relative atomic mass of neon, which consists of the isotopes $^{20}_{10}Ne$ and $^{22}_{10}Ne$, is 20.2. The percentage of $^{20}_{10}Ne$ atoms in the isotopic mixture is

  A 0.2

  B 2.0

  C 10.0

  D 10.1

  E 90.0

2 A pure liquid is found by experiment to contain 93.7% carbon and 6.3% hydrogen by mass. The empirical formula of the liquid is

  A CH

  B C_3H_2

  C C_5H_4

  D C_8H_6

  E $C_{15}H$

  (C = 12, H = 1)

3 Which of the following pieces of equipment should be rinsed with the reagent they are to contain rather than with water before beginning a titration?

  A X only

  B Y only

  C X and Z only

  D X and Y only

  E X, Y and Z

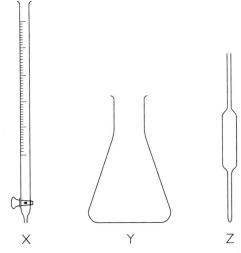

X   Y   Z

4 One of the compounds in both tea and coffee which acts as a stimulant is caffeine ($M_r = 194$). Analysis shows that caffeine contains 28.9% nitrogen by mass. The number of nitrogen atoms in one molecule of caffeine is

  A 1

  B 2

  C 4

  D 7

  E 8

  (N = 14)

5 $100 cm^3$ of $0.20 mol dm^{-3}$ K_2SO_4 are added to $100 cm^3$ of water and mixed thoroughly. The molarity of K^+ ions in the resulting solution is

  A 0.05

  B 0.10

  C 0.15

  D 0.20

  E 0.40

6 If the formula of a gaseous element is written as $X_2(g)$ we can deduce that it has

A an oxidation number of two.

B a relative molecular mass of two.

C a mass number of two.

D an atomic number of two.

E an atomicity of two.

7 The Avogadro constant is

A the number of electrons required to deposit one mole of atoms of any metal.

B the number of atoms in one mole of atoms of any element.

C the number of grams of any element containing 6×10^{23} atoms.

D the number of atoms in one gram of any element.

E the number of atoms in one mole of molecules of any element.

8 The table below shows the relative molecular masses of three compounds, I, II and III, and the percentage of element X in each of these compounds.

Compound	Relative molecular mass	Percentage of X
I	100	42
II	56	50
III	224	25

What is the probable relative atomic mass of X?

A 7

B 14

C 28

D 42

E 56

9 Careful analysis showed that 2.20 g of a compound containing only phosphorus and sulphur contained 1.24 g of phosphorus. What is the empirical formula of this compound?

($P = 31$, $S = 32$)

A P_2S_3

B P_2S_5

C P_3S_2

D P_3S_4

E P_4S_3

10 A molecular formula shows

A the ratio of atoms of the different elements in one molecule.

B the simplest whole number ratio for the atoms of different elements.

C the number of atoms in one molecule of a compound.

D the number of atoms of the different elements in one molecule.

E the number of atoms of the different elements in one mole.

11 Atoms of the same element have the same

A relative atomic mass.

B mass number.

C oxidation number.

D atomicity.

E atomic number.

12 60 g of the metal M ($M = 60$) combine with 24 g of oxygen ($O = 16$) to form an oxide. The formula of the oxide is

A MO

B M_2O

C M_2O_3

D M_3O_2

E M_5O_2

13 A lead–acid car battery requires 2 dm^3 of 4.0 mol dm^{-3} sulphuric acid (H_2SO_4). What mass of pure sulphuric acid is required for this? ($H_2SO_4 = 98$)

A $2 \times 4 \times 98$ g

B $\frac{2}{4} \times 98$ g

C $\frac{4}{2} \times 98$ g

D $\frac{98}{2} \times 4$ g

E $\frac{2}{98} \times 4$ g

14 Which of the following ionic compounds contains the greatest number of ions in 100 g of the substance? ($O = 16$, Na = 23, Mg = 24, Cl = 35.5, K = 39)

A Na_2O

B K_2O

C MgO

D NaCl

E $MgCl_2$

TEST 2
Reacting quantities and equations

This test is composed of twenty-one questions. For each question, five possible answers are suggested. These answers are labelled **A**, **B**, **C**, **D** and **E**. Select the most appropriate *one* of the answers and write its corresponding letter on a separate answer sheet.

Questions **1–4** concern the following equations.

A $N_2(g) + 3H_2(g) \rightarrow 2NH_3(g)$

B $2KOH(aq) + H_2SO_4(aq) \rightarrow K_2SO_4(aq) + 2H_2O(l)$

C $S(s) + O_2(g) \rightarrow SO_2(g)$

D $Ba^{2+}(aq) + SO_4^{2-}(aq) \rightarrow BaSO_4(s)$

E $Zn(s) + Cu^{2+}(aq) \rightarrow Zn^{2+}(aq) + Cu(s)$

Which *one* of the equations represents:

1 a reaction in which all the substances are small molecules?

2 a reaction which could be investigated using acid–base indicator?

3 a reaction which illustrates the relative reactivity of two elements?

4 a reaction which involves precipitation?

5 Which *one* of the following processes could be used to obtain the elements A and B from the compound AB?

A combustion

B distillation

C electrolysis

D precipitation

E synthesis

6 What mass of sodium contains the same number of atoms as 5 g of potassium? (Na = 23, K = 39)

A 5 g

B $\dfrac{5}{39} \times 23$ g

C $\dfrac{5}{23} \times 39$ g

D $\dfrac{23}{5} \times 39$ g

E 23 g

7 Which *one* of the following solutions contains the most sodium ions?

A 0.1 dm³ of 1.0 mol dm⁻³ Na_3PO_4

B 0.1 dm³ of 2.0 mol dm⁻³ NaCl

C 0.2 dm³ of 0.5 mol dm⁻³ Na_2CO_3

D 0.5 dm³ of 0.5 mol dm⁻³ NaOH

E 1.0 dm³ of 0.1 mol dm⁻³ Na_2SO_4

8 Which *one* of the following compounds produces the greatest mass of carbon dioxide on complete combustion of 1 g of the compound?

A methane CH_4

B ethene C_2H_2

C propane C_3H_8

D butene C_4H_8

E pentane C_5H_{12}

9 What is the maximum amount of aluminium which can be extracted from 102 kg of pure bauxite (Al_2O_3)?
(Al = 27, O = 16)

A $\dfrac{102}{2}$ kg

B $102 \times \dfrac{2}{5}$ kg

C 27 kg

D 54 kg

E 81 kg

10 Experiments show that 2.0 g of calcium reacts with 8.0 g of bromine to form 10.0 g of calcium bromide. How much calcium bromide will be produced if 2.0 g of calcium are heated with 6.0 g of bromine?

A 1.5 g

B 4.0 g

C 7.5 g

D 8.0 g

E 10.0 g

11 100 g of potassium hydrogencarbonate ($KHCO_3$) were heated to constant mass and the residue weighed 69 g. A possible equation for the decomposition is

A $2KHCO_3(s) \rightarrow K_2CO_3(s) + CO_2(g) + H_2O(g)$

B $KHCO_3(s) \rightarrow KOH(s) + CO_2(g)$

C $4KHCO_3(s) \rightarrow K_2O(s) + 2KOH(s) + H_2O(g) + 4CO_2(g)$

D $2KHCO_3(s) \rightarrow KOH(s) + KO(s) + 2CO_2(g)$

E $2KHCO_3(s) \rightarrow K_2O(s) + 2CO_2(g) + H_2O(g)$

(K = 39, H = 1, C = 12, O = 16)

12 0.1 mol of a chloride of sulphur was completely oxidised by nitric acid to chloride ions and sulphate ions. 0.1 moles of $PbCl_2$ and 0.2 moles of $BaSO_4$ were precipitated from this solution. The formula of the original compound was

A SCl

B S_2Cl

C SCl_2

D S_2Cl_2

E S_2Cl_4.

13 When 0.12 g of diamond are burnt in oxygen, 240 cm^3 of carbon dioxide are produced. What volume of carbon dioxide will be produced when 0.12 g of graphite are burnt in oxygen? (The volumes are measured at the same temperature and pressure.)

A 40 cm^3

B 60 cm^3

C 120 cm^3

D 240 cm^3

E 480 cm^3

14 The formula of a gas can be written as X_n. Two hundred cubic centimetres of X_n were heated and then cooled to the original temperature. Three hundred cubic centimetres of X_2 were produced. What is the value of n?

A $\frac{1}{2}$

B $\frac{1}{3}$

C 1

D 2

E 3

15 The volume of 0.10 $mol\,dm^{-3}$ hydrochloric acid, which is just enough to react completely with 50.0 cm^3 of 0.20 $mol\,dm^{-3}$ barium hydroxide is

A 12.5 cm^3

B 25.0 cm^3

C 50.0 cm^3

D 100.0 cm^3

E 200.0 cm^3.

16 100 cm^3 of 0.5 $mol\,dm^{-3}$ H_2SO_4 is added to 400 cm^3 of 0.1 $mol\,dm^{-3}$ KOH. The final concentration of hydrogen ions is

A very low because there is excess of OH^-

B $10^{-7}\,mol\,dm^{-3}$ since H^+ is neutralised by OH^-

C 0.01 $mol\,dm^{-3}$

D 0.06 $mol\,dm^{-3}$

E 0.12 $mol\,dm^{-3}$

17 The equation for the reaction of sulphur dioxide with oxygen to form sulphur trioxide is

$$2SO_2(g) + O_2(g) \rightarrow 2SO_3(g).$$

Given this equation it is possible to calculate

A the rate at which sulphur trioxide forms.

B the mass of sulphur dioxide in an equilibrium mixture of the gases.

C the heat produced when 1 mol of SO_3 forms.

D the percentage of sulphur in sulphur trioxide.

E the relative reactivity of sulphur and oxygen.

18 What are the values of x and y in the following equation when it is correctly balanced?

$$4FeS_2 + xO_2 \rightarrow 2Fe_2O_3 + ySO_2$$

A $x(10)\quad y(8)$

B $x(11)\quad y(4)$

C $x(11)\quad y(8)$

D $x(22)\quad y(4)$

E $x(22)\quad y(8)$

19 Which *one* of the following is the correct equation for the decomposition of gaseous N_xO_y into its elements at room temperature and pressure?

A $N_xO_y \rightarrow N_x + O_y$

B $2N_xO_y \rightarrow xN_2 + yO_2$

C $2N_xO_y \rightarrow N_{2x} + O_{2y}$

D $2N_xO_y \rightarrow 2N_{\frac{x}{2}} + 2O_{\frac{y}{2}}$

E $2N_xO_y \rightarrow yN_2 + xO_2$

20 When pure, dry silver chloride is exposed to sunlight it decomposes slowly into its elements. Which *one* of the following equations best represents the reaction which takes place?

A $AgCl(s) \rightarrow Ag(s) + Cl(g)$

B $2AgCl(s) \rightarrow Ag_2(s) + Cl_2(g)$

C $AgCl(s) \rightarrow Ag(s) + Cl^-(s)$

D $AgCl(s) \rightarrow Ag^+(s) + Cl^-(s)$

E $2AgCl(s) \rightarrow 2Ag(s) + Cl_2(g)$

21 Which *one* of the following ionic equations is correctly balanced?

A $S_2O_3^{2-} + 2H^+ \rightarrow H_2O + S + SO_2$

B $S_2O_3^{2-} + 2H^+ \rightarrow H_2O + 2S + SO_2$

C $S_2O_3^{2-} + H^+ \rightarrow 2S + OH^- + O_2$

D $S_2O_3^{2-} + 2H^+ \rightarrow H_2O + S^{2-} + SO_2$

E $S_2O_3^{2-} + H^+ \rightarrow S^{2-} + SO_2 + OH^-$

TEST 3
Redox

This test is composed of nineteen questions. For each question, five (or in some cases four) possible answers are suggested. These answers are labelled **A**, **B**, **C**, **D** and **E**. Select the most appropriate *one* of the answers and write its corresponding letter on a separate answer sheet.

1 Which *one* of the following can be described as a 'redox' reaction?

A $Br_2(l) \rightarrow 2Br(g)$

B $Na^+(g) + Br^-(g) \rightarrow NaBr(s)$

C $2HBr(aq) + Ca(OH)_2(aq) \rightarrow CaBr_2(aq) + 2H_2O(l)$

D $Br_2(l) + H_2O(l) \rightarrow HBr(aq) + HBrO(aq)$

E $AgBr(s) + 2NH_3(aq) \rightarrow [Ag(NH_3)_2]^+(aq) + Br^-(aq)$

2 The order of strength as oxidising agents for the ions Au^{3+}, Li^+, Ni^{2+} and Rb^+ is

strongest → weakest

A $Au^{3+} > Li^+ > Ni^{2+} > Rb^+$

B $Au^{3+} > Ni^{2+} > Li^+ > Rb^+$

C $Ni^{2+} > Au^{3+} > Li^+ > Rb^+$

D $Ni^{2+} > Au^{3+} > Rb^+ > Li^+$

E $Rb^+ > Li^+ > Ni^{2+} > Au^{3+}$

3 The oxidation number of tungsten in $Na_2W_4O_{13}.10H_2O$ is

A $+4$

B $+6$

C $+8$

D $+11$

E $+12$

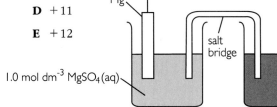

1.0 mol dm^{-3} MgSO$_4$(aq)

1.0 mol dm^{-3} ZnSO$_4$(aq)

Mg

Zn

salt bridge

4 In the electrochemical cell shown above,

A the reaction at the zinc electrode is $Zn \rightarrow Zn^{2+} + 2e^-$.

B electrons flow through the wire from the zinc to the magnesium electrode.

C a tiny current flows even when the salt bridge is removed.

D magnesium ions migrate into the salt bridge.

E the concentration of Mg^{2+} ions will decrease in the left-hand beaker.

5 $20\,cm^3$ of an acidified solution of $0.1\,mol\,dm^{-3}$ potassium manganate(VII) just reacted with $20\,cm^3$ of a solution of sodium sulphate(IV) (sodium sulphite). What is the concentration, in $mol\,dm^{-3}$, of the solution of sodium sulphate(IV)?

$$SO_3^{2-} + H_2O \rightarrow SO_4^{2-} + 2H^+ + 2e^-$$
$$MnO_4^- + 8H^+ + 5e^- \rightarrow Mn^{2+} + 4H_2O$$

A 0.50

B 0.25

C 0.10

D 0.04

E 0.02

6 Which *one* of the following conversions is an oxidation?

A $Cr_2O_3 \rightarrow Cr^{3+}$

B $CrO_4^{2-} \rightarrow Cr_2O_7^{2-}$

C $Cr^{3+} \rightarrow CrO_4^{2-}$

D $CrO_4^{2-} \rightarrow CrO_3$

E $CrO_4^{2-} \rightarrow Cr_2O_3$

7 $VO_4^{3-} + xH^+ + ye^- \rightarrow V^{3+} + zH_2O$
In the equation above, the values of x, y and z are

	x	y	z
A	8	3	4
B	8	2	4
C	8	2	2
D	4	2	4
E	4	1	2

8 Metal X is deposited at the cathode when a solution of its ions are electrolysed. Which *one* of the following will affect the mass of X deposited?

A the concentration of the solution

B the charge on the ions of X

C the temperature of the solution

D the area of the electrodes

E the distance between the electrodes

9 In which of the following equations does the *first* stated reagent act as a reducing agent?

A $Cl_2(g) + H_2(g) \rightarrow 2HCl(g)$

B $H^+(aq) + C_2O_4^{2-}(aq) \rightarrow HC_2O_4^-(aq)$

C $H^+(aq) + NH_3(g) \rightarrow NH_4^+(aq)$

D $H_2(g) + 2Na(s) \rightarrow 2NaH(s)$

E $Mg(s) + 2H^+(aq) \rightarrow Mg^{2+}(aq) + H_2(g)$

10 In the reaction $CH_4 + Cl_2 \rightarrow CH_3Cl + HCl$

A C in CH_4 is acting as oxidant and is oxidised.

B C in CH_4 is acting as oxidant and is reduced.

C H in CH_4 is acting as reductant and is reduced.

D C in CH_4 is acting as reductant and is reduced.

E C in CH_4 is acting as reductant and is oxidised.

11 An electron transfer reaction takes place when

A copper is added to $FeSO_4$ solution.

B silver is added to $Zn(NO_3)_2$ solution.

C iron is added to $AgNO_3$ solution.

D zinc is added to $Mg(NO_3)_2$ solution.

E lead is added to $Al_2(SO_4)_3$ solution.

12 Which *one* of the following equations is correctly balanced?

A $H_2O + 2I^- + 2H^+ \rightarrow 2H_2O + I_2$

B $Cr_2O_7^{2-} + Fe^{2+} + 14H^+ \rightarrow 2Cr^{3+} + Fe^{3+} + 7H_2O$

C $2NO_3^- + 2Cl^- + 4H^+ \rightarrow 2NO + Cl_2 + 2H_2O$

D $2MnO_4^- + 5Sn^{2+} + 16H^+ \rightarrow 2Mn^{2+} + 5Sn^{4+} + 8H_2O$

E $Zn + NO_3^- + 2H^+ \rightarrow Zn^{2+} + NO_2 + H_2O$

13 0.01 mol of a compound K_2XO_4 will just oxidise 0.04 mol of Fe^{2+} to Fe^{3+}. The final oxidation state of x is therefore

A $+6$

B $+5$

C $+4$

D $+3$

E $+2$

14 In which *one* of the following pairs of substances does the specified element have a different oxidation number in each substance?

A Cr in CrO_3 and $Cr_2O_7^{2-}$

B Cu in $Cu(NH_3)_4^{2+}$ and $CuCl_4^{2-}$

C F in ClF and HF

D Na in NaCl and NaH

E C in CH_4 and C_2H_6

15 A chemist isolated a compound which he described as 'manganese oxide-hydroxide, (MnOOH)'. The oxidation state of manganese in this compound is

A $+1$

B $+2$

C $+3$

D $+4$

E $+5$

Questions 16–18

$$Cr_2O_7^{2-} + 14H^+ + 6e^- \rightarrow 2Cr^{3+} + 7H_2O$$

$$Fe^{2+} \rightarrow Fe^{3+} + e^-$$

$$C_2O_4^{2-} \rightarrow 2CO_2 + 2e^-$$

16 The oxidation number of chromium in $Cr_2O_7^{2-}$ is

A $+2$

B -2

C $+3$

D $+6$

E $+7$

17 The number of moles of Fe^{2+} oxidised by one mole of $Cr_2O_7^{2-}$ is

A $\frac{1}{6}$

B 1

C 2

D 3

E 6

18 The number of moles of iron(II) ethanedioate (iron(II) oxalate, FeC_2O_4) oxidised by one mole of $Cr_2O_7^{2-}$ is

A $\frac{1}{2}$

B 1

C 2

D 3

E 6

19 w grams of metal, M $(A_r(M) = X)$ were deposited during electrolysis of a solution containing the ions M^{n+}. A current of I amps was used for t seconds. What is the value of n?
(1 Faraday $= 96\,500$ C)

A $\dfrac{XIt}{96\,500\,w}$

B $\dfrac{wIt}{96\,500\,X}$

C $\dfrac{It}{96\,500\,wX}$

D $\dfrac{96\,500\,w}{XIt}$

E $\dfrac{XIt}{w}$

TEST 4
Patterns and periodicity

This test is composed of nineteen questions. For each question, five possible answers are suggested. These answers are labelled **A**, **B**, **C**, **D** and **E**. Select the most appropriate *one* of the answers and write its corresponding letter on a separate answer sheet.

Questions **1–5**

The statements below relate to five of the elements in the third period of the periodic table, labelled **A**, **B**, **C**, **D** and **E**. In each case, select the letter of the element that has the stated characteristic.

    A sodium

    B aluminium

    C silicon

    D phosphorus (white)

    E chlorine

1 Which element exists as separate molecules in the solid state at room temperature?

2 Which element forms an amphoteric oxide?

3 Which element forms a gaseous hydride which is slightly basic?

4 Which element has the highest atomic electrical conductance?

5 Which element is the strongest oxidising agent?

Questions **6–8**

Consider the following five elements in the *solid* state in answering the questions below.

    A aluminium

    B carbon (diamond)

    C phosphorus (white)

    D potassium

    E xenon

6 Which element is composed of monatomic molecules held together by Van der Waals' forces?

7 Which element is a solid with a low melting point and high electrical conductivity?

8 Which element is a low melting non-conducting solid composed of symmetrical polyatomic molecules?

9 The elements, X, Y and Z are in the same period of the periodic table. The oxide of X is acidic, the oxide of Y is amphoteric and that of Z is basic. The order of these elements in increasing atomic number is likely to be

    A XYZ

    B XZY

    C YZX

    D ZXY

    E ZYX

10 The elements in the periodic table are listed in order of increasing

    A relative atomic mass.

    B atomic weight.

    C relative isotopic mass.

    D nuclear mass.

    E nuclear charge.

11 Element Q forms an ionic compound with sodium. Q is most likely to be a member of groups

    A III and IV

    B III and V

    C IV and V

    D IV and VI

    E V and VI

12 Elements in the same short period of the periodic table are likely to have

    A the same oxidation state.

    B similar physical properties.

    C similar atomic radii.

    D different numbers of electrons in their outer shell.

    E similar ionic radii.

13 Which of the following statements is the *best* description of the element of atomic number 14?

    A a reactive metal

    B a poor metal

    C a metalloid

    D a non-metal

    E a transition metal

14 Which *one* of the following elements does not form both ionic and simple molecular binary compounds?

A hydrogen

B lithium

C beryllium

D nitrogen

E oxygen

15 Which of the following elements has the highest molar volume at room temperature?

A lithium

B carbon

C sodium

D aluminium

E potassium

16 The elements X, Y and Z are in the *same* short period of the periodic table. Element X has a giant molecular structure, element Y is metallic and element Z is composed of simple molecules. The order of these elements in increasing atomic number is

A XYZ

B XZY

C YXZ

D YZX

E ZXY

17 0.25 mol of gaseous chlorine produced 0.10 mol of the chloride of element M. The formula of this chloride could be

A MCl_3

B $MCl_{2.5}$

C MCl_5

D M_2Cl_3

E M_5Cl_2

18 Which *one* of the following elements forms a soluble basic oxide?

A caesium

B nickel

C phosphorus

D tin

E zinc

19 Along which *one* of the following series of three elements do the melting points of the elements rise?

A B, C, N

B Na, Mg, Al

C Al, Si, P

D C, Si, Ge

E S, Cl, Ar

TEST 5
Atomic structure

This test is composed of fifteen questions. For each question, five possible answers are suggested. These answers are labelled **A**, **B**, **C**, **D** and **E**. Select the most appropriate *one* of the answers and write its corresponding letter on a separate answer sheet.

1 Which *one* of the following instruments could be used to detect a stream of beta-particles?

   A a spectrophotometer

   B a gold-leaf electroscope

   C a mass spectrometer

   D a radiographer

   E a magnetometer

2 X-rays

   A are affected by electric and magnetic fields.

   B are formed by the loss of electrons from atoms.

   C have lower frequencies than visible light.

   D are formed when a solid target is bombarded by cathode rays.

   E consist of smaller particles than electrons.

3 Using a mass spectrometer, it is possible to determine the number of

   A protons in an atom.

   B energy levels in an atom.

   C atoms in one mole of an element.

   D isotopes of an element.

   E neutrons in an atom.

4 When a parallel beam of alpha-particles is directed towards a thin metal foil, most of the particles pass through, but a small fraction appear to rebound from the foil. This is because the alpha-particles

   A are very small and have no charge.

   B have widely different velocities.

   C are repelled by electrons in the foil.

   D are repelled by the nuclei of atoms in the foil.

   E obey the law of conservation of momentum.

5 The relative atomic mass of an element is

   A the mass of 6×10^{23} atoms of the element.

   B the weighted mean of the relative isotopic masses on the scale $^{12}_{6}C = 12$.

   C the average of the relative isotopic masses on the scale $^{12}_{6}C = 12$.

   D the mass in atomic mass units of one atom on the scale $^{12}_{6}C = 12$.

   E one twelfth the weighted mean of the isotopic masses.

6 The isotope $^{40}_{19}K$ emits a beta-particle during radioactive decay. The other product is

   A $^{40}_{20}Ca$

   B $^{40}_{18}Ar$

   C $^{39}_{19}K$

   D $^{40}_{20}K$

   E $^{36}_{17}Cl$

7 Which *one* of the following particles has seven protons, eight neutrons and nine electrons?

   A $^{8}_{7}N^{-}$

   B $^{14}_{7}N^{2-}$

   C $^{15}_{7}N^{-}$

   D $^{15}_{8}N^{2-}$

   E $^{15}_{7}N^{2-}$

8 The isotopes W, X, Y and Z form compounds WX, WY and WZ. The compounds WX and WY are both radioactive but WZ is not. Which of the following conclusions is correct?

   A Only one of the isotopes is radioactive.

   B Two of the isotopes are radioactive.

   C Three of the isotopes are radioactive.

   D XZ will not be radioactive.

   E W is radioactive in some compounds.

9 Atoms with different atomic numbers must have different

   A numbers of electrons.

   B numbers of neutrons.

   C mass numbers.

   D isotopic masses.

   E molar masses.

10 The accurate relative isotopic masses of five isotopes are

$^1_1H = 1.0078$, $^2_1H = 2.0141$, $^{12}_6C = 12.000$,

$^{14}_7N = 14.0031$, $^{16}_8O = 15.9949$.

Using a high resolution mass spectrometer, a certain gas was found to have a relative molecular mass of 28.0172. The gas could be

A $^{14}_7N_2$

B $^{12}_6C_2\,^1_1H_4$

C $^2_1H\,^{12}_6C\,^{14}_7N$

D $^{12}_6C_2\,^2_1H_2$

E $^{12}_6C\,^{16}_8O$

11 The mass spectrometer trace for naturally occurring magnesium is shown below. Assuming that all three peaks relate to ions with one positive charge, what is the relative atomic mass for magnesium?

A 24.2

B 24.3

C 24.4

D 24.7

E 24.8

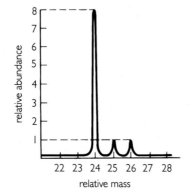

12 The diagram below shows the mass spectrometer trace of the substance X in the region of relative mass 10 to 20 units. Which of the following substances is X most likely to be?

A O_2

B N_2

C NH_3

D H_2O

E CH_4

13 The atomic number of an element is the number of

A atoms in one molecule.

B electrons in the neutral atom.

C protons plus neutrons in the atom.

D protons plus electrons in the atom.

E atoms in one mole.

14 The graph below shows the square root of the frequency of the X-rays produced by electron bombardment of solid elements, ν, against the atomic number of the target element, Z.

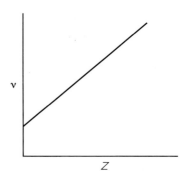

Which *one* of the following statements represents the correct relationship between ν and Z? (*b* is a constant)

A $\nu \propto Z$

B $\nu \propto Z^2$

C $\nu \propto (Z - b)^2$

D $\nu \propto Z - b$

E $\nu \propto \sqrt{(Z - b)}$

15 In an attempt to determine the charge carried by *one* electron, a student bombarded tiny oil droplets with a stream of electrons and then measured the total charge on individual oil drops. The charges on 3 different oil drops were found to be 12.8×10^{-19} C, 16.0×10^{-19} C and 25.6×10^{-19} C respectively. These figures suggest that the largest possible charge on the electron is

A 25.6×10^{-19} C

B 12.8×10^{-19} C

C 6.4×10^{-19} C

D 3.2×10^{-19} C

E 1.6×10^{-19} C

TEST 6
Electronic structure

This test is composed of eighteen questions. For each question, five possible answers are suggested. These answers are labelled **A**, **B**, **C**, **D** and **E**. Select the most appropriate *one* of the answers and write its corresponding letter on a separate answer sheet.

1 Which *one* of the following equations relates to the second ionisation energy of element M?

   A $M(s) \rightarrow M^{2+}(s) + 2e^-$

   B $M(s) \rightarrow M^{2+}(g) + 2e^-$

   C $M(g) \rightarrow M^{2+}(g) + 2e^-$

   D $M^+(s) \rightarrow M^{2+}(g) + e^-$

   E $M^+(g) \rightarrow M^{2+}(g) + e^-$

2 Which of the following elements has the highest (most endothermic) second ionisation energy?

   A oxygen

   B fluorine

   C neon

   D sodium

   E magnesium

3 The third ionisation energies of six consecutive elements in the periodic table are shown below. To which group of the periodic table is element X likely to belong?

   A II

   B III

   C IV

   D V

   E VI

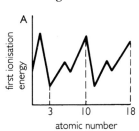

4 The first, second, third and fourth ionisation energies of element Y are 740, 1500, 7700 and $10\,500\,kJ\,mol^{-1}$ respectively. To which group of the periodic table is element Y likely to belong?

   A I   **B** II   **C** III   **D** IV   **E** O

5 In any one group of the periodic table, the first ionisation energy decreases with increasing atomic number. Which *one* of the following factors is most responsible for this?

   A the increasing atomic radius

   B the decreasing effective nuclear charge

   C the decreasing bond energy

   D the increasing nuclear charge

   E the increasing atomic mass

6 Which *one* of the graphs below represents a plot of the first ionisation energy against atomic number for the first eighteen elements?

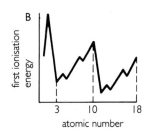

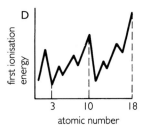

7 Which *one* of the following graphs shows the logarithm to base ten of the successive ionisation energies (log ionisation energy) of nitrogen against the ionisation number?

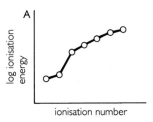

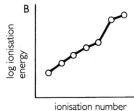

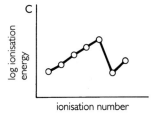

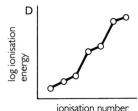

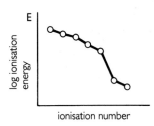

8 Which *one* of the following statements regarding electronic orbitals is correct?

  A Each *p*-orbital can hold a maximum of six electrons.

  B The 3*p*-orbitals have a higher energy level than the 3*s*-orbital.

  C The three 3*p*-orbitals have slightly different energy levels.

  D The charge clouds for *p*-orbitals are spherical.

  E The 1*s*-orbital has the same size and shape as the 2*s*-orbital.

9 Which *one* of the following diagrams represents the visible region of the atomic hydrogen spectrum?

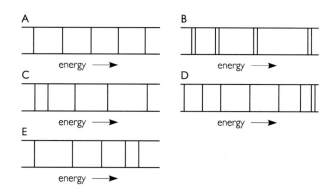

10 When electrons (with a charge of 1.6×10^{-19} C) were accelerated through a sample of xenon, ionisation first occurred when the accelerating potential was 12 V. Which *one* of the following values would this suggest for the first ionisation energy of xenon in $J \, mol^{-1}$?

  A $1.6 \times 10^{-19} \times 12$

  B $\dfrac{1.6 \times 10^{-19}}{12} \times 6 \times 10^{23}$

  C $\dfrac{1.6 \times 10^{-19}}{6 \times 10^{23}} \times 12$

  D $\dfrac{12 \times 6 \times 10^{23}}{1.6 \times 10^{-19}}$

  E $1.6 \times 10^{-19} \times 12 \times 6 \times 10^{23}$

11 The diagram below shows the logarithms of the first seven ionisation energies of element Q. Element Q could be

  A aluminium

  B beryllium

  C boron

  D nitrogen

  E silicon

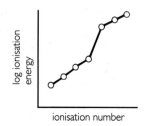

12 The first ionisation energy of oxygen is greater than that of magnesium. Which *one* of the following factors is responsible for this?

  A There is a greater nuclear charge on oxygen.

  B The number of electrons in the outer shell is greater for oxygen.

  C The outermost electrons are further from the nucleus in oxygen.

  D The shielding by inner-shell electrons is greater for magnesium.

  E Interatomic bonding is stronger in oxygen.

13 The alkali metals are chemically similar because

  A their outermost electrons have the same quantum number.

  B their outermost electrons have the same energy.

  C their outermost shell contain only *s* electrons.

  D their outermost shells contain only one electron.

  E they have low first ionisation energies.

14 Which *one* of the following notations represents the electronic structure of nitrogen?

  A $1s^2 2s^2 3p_x^1 3p_y^1 3p_z^1$ **D** $1s^2 2s^2 2p_x^1 2p_y^1 2p_z^1$

  B $1s^2 2s^2 2p_x^2 2p_y^1$ **E** $1s^2 2s^2 3p_x^2 3p_y^1$

  C $1s^2 2s^2 2p_x^1 2p_y^2$

15 The electron configuration of the outermost shell of an atom of the element R is $3s^2 3p^5$. The element R is

  A aluminium   **D** nitrogen

  B chlorine   **E** phosphorus

  C fluorine

16 The atomic number of the element with electron configuration $(Ne)3s^2 3p^3$ is

  A 5   **D** 13

  B 7   **E** 15

  C 10

17 The number of electrons required to fill the first seven energy levels (1*s*, 2*s*, 2*p*, 3*s*, 3*p*, 3*d*, 4*s*) is

  A 18   **D** 30

  B 20   **E** 36

  C 24

18 Which *one* of the following represents the electron configuration of the outermost shell of an atom of an element in Group V?

  A $2s^2 2p^5$ **D** $4s^2 4p^3$

  B $3p^5$ **E** $5s^2 5d^3$

  C $3d^3 4s^2$

TEST 7
Nuclear structure and radioactivity

This test is composed of eighteen questions. For each question, five possible answers are suggested. These answers are labelled **A**, **B**, **C**, **D** and **E**. Select the most appropriate *one* of the answers and write its corresponding letter on a separate answer sheet.

1 Gamma-rays are

   A attracted by an electric field.

   B deflected by a magnetic field.

   C composed of particles smaller than electrons.

   D diffracted by a crystal lattice.

   E unable to penetrate thin metal foil.

2 As atomic number increases, the neutron/proton ratio (n/p) for stable isotopes

   A remains constant.

   B slowly increases.

   C slowly decreases.

   D rises and then falls.

   E falls and then rises.

3 Bismuth-212 has a half-life of 1 hour. If 16 g of the isotope are allowed to decay, what mass of the isotope remains after 4 hours?

   A 12 g

   B 4 g

   C 2 g

   D 1 g

   E 0 g

4 The emission of gamma-rays by an element results in the loss of

   A electrons

   B charge

   C energy

   D stability

   E atoms

5 In a nuclear reactor, rods of natural uranium are inserted in channels surrounded by blocks of graphite. The main purpose of the graphite is to

   A slow down the neutrons from fission of U-235.

   B absorb the neutrons from fission of U-235.

   C control the temperature of the reactor.

   D ensure a steady production of energy.

   E absorb the radioactive emissions of the fission process.

6 In a nuclear reactor, rods of natural uranium are surrounded by graphite. This graphite is also penetrated by rods of cadmium or boron. The main purpose of the cadmium or boron is to

   A slow down the neutrons from fission of U-235.

   B absorb the neutrons from fission of U-235.

   C conduct away the heat produced from fission of U-235.

   D absorb the radioactive emissions of the fission process.

   E ensure that the uranium never reaches the critical size.

7 The isotope $^{32}_{11}P$ emits a beta-particle during a radioactive decay. Which *one* of the following isotopes is the other product of disintegration?

   A $^{32}_{14}Si$

   B $^{32}_{16}S$

   C $^{31}_{15}P$

   D $^{33}_{15}P$

   E $^{33}_{16}S$

8 Rutherford showed that the charge/mass ratio for a certain particle, X, was half the value of the charge/mass ratio for a proton ($^{1}_{1}H^{+}$). Which *one* of the following particles could X be?

   A $^{2}_{1}H^{2+}$

   B $^{2}_{2}He^{2+}$

   C $^{4}_{2}He$

   D $^{4}_{2}He^{+}$

   E $^{6}_{3}Li^{3+}$

9 Which *one* of the following statements describes the half-life of a radioactive isotope *incorrectly*?

   A The time taken for half of the mass of the isotope to disappear.

   B The time taken for the concentration of an aqueous isotope to fall to half its initial value.

   C The time taken for the number of atoms of the isotope to fall to half its original value.

   D The time taken for the rate of decay of the isotope to fall to half its initial value.

   E The time taken for the mass of the isotope to fall from half its initial value to zero.

10 Living organisms produce 15.3 ± 0.1 disintegrations of carbon-14 atoms per minute per gram of carbon. A sample, X, produces 1.9 ± 0.1 disintegrations of carbon-14 atoms per minute per gram of carbon. Assuming that the half-life of carbon-14 is 5600 years, which *one* of the following provides the best estimate for the age of X?

A $5600 \times \dfrac{15.3}{1.9}$ years

B $5600 \times \dfrac{1.9}{15.3}$ years

C $5600 \times (15.3 - 1.9)$ years

D 5600×3 years

E $5600 \times 15.3 \times 1.9$ years

11 Certain isotopes, such as $^{14}_{6}C$, have a neutron/proton ratio which is above the stable value. A common process by which these isotopes achieve stability is

A electron capture.

B alpha-decay.

C neutron emission.

D proton capture.

E beta-decay.

12 In a radioactivity experiment the background count was found to be 24 counts per minute, and a radioactive specimen, X, gave a count of 220 counts per minute (including background radiation) at the start. Assuming that X has a half-life of 10 minutes and that it decays directly to a stable isotope, what is the count rate (in counts per minute, including background radiation) 20 minutes after the start of the experiment?

A 0

B 24

C 55

D 73

E 79

13 Which *one* of the following statements provides the most accurate description of atomic fission?
Atomic fission is the disintegration of a nucleus involving

A the formation of alpha-particles.

B the formation of two or more neutrons.

C the formation of two large nuclei.

D a chain reaction.

E the emission of gamma-radiation.

14 The radioactive isotopes X and Y have half-lives of 2000 years and 6000 years respectively. A sample of rock contains four atoms of X for each atom of Y. The rock will contain the same number of atoms of X and Y after

A 2000 years.

B 4000 years.

C 6000 years.

D 8000 years.

E 12 000 years.

15 Bombardment of $^{7}_{3}Li$ with gamma-rays produces a proton and another nucleus. This other nucleus is

A $^{6}_{3}Li$

B $^{7}_{2}He$

C $^{6}_{2}He$

D $^{4}_{2}He$

E $^{7}_{4}Be$

16 Naturally occurring chlorine contains two stable isotopes, $^{35}_{17}Cl$ and $^{37}_{17}Cl$, which occur in the relative proportions $3:1$. The relative proportions of the three molecules of chlorine $^{35}_{17}Cl_2$, $^{35}_{17}Cl^{37}_{17}Cl$ and $^{37}_{17}Cl_2$ will be

A $9:6:3$

B $9:6:1$

C $9:3:1$

D $6:6:1$

E $6:3:1$

17 The half-life of strontium-90 ($^{90}_{38}Sr$) is 28 years. This means that

A half the atoms in a sample of strontium-90 decay in 28 years

B all the atoms in a sample of strontium-90 decay in 56 years.

C all the atoms in a sample of strontium-90 decay in 14 years.

D half a mole of strontium-90 decays in 28 years.

E one mole of strontium-90 decays in 14 years.

18 The nuclear transformation $^{1}_{0}n \rightarrow {^{1}_{1}H}$ is an example of

A electron capture

B fission

C fusion

D beta-decay

E alpha-decay

TEST 8
The electronic theory and chemical bonding

This test is composed of eighteen questions. For each question, five possible answers are suggested. These answers are labelled **A**, **B**, **C**, **D** and **E**. Select the most appropriate *one* of the answers and write its corresponding letter on a separate answer sheet.

1   In which *one* of the following substances is ionic bonding present?

   A ice

   B silicon

   C brass

   D lime

   E sugar

2   Which *one* of the following species has a different number of electrons from the K^+ ion?

   A Ar

   B Br^-

   C HS^-

   D PH_4^+

   E SiH_4

3   Element X has atomic number 19 and element Y has atomic number 35. Which *one* of the following binary compounds are X and Y most likely to form?

   A an ionic compound, X^+Y^-

   B an ionic compound, X^-Y^+

   C an ionic compound, $(X^+)_3Y^{3-}$

   D a molecular compound, XY

   E a molecular compound, XY_3

4   The formation of a co-ordinate (dative) bond between the phosphorus atom in PH_3 and the boron of BF_3 involves

   A increasing the number of electrons in the outer shell of phosphorus.

   B reducing the number of electrons in the outer shell of phosphorus.

   C transferring electrons from phosphorus to boron.

   D transferring electrons from boron to phosphorus.

   E sharing a pair of electrons between boron and phosphorus.

5   The elements X and Y form a compound of formula XY_3. The atomic numbers of X and Y could be

   A 3 and 5

   B 3 and 9

   C 5 and 7

   D 7 and 9

   E 7 and 13

6   Elements Q and R are in the same short period of the periodic table and have 4 and 6 outer shell electrons respectively. The formula of the compound they form together is most likely to be

   A QR

   B QR_2

   C Q_2R

   D Q_2R_3

   E Q_3R_2

7   Which *one* of the following species has the same electronic structure as Br^-?

   A Cl^-

   B K^+

   C Se^{2-}

   D Ar

   E Xe

8   In 1874, before modern instrumental methods of analysis became available, Van't Hoff and Le Bel predicted quite correctly that the methane molecule was tetrahedral rather than square planar. Which *one* of the following pieces of information would have provided the most convincing evidence for methane's tetrahedral shape?

   A Methane forms only one dichloro-compound.

   B Methane can substitute four chlorine atoms.

   C Methane is a gaseous hydrocarbon.

   D Monochloromethane is a polar substance.

   E Methane is a non-polar substance.

9 Which *one* of the following compounds has the greatest degree of ionic character?

    A beryllium oxide

    B beryllium sulphide

    C calcium oxide

    D calcium sulphate

    E magnesium oxide

10 Which *one* of the following molecules has a bond angle greater than $109° 28'$?

    A SCl_2

    B CS_2

    C H_2S

    D CCl_4

    E NH_3

11 In which of the following does the covalent bond show the greatest departure from equal sharing of the electron pair?

    A F_2

    B SiH_4

    C C (graphite)

    D HCl

    E BrCl

Questions 12–18

The shapes of simple molecules (with respect to their constituent atoms) can be described as

    A linear

    B V-shaped (bent)

    C trigonal planar

    D pyramidal

    E tetrahedral

Select the shape (with respect to atoms) of each of the following species.

12 F_2O

13 NH_4^+

14 NF_3

15 gaseous $BeCl_2$

16 gaseous $AlCl_3$

17 $GeCl_4$

18 C_2H_2

TEST 9
Intermolecular forces

This test is composed of twenty questions. For each question, five possible answers are suggested. These answers are labelled **A**, **B**, **C**, **D** and **E**. Select the most appropriate *one* of the answers and write its corresponding letter on a separate answer sheet.

1 Which *one* of the following compounds has no permanent dipole?

 A CH_2Cl_2

 B C_2Cl_6

 C CH_3OCH_3

 D NCl_3

 E CH_3CCl_3

2 In which *one* of the following compounds would hydrogen bonding not occur?

 A CH_3OCH_3

 B NH_2Cl

 C $(CH_3)_2NOH$

 D C_6H_5OH

 E H_2O_2

3 Compound X, empirical formula CHBr, was found to have zero dipole moment. Which one of the following structural formulae could be that of X?

4 Molecules of the compound ZCl_3 have zero dipole moment. What is their shape, with respect to constituent atoms?

 A linear

 B trigonal planar

 C tetrahedral

 D pyramidal

 E square planar

5 Which *one* of the following values would you use in estimating an approximate value for the strength of the hydrogen bond between ammonia molecules?

 A the enthalpy change of fusion of $NH_3(s)$

 B the enthalpy change of vaporisation of $NH_3(l)$

 C the N–H bond energy in $NH_3(l)$

 D the enthalpy change of formation of $NH_3(l)$

 E the enthalpy change of solution of $NH_3(g)$

6 In which *one* of the following molecules does the covalent bond show the greatest departure from equal sharing of the electron pair?

 A Cl_2

 B HI

 C F_2

 D HCl

 E ClF

7 As atomic number increases from sodium to chlorine across period 3, the electronegativity of the elements

 A increases steadily.

 B decreases steadily.

 C increases to a maximum and then decreases.

 D decreases to a minimum and then increases.

 E stays almost constant.

8 According to the kinetic theory of gases, the molecules of an ideal gas

 A all have the same velocity.

 B are tiny charged particles.

 C attract each other strongly.

 D occupy a negligible volume.

 E lose energy on collision.

9 In the Van der Waals' Real Gas Equation,

$$\left(p + \frac{a}{V^2}\right)(V - b) = RT,$$

the term $\frac{a}{V^2}$ is inserted to allow for

A the volume of the molecules.

B the non-elastic molecular collisions.

C the intermolecular attractions.

D the different molecular velocities.

E collisions with the walls of the vessel.

10 Which *one* of the following types of bond is responsible for the surface tension of liquid tetrachloromethane (CCl_4)?

A covalent bonding

B hydrogen bonding

C permanent dipole attractions

D induced dipole attractions

E co-ordinate bonding

11

	melting point /K	boiling point /K
X Br	823	1583
Z Br	315	389

From the data above concerning the two bromides, XBr and ZBr, it is reasonable to conclude that

A ZBr has an ionic structure.

B X and Z are in the same group of the periodic table.

C XBr has a giant molecular structure.

D ZBr is very soluble in water.

E X is a metal and Z is a non-metal.

12 The boiling point of SiH_4 is higher than that of CH_4 because

A molecules of SiH_4 are polar unlike those of CH_4.

B molecules of SiH_4 are hydrogen-bonded but those of CH_4 are not.

C SiH_4 has a giant structure but CH_4 is composed of simple molecules.

D molecules of SiH_4 have permanent dipole–dipole attractions.

E intermolecular forces are stronger in SiH_4 than in CH_4.

13 The atoms P and Q have the electron configurations $1s^2 2s^2 2p^6 3s^2$ and $1s^2 2s^2 2p^3$ respectively. The formula of the compound they form together is most likely to be

A PQ_2

B P_2Q_3

C P_2Q_5

D P_3Q

E P_3Q_2

14 Which *one* of the following represents the order of increasing dipole moment for the trichlorobenzenes X, Y and Z shown below?

A XYZ

B YXZ

C YZX

D ZXY

E ZYX

15 The enthalpy change of sublimation of solid chlorine is $25\,kJ\,mol^{-1}$ and the Cl–Cl bond energy is $245\,kJ\,mol^{-1}$. The energy required to tear one chlorine molecule away from its neighbours in solid chlorine is therefore

A $\dfrac{25}{6 \times 10^{23}}$ kJ

B $\dfrac{245}{6 \times 10^{23}}$ kJ

C $\dfrac{270}{6 \times 10^{23}}$ kJ

D $\dfrac{220}{6 \times 10^{23}}$ kJ

E $\dfrac{2 \times 270}{6 \times 10^{23}}$ kJ

Questions **16–20** concern the following classes of organic compound:

A carbohydrate

B nucleic acid

C protein

D fat

E amino acid

Select from **A** to **E** the class into which you would place a compound which

16 catalyses the decomposition of urea in mammals.

17 is more soluble in tetrachloromethane than in water.

18 relies entirely on −OH groups for hydrogen bonding.

19 acts as a structural polymer in plants.

20 is responsible for the similarity of a child to its parents.

TEST 10
Structure, bonding and properties: the solid state

This test is composed of twenty-one questions. For each question, four or five possible answers are suggested. These answers are labelled **A**, **B**, **C**, **D** and **E**. Select the most appropriate *one* of the answers and write its corresponding letter on a separate answer sheet.

1 Crystalline solids have good cleavage planes because the particles in the crystal are

A weakly bonded together.

B separated by large distances.

C arranged in a regular fashion.

D spherically symmetrical.

E sometimes separated by dislocations.

2 The number of nearest neighbours to each metal atom in a body-centred cubic structure is

A 4

B 6

C 8

D 10

E 12

3 Which *one* of the following would favour the formation of an ionic compound with the largest degree of covalent character?

A a small anion with a multiple charge

B a small anion with a single charge

C a large cation with a multiple charge

D a small cation with a single charge

E a small cation with a multiple charge

4 The co-ordination number of carbon in graphite is

A 3

B 4

C 5

D 6

E 7

5 The co-ordination number of carbon in diamond is four. This means that each carbon atom has

A four covalent bonds.

B four outer electrons.

C an oxidation number of four.

D four nearest neighbours.

E four hybrid sp^3 electrons.

6 Hydrogen atoms are difficult to detect by X-ray diffraction because

A the mass of the hydrogen atom is too small.

B the electron density of hydrogen atoms is too low.

C the radius of the hydrogen atom is too small.

D there are no neutrons in hydrogen atoms.

E the bonds to hydrogen atoms are too short.

7 Graphite and diamond are allotropes of carbon because

A they are different physical states of the same element.

B their atoms contain different numbers of neutrons.

C they are different crystalline structures of the same element.

D their molecules contain different numbers of atoms.

E they give equal volumes of carbon dioxide on heating.

Questions 8–11

The following diagram shows a unit cell of the compound formed between the metal X and the non-metal Y.

The ion of X is represented by an open circle at the centre of the unit cell and ions of Y are represented by black circles at the corners of the cell.

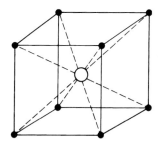

8 The formula of the compound formed between X and Y is

A XY

B XY_2

C XY_4

D XY_6

E XY_8

9 The number of ions of Y in the unit cell is

   A $\frac{1}{2}$

   B 1

   C 2

   D 4

   E 8

10 The co-ordination numbers of ions of X and Y are respectively

   A 1:1

   B 1:4

   C 1:8

   D 4:4

   E 8:8

11 If the volume of 1 mol of the compound is V dm^3 and the volume of a unit cell is v dm^3, the Avogadro constant, L, is given by

   A $\dfrac{V}{v} \times \dfrac{1}{8}$

   B $\dfrac{V}{v} \times \dfrac{1}{4}$

   C $\dfrac{V}{v}$

   D $\dfrac{V}{v} \times 4$

   E $\dfrac{V}{v} \times 8$

Questions **12–18**

Crystalline solids may be divided into four distinct structures labelled **A**, **B**, **C** and **D** below:

   A giant metallic

   B giant ionic

   C giant molecular

   D simple molecular

In each of the following questions select the most likely structure for the substance with the stated property.

12 A hard, brittle substance which conducts electricity when molten.

13 A clear substance which gradually softens between 400 and 800°C.

14 An element whose relative molecular mass is four times its relative atomic mass.

15 An element which boils at 1100°C to give a monatomic vapour.

16 A solid mixture of two elements which conducts electricity.

17 A monatomic substance held together by Van der Waals' forces.

18 A substance boiling at 190 K which reacts with water to form a solution which conducts electricity.

Questions **19–21**

The following diagram shows a unit cell of TiO$_2$. The black dots represent titanium atoms. One of these is at the centre of the unit cell. The other titanium atoms are at the corners of the cell. The six open circles represent oxygen atoms. Four of these oxygens are on face diagonals and the other two are on a body diagonal.

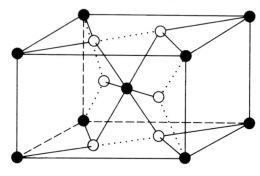

19 How many oxygen atoms are there inside the unit cell?

   A 1

   B 2

   C 3

   D 4

   E 6

20 What are the respective co-ordination numbers of titanium and oxygen?

   A 6:3

   B 6:2

   C 4:3

   D 4:2

   E 2:3

21 If the volume of 1 mol of TiO$_2$ is V cm^3 and the volume of the unit cell is v cm^3, what is the value of the Avogadro constant?

   A $\dfrac{V}{v} \times \dfrac{1}{2}$

   B $\dfrac{V}{v}$

   C $\dfrac{V}{v} \times 2$

   D $\dfrac{V}{v} \times 4$

   E $\dfrac{V}{v} \times 6$

TEST 11
The gaseous state

This test is composed of nineteen questions. For each question five possible answers are suggested. These answers are labelled **A**, **B**, **C**, **D** and **E**. Select the most appropriate *one* of the answers and write its corresponding letter on a separate answer sheet.

1   The temperature of $4 \, dm^3$ of an ideal gas rises from $200 \, K$ to $400 \, K$ and, at the same time, the pressure on the gas is halved. What is the final volume of the gas?

   A $1 \, dm^3$

   B $2 \, dm^3$

   C $4 \, dm^3$

   D $8 \, dm^3$

   E $16 \, dm^3$

2   What volume of oxygen is required to react completely with a mixture of $10 \, cm^3$ of hydrogen and $20 \, cm^3$ of carbon monoxide?
(All volumes are measured at the same temperature and pressure.)

   A $10 \, cm^3$

   B $15 \, cm^3$

   C $20 \, cm^3$

   D $25 \, cm^3$

   E $30 \, cm^3$

3   $10 \, cm^3$ of a hydrocarbon react completely with exactly $40 \, cm^3$ of oxygen to produce $30 \, cm^3$ of carbon dioxide. What is the formula of the hydrocarbon?
(All volumes are measured at the same temperature and pressure.)

   A CH_4

   B C_2H_6

   C C_3H_4

   D C_3H_6

   E C_3H_8

Questions **4–6** concern the analysis of a volatile hydrocarbon, X. ($C = 12$, $H = 1$)

   A $C_{\frac{1}{2}}H$

   B CH

   C CH_2

   D C_6H

   E C_7H_4

5   When $0.14 \, g$ of X was vaporised at $100°C$, it occupied $62 \, cm^3$. Assuming that one mole of X occupies $22\,400 \, cm^3$ at s.t.p., the relative molecular mass of X is

   A $\dfrac{0.14 \times 22\,400}{373 \times 62}$

   B $\dfrac{0.14 \times 22\,400 \times 373 \times 62}{273}$

   C $\dfrac{0.14 \times 62 \times 373}{22\,400}$

   D $\dfrac{0.14 \times 22\,400 \times 373}{62 \times 273}$

   E $\dfrac{0.14 \times 22\,400 \times 273}{62 \times 373}$

6   The accurate relative molecular mass of X (to the nearest integer) is

   A 37

   B 65

   C 69

   D 70

   E 73

Questions **7–9**

Two identical flasks at the same temperature contain $4 \, g$ of helium and $4 \, g$ of hydrogen respectively.

($He = 4$, $H = 1$)

7   The ratio, number of molecules of He : number of molecules of hydrogen is

   A $1:1$

   B $1:2$

   C $1:4$

   D $2:1$

   E $4:1$

8   The ratio, pressure of helium : pressure of hydrogen is

   A $1:1$

   B $1:2$

   C $1:4$

   D $2:1$

   E $4:1$

9 The ratio, average kinetic energy per helium molecule : average kinetic energy per hydrogen molecule, is

A $1:1$

B $1:2$

C $1:4$

D $2:1$

E $4:1$

10 $100\,cm^3$ of a gaseous oxide of nitrogen was completely decomposed into nitrogen and oxygen.

$$2N_xO_y \rightarrow xN_2(g) + yO_2(g)$$

After decomposition, the volume of gas was $150\,cm^3$. After passing the decomposition products over heated copper, the volume decreased to $100\,cm^3$. All volumes were measured at room temperature and pressure. What is the formula of the original gas?

A NO

B NO_2

C N_2O

D N_2O_2

E N_2O_3

11 $10\,cm^3$ of a gaseous element, Y reacts with excess hydrogen to form $40\,cm^3$ of a gaseous compound containing Y and hydrogen, all volumes being measured under the same conditions of temperature and pressure. From this information, we can deduce that one molecule of the reactant, Y, could contain

A one atom of Y.

B two atoms of Y.

C one or two atoms of Y.

D two or four atoms of Y.

E four atoms of Y.

12 The molecules of a *real* gas

A occupy zero volume.

B exert no forces on one another.

C all have the same speed.

D collide with equal momentum.

E collide inelastically.

13 The mass of air inside a telephone kiosk ($1\,m \times 1\,m \times 2\,m$) is about

A $0.25\,kg$

B $1.3\,kg$

C $2.5\,kg$

D $5\,kg$

E $25\,kg$

14 Flask A contains $1\,dm^3$ of nitrogen at $1 \times 10^5\,Pa$ and flask B contains $2\,dm^3$ of oxygen at $3 \times 10^5\,Pa$. If the flasks are connected, at constant temperature, what is the final pressure in pascals?

A $1\frac{1}{3} \times 10^5$

B 2×10^5

C $2\frac{1}{3} \times 10^5$

D $2\frac{1}{2} \times 10^5$

E 4×10^5

Questions **15–19** refer to the five graphs of a quantity Y plotted against a quantity X labelled **A**, **B**, **C**, **D** and **E** in the figure below.

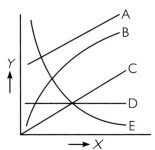

Choose the graphs which describes the relationship between X and Y most accurately in each of the following questions. Each graph may be used once, more than once, or not at all.

15 Y is the pressure of nitrogen (p) and X is the volume of the nitrogen (V) at constant temperature.

16 Y is the pressure of nitrogen (p) and X is the reciprocal of the volume of nitrogen ($1/V$) at constant temperature.

17 Y is the product pressure × volume (i.e. pV) and X is the volume (V) for a constant number of moles of a perfect gas at constant temperature.

18 Y is the volume of gas (V) and X is the temperature in degrees Celsius ($T/°C$) for a constant number of moles of a perfect gas at constant pressure.

19 Y is the product pressure × volume (i.e. pV) and X is the absolute temperature (T/K) for a constant number of moles of ideal gas.

TEST 12
Energy changes and bonding

This test is composed of twenty questions. For each question five possible answers are suggested. These answers are labelled **A**, **B**, **C**, **D** and **E**. Select the most appropriate *one* of the answers and write its corresponding letter on a separate answer sheet.

1 Which *one* of the following equations relates to the enthalpy change of atomisation of bromine?

A $Br_2(g) \rightarrow 2Br(g)$

B $\frac{1}{2}Br_2(g) \rightarrow Br(g)$

C $Br_2(l) \rightarrow 2Br(g)$

D $\frac{1}{2}Br_2(l) \rightarrow Br(g)$

E $\frac{1}{2}Br_2(s) \rightarrow Br(g)$

2 Using the data:

C (graphite) $+O_2(g) \rightarrow CO_2(g)$

$\Delta H^{\ominus} = -394\,kJ\,mol^{-1}$,

$H_2(g) + \frac{1}{2}O_2(g) \rightarrow H_2O(l)$

$\Delta H^{\ominus} = -286\,kJ\,mol^{-1}$,

$CH_4(g) + 2O_2(g) \rightarrow CO_2(g) + 2H_2O(l)$

$\Delta H^{\ominus} = -890\,kJ\,mol^{-1}$,

the standard enthalpy change of formation of methane is

A $-1856\,kJ\,mol^{-1}$.

B $-210\,kJ\,mol^{-1}$.

C $-76\,kJ\,mol^{-1}$.

D $+76\,kJ\,mol^{-1}$.

E $+210\,kJ\,mol^{-1}$.

3 When $100\,cm^3$ of $0.1\,mol\,dm^{-3}$ NaOH is neutralised by excess hydrochloric acid, the final volume of the solution is $130\,cm^3$ and the temperature of the mixture rises by $1.1°C$. Ignoring the thermal capacity of the container and assuming the specific heating capacity of all the solutions to be $4.0\,J\,g^{-1}\,K^{-1}$, what is the enthalpy change of neutralisation of NaOH by HCl in $J\,mol^{-1}$?

A $130 \times 1.1 \times 4$

D $100 \times 1.1 \times 4$

B $130 \times 1.1 \times 4 \times 10$

E $100 \times 1.1 \times 4 \times 100$

C $130 \times 1.1 \times 4 \times 100$

4 The enthalpy changes of formation of $P_4(s)$, $P_4(g)$ and $P(g)$ at 298 K are 0, 52 and $316\,kJ\,mol^{-1}$ respectively. What is the enthalpy change of atomisation of phosphorus in $kJ\,mol^{-1}$?

A 52

D $316 + \frac{52}{4}$

B $\frac{316}{4}$

E $316 + 52$

C 316

5 The energy released when *one* electron is added to a gaseous atom would be expected to be highest for elements in group

A I   **B** II   **C** VI   **D** VII   **E** O

6 Which *one* of the following spontaneous changes is endothermic?

A the mixing of two ideal liquids at room temperature.

B the condensation of water vapour at room temperature.

C the decomposition of ozone into oxygen at room temperature.

D the conversion of cyclopropane to propene at room temperature.

E the melting of sulphur at its melting point.

7 The standard enthalpy changes of formation for $CO(g)$ and $COCl_2(g)$ are $-110\,kJ\,mol^{-1}$ and $-223\,kJ\,mol^{-1}$ respectively. The standard enthalpy change in $kJ\,mol^{-1}$ for the reaction

$$CO(g) + Cl_2(g) \rightarrow COCl_2(g)$$

is therefore

A -333 **C** $+113$ **E** not obtainable without further data.

B -113 **D** $+333$

8 Which *one* of the following substances supports the fact that the thermal stability of a compound *cannot* always be related to its enthalpy change of formation?

	Substance	$\Delta H_f^{\ominus}/kJ\,mol^{-1}$	Stability
A	V	-10	stable
B	W	-1000	stable
C	X	-100	unstable
D	Y	$+10$	unstable
E	Z	$+1000$	unstable

9 Which of the following pairs of substances will have the closest values of their molar enthalpy changes of combustion?

A propane and butane

B cyclohexane and hexane

C cyclopropane and propene

D propan-1-ol and methoxyethane

E *cis*-but-2-ene and *trans*-but-2-ene

10 In order to calculate the average C–H bond energy in methane it is necessary to know the standard enthalpy change of formation of methane and also

A the molar enthalpy change of vaporisation of methane.

B the standard enthalpy changes of atomisation of carbon and hydrogen.

C the standard enthalpy changes of combustion of methane, hydrogen and carbon.

D the electron affinity of hydrogen and the first four ionisation energies of carbon.

E the standard enthalpy changes of formation of carbon and hydrogen.

11 Some average bond energies at 298 K in $kJ\,mol^{-1}$ are: $C\equiv C$ 835; $C=C$ 610; $C–C$ 346; $C–H$ 413; $H–H$ 436.
What is the value of $\Delta H^{\ominus}_{298}$, in $kJ\,mol^{-1}$, for the reaction $2H_2(g) + HC\equiv CH(g) \rightarrow CH_3CH_3(g)$?

A −665   **D** +319

B −291   **E** +665

C +291

12 Which *one* of the following equations summarises the process relating to the lattice energy of calcium oxide?

A $Ca^{2+}(g) + O^{2-}(g) \rightarrow CaO(s)$

B $Ca^{2+}(s) + O^{2-}(g) \rightarrow CaO(s)$

C $Ca^{2+}(aq) + O^{2-}(aq) \rightarrow CaO(s)$

D $Ca^{2+}(g) + O^{2-}(g) \rightarrow CaO(g)$

E $Ca(g) + \frac{1}{2}O_2(g) \rightarrow CaO(s)$

13 $\Delta H_f^{\ominus}$ for the hypothetical compound Ar^+Br^- would have a high positive value. The main reason for this is that

A bromine has a large enthalpy change of atomisation.

B bromine has a small electron affinity.

C bromine has a large first ionisation energy.

D argon has a large enthalpy change of atomisation.

E argon has a large first ionisation energy.

14 Assuming that both NaCl(s) and MgS(s) have simple cubic structures, that the lattice energy of sodium chloride is $-800\,kJ\,mol^{-1}$ and that the distance between the centres of Na^+ and Cl^- ions in NaCl is very similar to that between Mg^{2+} and S^{2-} ions in MgS, which of the following provides the best estimate for the lattice energy of magnesium sulphide?

A $-3200\,kJ\,mol^{-1}$ **D** $-400\,kJ\,mol^{-1}$

B $-1600\,kJ\,mol^{-1}$ **E** $-200\,kJ\,mol^{-1}$

C $-800\,kJ\,mol^{-1}$

15 The first, second and third ionisation energies of element X are 500, 1000 and $2000\,kJ\,mol^{-1}$ respectively. The hydration energies of ions X^+, X^{2+} and X^{3+} are −400, −1800 and $3800\,kJ\,mol^{-1}$ respectively. A consideration of enthalpy changes suggests that in aqueous solution, X is likely to form

A $X^+(aq)$ ions only.   **D** $X^+(aq)$ and $X^{2+}(aq)$ ions.

B $X^{2+}(aq)$ ions only.   **E** $X^{2+}(aq)$ and $X^{3+}(aq)$ ions.

C $X^{3+}(aq)$ ions only.

Questions **16–20** refer to the diagram below.

$$Ca(g) + Cl_2(g) \quad \xrightarrow{\Delta H_3^{\ominus}=c\,kJ} \quad Ca(g) + 2Cl(g)$$

$$\Delta H_2^{\ominus}=b\,kJ \uparrow \qquad\qquad \Delta H_4^{\ominus}=d\,kJ$$

$$Ca(s) + Cl_2(g) \qquad\qquad Ca^{2+}(g) + 2e^- + 2Cl(g)$$

$$\Delta H_1^{\ominus}=a\,kJ \qquad\qquad \Delta H_5^{\ominus}=e\,kJ$$

$$CaCl_2(s) \quad \xrightarrow{\Delta H_6^{\ominus}=f\,kJ} \quad Ca^{2+}(g) + 2Cl^-(g)$$

16 Which *one* of the following changes represents the standard enthalpy change of formation of $CaCl_2(s)$?

A $\Delta H_1^{\ominus}$ **D** $-\Delta H_2^{\ominus} - \Delta H_1^{\ominus}$

B $-\Delta H_1^{\ominus}$ **E** $-\Delta H_3^{\ominus} - \Delta H_2^{\ominus} - \Delta H_1^{\ominus}$

C $\Delta H_6^{\ominus}$

17 What is the standard enthalpy change of atomisation of chlorine in $kJ\,mol^{-1}$?

A $\dfrac{c}{2}$ **D** $c + e$

B $-c$ **E** $\dfrac{c + e}{2}$

C c

18 What is the standard enthalpy change in kJ for the process $Ca(s) \rightarrow Ca^{2+}(g) + 2e^-$?

A $b + c$ **D** $b + c + d$

B $b + d$ **E** $b + c + d + e$

C $b + e$

19 Which of the six changes shown in the diagram is/are exothermic in the direction indicated?

A $\Delta H_1^{\ominus}$ only   **D** $\Delta H_1^{\ominus}, \Delta H_5^{\ominus}$ and $\Delta H_6^{\ominus}$

B $\Delta H_5^{\ominus}$ only   **E** $\Delta H_5^{\ominus}$ and $\Delta H_6^{\ominus}$

C $\Delta H_6^{\ominus}$ only

20 The enthalpy change denoted by $\Delta H_5^{\ominus}$ represents

A the sum of the first two electron affinities of Cl(g).

B the sum of the first two ionisation energies of Cl(g).

C the sum of the electron affinities of Cl(g) and $Cl^-(g)$.

D twice the electron affinity of Cl(g).

E twice the first ionisation energy of Cl(g).

TEST 13
Patterns across the periodic table

This test is composed of twenty-five questions. For each question five possible answers are suggested. These answers are labelled **A**, **B**, **C**, **D** and **E**. Select the most appropriate *one* of the answers and write its corresponding letter on a separate answer sheet.

1 Which of the following elements has the largest second ionisation energy?

   A sodium

   B magnesium

   C fluorine

   D potassium

   E neon

2 In which of the following is the radius ratio the smallest?

   A $\dfrac{Li^+}{Li}$ **D** $\dfrac{Na^+}{Na}$

   B $\dfrac{B^{3+}}{B}$ **E** $\dfrac{F^-}{F}$

   C $\dfrac{N^{3-}}{N}$

3 Which *one* of the following sets of data represents the first five successive ionisation energies of magnesium in $kJ\,mol^{-1}$?

   A   500   4600   6900   9500   13 400

   B 2080   4000   6100   9400   12 200

   C   580   1800   2700   11 600   14 800

   D   740   1500   7700   10 500   13 600

   E   790   1600   3200   4400   16 100

4 The first ionisation energy of phosphorus is greater than the first ionisation energy of potassium. One of the factors responsible for this is that

   A the outermost electron is further from the nucleus in potassium atoms than in phosphorus atoms.

   B there are more electrons in the outer quantum shell of phosphorus than potassium.

   C the inner quantum shells provide greater shielding in phosphorus than in potassium.

   D the nuclear charge is greater for phosphorus than potassium.

   E the covalent bonding in P_4 molecules is stronger than the metallic bonding in potassium.

5 The covalent radius for chlorine is half the distance between the centres of

   A two chlorine atoms in gaseous chlorine.

   B two chlorine atoms in solid chlorine.

   C two chlorine atoms in a chlorine molecule.

   D two neighbouring, but unbonded chlorine atoms.

   E two chlorine atoms in a dichloro-compound.

6 The series of elements Na, Mg, Al, P and S were heated in a stream of chlorine to obtain their chlorides. The heat evolved per mole of chlorine atoms will

   A increase to a maximum and then decrease along the series.

   B decrease to a minimum and then increase along the series.

   C rise progressively along the series.

   D fall progressively along the series.

   E remain approximately constant.

7 Separate samples of NaCl, $MgCl_2$, Al_2Cl_6, PCl_3 and S_2Cl_2 were added to water and the resulting mixtures were tested with full-range indicator paper. The pHs of the solutions obtained will

   A increase from 7 to a maximum and then decrease.

   B increase from 7 to a maximum and remain high.

   C decrease from 11 to a minimum and then increase.

   D decrease from 11 to a minimum and remain low.

   E decrease from 7 to a minimum and remain low.

8 Elements X, Y and Z are in the same short period of the periodic table. The hydrides of X and Y are gaseous, but that of Z is a solid at room temperature. The hydride of X is insoluble in water, that of Y gives an acidic solution with water and that of Z gives an alkaline solution. The elements arranged in order of atomic number are

   A XZY

   B YXZ

   C YZX

   D ZXY

   E ZYX

9 The hydride of element Q reacts with water producing hydrogen and an alkaline solution. Q is probably

   A an alkali metal.

   B a transition metal.

   C a metal low in the activity series.

   D an element in Group V.

   E a metal in Group IV.

Questions **10–14** refer to the five graphs below showing various physical quantities, labelled Y, against atomic number.

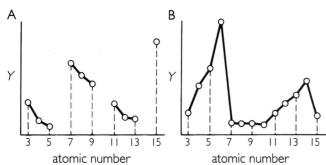

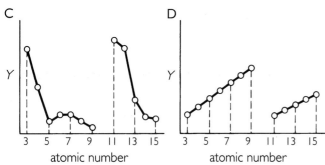

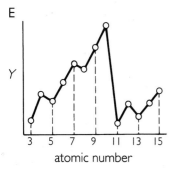

Which of the graphs is appropriate when Y is the physical quantity indicated below? Each graph may be used once, more than once, or not at all.

10 Electronegativity

11 The ionic radius of the most stable ion

12 The boiling point of the chloride

13 The first ionisation energy

14 The melting point of the element

Questions **15–20**

Five classes into which oxides may be divided are

   A acidic

   B amphoteric

   C basic

   D neutral

   E peroxide

Assign each of the following oxides to its appropriate class.

15 Cl_2O

16 CO

17 Cs_2O

18 SiO_2

19 BaO_2

20 Al_2O_3

Questions **21–24**

When the chloride of an element is shaken with water, the product may contain the element as

   A an insoluble unchanged ionic solid chloride.

   B unchanged simple molecules of the chloride.

   C hydrated cations.

   D a precipitate of hydrated oxide or hydroxide.

   E molecules and anions of a dissolved oxyacid.

Choose from **A** to **E**, the state in which each of the following elements will exist when its chloride is shaken with excess water.

21 Potassium

22 Silicon

23 Carbon

24 Phosphorus

25 In order to determine the formula of a chloride of the element Q, 0.1 mol of the chloride was dissolved in $500\,cm^3$ of water. $50\,cm^3$ of this solution just reacted with $300\,cm^3$ of $0.1\,mol\,dm^{-3}$ $AgNO_3(aq)$. Which *one* of the following is a possible formula for the chloride?

   A Q_3Cl

   B Q_2Cl_6

   C QCl

   D Q_2Cl_3

   E QCl_6

TEST 14
Competition processes

This test is composed of sixteen questions. For each question five possible answers are suggested. These answers are labelled **A, B, C, D** and **E**. Select the most appropriate *one* of the answers and write its corresponding letter on a separate answer sheet.

Questions **1–3** concern the arrangement shown in the diagram below, which is composed of the following half-cells:

$Cr^{3+}(aq)/Cr(s)$, $E^{\ominus} = -0.74\,V$ and $Ag^+(aq)/Ag(s)$, $E^{\ominus} = +0.80\,V$.

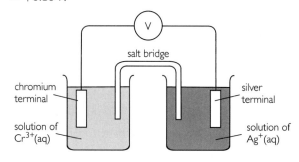

1 What is the standard e.m.f. of the cell $Cr(s)|Cr^{3+}(aq)\|Ag^+(aq)|Ag(s)$?

A $(0.80 + 0.74)$ V

B $(0.80 - 0.74)$ V

C $\left(0.80 + \dfrac{0.74}{3}\right)$ V

D $(-0.80 + 0.74)$ V

E $\left(\dfrac{0.80 + 0.74}{3}\right)$ V

2 The e.m.f. of the cell can be reduced by reducing

A the area of the silver terminal.

B the cross-sectional area of the salt bridge.

C the thickness of the connecting wire.

D the concentration of $Cr^{3+}(aq)$.

E the concentration of $Ag^+(aq)$.

3 When the cell operates normally

A electrons flow through the voltmeter from silver to chromium.

B the silver terminal is more negative than chromium.

C the concentration of $Cr^{3+}(aq)$ will fall.

D both positive and negative ions move through the salt bridge.

E reduction occurs at the chromium terminal.

Questions **4–6** refer to the table of standard redox potentials below.

	$E^{\ominus}/V$
$Ce^{3+}(aq) + 3e^- \rightarrow Ce(s)$	-2.33
$Th^{4+}(aq) + 4e^- \rightarrow Th(s)$	-1.90
$Ni^{2+}(aq) + 2e^- \rightarrow Ni(s)$	-0.25
$Cu^{2+}(aq) + 2e^- \rightarrow Cu(s)$	$+0.34$
$Tl^{3+}(aq) + 2e^- \rightarrow Tl^+(aq)$	$+1.25$

4 Which of the following species is the most powerful reducing agent?

A Ce^{3+} **D** Tl^+

B Ni   **E** Th

C Tl^{3+}

5 The e.m.f. between electrodes connecting the two standard half-cells

$Pt(s)|Tl^+(aq), Tl^{3+}(aq)$ and $Ni(s)|Ni^{2+}(aq)$ is

A 2.00 V   **D** 0.75 V

B 1.50 V   **E** 0.50 V

C 1.00 V

6 Excess copper was added to $100\,cm^3$ of $0.1\,mol\,dm^{-3}$ $Tl(NO_3)_3$ solution. What mass of copper would react? $(Cu = 64)$

A 1.28 g

B 0.96 g

C 0.64 g

D 0.42 g

E 0.32 g

Questions **7** and **8** refer to the following equations involving reactions of ammonia.

A $NH_3 + NH_3 \rightarrow NH_4^+ + NH_2^-$

B $2Na + 2NH_3 \rightarrow 2NaNH_2 + H_2$

C $3CuO + 2NH_3 \rightarrow 3Cu + N_2 + 3H_2O$

D $NH_3 + NH_2Cl \rightarrow H_2NNH_2 + HCl$

E $NH_3 + H_2S \rightarrow NH_4HS$

7 In which reaction does ammonia behave as an oxidising agent?

8 In which reaction does ammonia behave as both an acid and a reducing agent?

9 Which *one* of the following is a redox reaction?

A $Cu^+ + 2NH_3 \rightarrow [Cu(NH_3)_2]^+$

B $Cu^+ + 4Cl^- \rightarrow [CuCl_4]^{3-}$

C $Cu^+ + Cl^- \rightarrow CuCl$

D $2Cu^+ \rightarrow Cu + Cu^{2+}$

E $[Cu(NH_3)_2]^+ + 2H^+ \rightarrow Cu^+ + 2NH_4^+$

10 In the equation, $Cu + Cu^{2+} + 4Cl^- \rightarrow 2[CuCl_2]^-$, Cl^- is behaving as

A an oxidising agent.

B a reducing agent.

C a ligand.

D a base.

E a complex ion.

11 When hydrogen reacts with sodium to form sodium hydride, it behaves as

A an acid.

B a base.

C a nucleophile.

D an oxidising agent.

E a reducing agent.

12 $30\,cm^3$ of a $0.1\,mol\,dm^{-3}$ solution of a stable cation of element Q react exactly with $12\,cm^3$ of $0.1\,mol\,dm^{-3}$ acidified potassium manganate(VII).

$$MnO_4^- + 8H^+ + 5e^- \rightarrow Mn^{2+} + 4H_2O$$

Which *one* of the following equations could represent the change in oxidation of Q correctly?

A $Q^+ \rightarrow Q^{2+}$

B $Q^+ \rightarrow Q^{3+}$

C $Q^+ \rightarrow Q^{4+}$

D $Q^{2+} \rightarrow Q^{3+}$

E $Q^{4+} \rightarrow Q^{2+}$

13 The size and sign of an electrode potential provides an indication of

A the energetic favourability of a reaction.

B the kinetic feasibility of a reaction.

C the overall stoichiometry of a reaction.

D the activation energy of a reaction.

E the quantity of materials reacting.

14 Which *one* of the following species is the conjugate base to HSO_4^-?

A H_2SO_4

B SO_4^{2-}

C SO_3

D OH^-

E HSO_3^-

15 Lead(II) chloride is precipitated from solutions of lead salts by adding dilute hydrochloric acid. However, this precipitate dissolves when sufficient concentrated hydrochloric acid is added because

A lead chloride is soluble in acid.

B lead chloride complexes with Cl^- ions.

C chloride ions combine readily with H^+ ions.

D chloride ions complex with HCl.

E excess Cl^- ions reverse the equilibrium.

16 When an acid, H_3PO_2 is treated with excess sodium hydroxide, the only sodium salt obtained has the formula NaH_2PO_2. Which *one* of the following structures for H_3PO_2 best fits this data?

TEST 15
Groups I and II—the alkali metals and the alkaline-earth metals

This test is composed of seventeen questions. For each question five possible answers are suggested. These answers are labelled **A**, **B**, **C**, **D** and **E**. Select the most appropriate *one* of the answers and write its corresponding letter on a separate answer sheet.

1   On descending Group I from lithium to francium there is a steady increase in

   A electronegativity.

   B ionisation energy.

   C boiling point.

   D standard electrode potential.

   E molar volume.

2   The sodium ion, Na^+, is isoelectronic with

   A P^{3-}

   B Ar

   C K^+

   D F^-

   E Na

3   Given below are the first four ionisation energies, in $kJ\,mol^{-1}$, of aluminium, calcium, magnesium, rubidium and strontium (not in order). Which is the series for calcium?

   A 590   1100   4900   6500

   B 400   2700   3800   5100

   C 740   1500   7700   10 500

   D 580   1800   2700   11 600

   E 550   1050   4200   5500

4   Alkali metals

   A are reduced by hydrogen.

   B form reactive cations.

   C are stored under water.

   D readily form complex ions.

   E are oxidised by water.

5   Metals in Group I of the periodic table have *no*

   A coloured compounds.

   B insoluble compounds.

   C amphoteric oxides.

   D reaction with hydrogen.

   E stable nitrides.

6   Which *one* of the following equations represents correctly the thermal decomposition of potassium nitrate?

   A $2KNO_3 \rightarrow K_2O + 2NO_2 + \frac{1}{2}O_2$

   B $2KNO_3 \rightarrow K_2O + 2NO + \frac{3}{2}O_2$

   C $2KNO_3 \rightarrow K_2O + NO + NO_2 + O_2$

   D $2KNO_3 \rightarrow K_2O_2 + 2NO_2$

   E $2KNO_3 \rightarrow 2KNO_2 + O_2$

7   Lithium differs from sodium and potassium in that it forms

   A an ionic hydride which reacts with water.

   B a carbonate which decomposes readily to the oxide.

   C a peroxide when it reacts with oxygen.

   D a nitrate which decomposes on heating.

   E a hydroxide which does not decompose on heating.

8   Which *one* of the following metal ions in aqueous solution would give a white precipitate with aqueous sodium ethanedioate (oxalate), but no precipitate with aqueous potassium chromate(VI)?

   A Mg^{2+}

   B Ca^{2+}

   C Sr^{2+}

   D Ba^{2+}

   E Ra^{2+}

9 A solid compound of calcium was warmed with an equal volume of water evolving a gas which neither burned nor supported combustion. The formula of this compound could be

A CaC_2

B $CaCl_2$

C CaH_2

D Ca_3N_2

E CaO_2

10 On descending Group II from magnesium to barium, there is a steady increase in the solubility in water of the

A carbonates.

B hydroxides.

C phosphates(V).

D chromates(VI).

E sulphates(VI).

11 Magnesium does *not* form Mg^{3+} ions because, relatively speaking, it has

A a low second ionisation energy.

B a low third ionisation energy.

C a low fourth ionisation energy.

D a high second ionisation energy.

E a high third ionisation energy.

12 Which *one* of the following compounds would be expected to have the highest degree of ionic character?

A caesium sulphide

B caesium selenide

C francium sulphide

D rubidium sulphide

E rubidium selenide

13 The alkali metals and the alkaline-earth metals are usually extracted by

A reduction of the carbonate with coke.

B electrolysis of the molten chloride.

C electrolysis of the oxide in molten cryolite.

D thermite reduction of the oxide with aluminium.

E roasting the carbonate in air.

14 Which *one* of the following sodium salts could decolorise an aqueous solution of iodine?

A sodium chloride

B sodium sulphate(VI)

C sodium thiosulphate

D sodium nitrate(V)

E sodium chromate(VI)

15 Which *one* of the following ions might be responsible for the hardness of a sample of tap water?

A Cl^-

B CO_3^{2-}

C HCO_3^-

D Mg^{2+}

E SO_4^{2-}

16 Which *one* of the following chlorides is likely to be that of a Group II element?

	Melting point/°C	pH of aqueous solution	Conductivity of aqueous solution
A	sublimes	acidic	good
B	405	acidic	good
C	280	neutral	poor
D	455	insoluble	—
E	872	neutral	good

17 The diagrams below represent molecules of $BeCl_2$ and Cl_2.

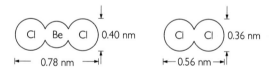

What is the covalent radius of Be in $BeCl_2$?

A 0.10 nm

B 0.11 nm

C 0.20 nm

D 0.21 nm

E 0.22 nm

TEST 16
Aluminium

This test is composed of fifteen questions. For each question, five possible answers are suggested. These answers are labelled **A**, **B**, **C**, **D** and **E**. Select the most appropriate *one* of the answers and write its corresponding letter on a separate answer sheet.

1   Which *one* of the following represents the ground-state electronic configuration of gallium, the element immediately below aluminium in Group III?

   A $1s^2 2s^2 2p^6 3s^2 3p^6 4s^1 4p^2$

   B $1s^2 2s^2 2p^6 3s^2 3p^6 4s^2 4p^1$

   C $1s^2 2s^2 2p^6 3s^2 3p^6 4d^{10} 4s^2 4p^1$

   D $1s^2 2s^2 2p^6 3s^2 3p^6 3d^{10} 4s^2 4p^1$

   E $1s^2 2s^2 2p^6 3s^2 3p^6 3d^{10} 4s^2 4p^3$

2   Which *one* of the following minerals does *not* contain aluminium?

   A emery

   B mica

   C anhydrite

   D emerald

   E beryl

3   The elements calcium and aluminium are similar in having

   A amphoteric hydroxides.

   B soluble hydroxides.

   C insoluble sulphates.

   D volatile chlorides.

   E ionic fluorides.

4   The chemistry of $Be^{2+}(aq)$ resembles that of $Al^{3+}(aq)$. The principal reason for this is that Be^{2+} and Al^{3+} have similar

   A ionic radii.

   B charge densities.

   C hydration energies.

   D elecron structures.

   E solvation numbers.

5   What are the relative positions of the chlorine atoms around one of the aluminium atoms in a molecule of Al_2Cl_6?

   A tetrahedral

   B trigonal planar

   C square planar

   D octahedral

   E pyramidal

6   Which of the following properties could refer to aluminium chloride?

	State at 20°C	b.pt./°C	pH of aqueous solution
A	solid	1400	7
B	solid	800	6
C	solid	200	3
D	solid	220	9
E	liquid	200	4

7   The elements in Group III, considered in order of increasing atomic number, show a *decrease* in

   A molar volume.

   B first ionisation energy.

   C ionic radius.

   D nuclear charge.

   E strength as reducing agents.

8   With which *one* of the following reagents does aluminium react most readily?

   A concentrated H_2SO_4

   B dilute HNO_3

   C hot dilute NaOH

   D concentrated NH_3

   E concentrated $KMnO_4$

9 Aluminium is obtained from bauxite—hydrated aluminium oxide containing impurities such as iron(III) oxide and silicon(IV) oxide. On which *one* of the following essential features of aluminium oxide is the purification of bauxite based?

A its amphoteric nature

B its stability on heating

C its insolubility in water

D its conductivity when molten

E its insolubility in weak acids

10 Aluminium is obtained industrially by

A reducing aluminium oxide with coke.

B electrolysing molten aluminium chloride.

C electrolysing molten aluminium oxide.

D electrolysing aluminium oxide in molten cryolite.

E reducing aluminium oxide with iron.

11 Aluminium articles form only a thin coating of oxide on exposure to the atmosphere, but iron objects eventually corrode away completely. Which *one* of the following statements helps to explain this difference?

A Aluminium oxide is covalently bonded.

B Aluminium oxide forms a giant structure.

C Aluminium oxide is insoluble in water.

D Rust is readily penetrated by water.

E Rust is soluble in rain water.

Questions **12–15**

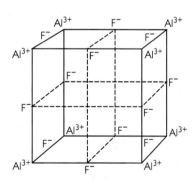

The diagram above represents a unit cell of aluminium fluoride.

12 What is the number of F^- ions in *one* unit cell?

A 12

B 6

C 4

D 3

E 1

13 If the volume of 1 mol of aluminium fluoride is $V \, dm^3$ and the volume of a unit cell is $v \, dm^3$, what is the value of the Avogadro constant, L?

A $\dfrac{V}{v} \times \dfrac{1}{12}$

B $\dfrac{V}{v} \times \dfrac{1}{8}$

C $\dfrac{V}{v} \times \dfrac{1}{3}$

D $\dfrac{V}{v}$

E $\dfrac{V}{v} \times 3$

14 What are the co-ordination numbers of the Al^{3+} ion and the F^- ion respectively?

A 1 and 3

B 3 and 1

C 6 and 2

D 8 and 12

E 12 and 8

15 In the crystalline structure of aluminium fluoride, the arrangement of Al^{3+} ions is

A tetrahedral.

B body-centred cubic.

C face-centred cubic.

D cubic close-packed.

E simple cubic.

TEST 17
Group VII—the halogens

This test is composed of twenty questions. For each question, five possible answers are suggested. These answers are labelled **A**, **B**, **C**, **D** and **E**. Select the most appropriate *one* of the answers and write its corresponding letter on a separate answer sheet.

1 The halogens differ from the alkali metals in having some

   A insoluble compounds.

   B coloured compounds.

   C covalent compounds.

   D reactive compounds.

   E abundant compounds.

2 When bromine is prepared by warming a mixture of solid manganese(IV) oxide, solid sodium bromide and concentrated sulphuric acid, the liquid bromine which collects is contaminated with hydrogen bromide. Which *one* of the following techniques would purify the bromine most effectively?

   A washing with water

   B washing with concentrated H_2SO_4

   C ether extraction

   D fractional distillation

   E standing over NaOH(s)

3 Fluorine is manufactured by electrolytic rather than chemical oxidation because chemical oxidants

   A will not oxidise fluorides.

   B produce impure fluorine.

   C are difficult to control.

   D react with fluorine.

   E attack the reaction vessel.

4 Which *one* of the following statements helps to explain why sodium and fluorine react more vigorously than sodium and chlorine?

   A Fluorine is more volatile than chlorine.

   B Fluorine has a smaller nuclear charge than chlorine.

   C Fluorine has a larger first ionisation energy than chlorine.

   D Fluorine has a smaller bond energy than chlorine.

   E Fluorine has a more positive electron affinity than chlorine.

5 When $Cl_2(g)$ is bubbled into cold dilute NaOH(aq) the principal products of the reaction are

   A NaCl and NaClO

   B NaClO and $NaClO_2$

   C NaCl and $NaClO_3$

   D NaClO and $NaClO_3$

   E NaCl and $NaClO_4$

6 Br^- is produced in the reaction between Br_2 and

   A Cl_2

   B Cl^-

   C HCl

   D I_2

   E I^-

7 Fluorine

   A readily forms fluorates(V).

   B cannot form a stable oxide.

   C forms an insoluble silver salt.

   D forms a compound with krypton.

   E disproportionates with alkali.

8 Which *one* of the following properties of the halogens *increases* with increasing relative atomic mass from fluorine to iodine?

   A tendency to form complex trihalide ions (Hal_3^-)

   B the solubility of Ag^+ salts

   C vigour of reaction with H_2

   D strength as oxidising agents

   E vigour of reaction with Na

9 Which *one* of the following properties of the halogens *decreases* as relative atomic mass increases from fluorine to iodine?

   A absorption of visible light

   B melting point

   C metallic character

   D atomic radius

   E first ionisation energy

10 Which *one* of the following reactions could be used to prepare gaseous hydrogen iodide?

   A Pass $H_2(g)$ over heated $I_2(s)$.

   B Warm concentrated HNO_3 with $I_2(s)$.

   C Warm concentrated H_3PO_4 with $NaI(s)$.

   D Warm concentrated H_2SO_4 with $NaI(s)$ and $MnO_2(s)$.

   E Heat $H_2O(g)$ and $I_2(g)$ to red heat.

11 The hydrogen halides

   A are coloured compounds.

   B form soluble lead salts.

   C increase in stability from HF to HI.

   D donate protons to water.

   E are liquids at 20°C.

12 When a solution of potassium bromide is treated with silver nitrate(V) solution it forms

   A a white precipitate soluble in dilute $NH_3(aq)$.

   B a white precipitate insoluble in dilute $NH_3(aq)$.

   C a cream precipitate soluble in dilute $NH_3(aq)$.

   D a cream precipitate insoluble in dilute $NH_3(aq)$.

   E a yellow precipitate insoluble in dilute $NH_3(aq)$.

13 Iodine exists in different oxidation states from -1 to $+7$. Which *one* of the following iodine-containing ions could *not* undergo disproportionation?

   A I^+

   B I^-

   C IO^-

   D ICl_2^+

   E IO_3^-

14 The measured electrode potential for the reaction $2Cl^-(aq) \rightleftharpoons Cl_2(g) + 2e^-$ is independent of
   A the temperature.

   B the size of the electrode.

   C the nature of the electrode.

   D the pressure of $Cl_2(g)$.

   E the purity of $Cl^-(aq)$.

15 Naturally occurring chlorine is composed of two isotopes, $^{35}_{17}Cl$ and $^{37}_{17}Cl$, in the relative proportions $3:1$. What are the relative proportions in gaseous chlorine of $^{35}_{17}Cl_2 : ^{35}_{17}Cl^{37}_{17}Cl : ^{37}_{17}Cl_2$ in gaseous chlorine?

   A $3:2:1$

   B $6:2:1$

   C $6:3:1$

   D $9:3:1$

   E $9:6:1$

16 The mass of sodium thiosulphate-5-water ($Na_2S_2O_3.5H_2O$) required to make up $250\,cm^3$ of a $0.5\,mol\,dm^{-3}$ solution is ($Na = 23$, $S = 32$, $O = 16$, $H = 1$)

   A $158 \times 0.5 \times \dfrac{250}{1000}$

   D $248 \times 0.5 \times 250$

   B $158 \times 0.5 \times \dfrac{1000}{250}$

   E $248 \times \dfrac{1}{0.5} \times \dfrac{250}{1000}$

   C $248 \times 0.5 \times \dfrac{250}{1000}$

17 Which *one* of the following pairs of compounds contains halogen atoms whose combined oxidation numbers total $+8$?

   A $KClO_4$, $NaBrO_4$

   B $KClO_3$, $NaBrO_3$

   C ClO_2, I_2O_5

   D $NaClO_2$, HIO_3

   E $NaCl$, $KClO_4$

18 Suppose you thought that you had discovered a new element in Group VII. Which of the following properties should your new element possess?

   A It should be a highly reactive gaseous element.

   B It should react rapidly with hydrogen forming a gas.

   C It should react more vigorously than the other halogens with sodium.

   D It should have a second ionisation energy very much larger than the first.

   E It should have some properties resembling those of metals.

19 An excess of potassium iodide solution was added to bromine water and then excess sodium thiosulphate solution was added. At the end of the reactions, the two halogens are present as

   A Br_2 and I_2

   B Br_2 and I^-

   C Br^- and I_2

   D Br^- and I^-

   E Br^-, I^- and I_2

20 When concentrated sulphuric acid is added to solid samples of sodium chloride, sodium bromide and sodium iodide, which of the following halogen-containing compounds are produced?

   A HCl, HBr and HI only

   B HCl, HBr and I_2 only

   C HCl, HBr, Br_2, HI and I_2 only

   D HCl, Cl_2, Br_2 and I_2 only

   E Cl_2, Br_2 and I_2 only

TEST 18
Group IV—carbon to lead, non-metal to metal

This test is composed of fifteen questions. For each question, five possible answers are suggested. These answers are labelled **A**, **B**, **C**, **D** and **E**. Select the most appropriate *one* of the answers and write its corresponding letter on a separate answer sheet.

1 Diamond and graphite are classed as allotropes because

   A they are different crystalline forms of the same element.

   B they have different melting points and boiling points.

   C their atoms contain different numbers of neutrons.

   D the bonding in their structures is different.

   E they form different oxides on burning in oxygen.

2 Graphite conducts electricity because

   A it is crystalline.

   B it contains an excess of electrons.

   C its atoms are close together.

   D it contains carbon ions.

   E its electrons are de-localised.

3 The half-life of radioactive $^{14}_{6}C$ is 5000 years. 12 g of this isotope will

   A contain 6×10^{23} atoms.

   B decay to 3 g in 10 000 years.

   C decay to 9 g in 2500 years.

   D disappear in 10 000 years.

   E eventually decay to $^{12}_{6}C$.

4 All the elements in Group IV form

   A simple molecular chlorides.

   B amphoteric oxides.

   C more than one hydride.

   D stable hydrides.

   E ionic sulphides.

5 Which *one* of the following oxides is most stable on heating in air at 750°C?

   A CO

   B SiO

   C GeO

   D SnO

   E PbO

6 CO_2 and SiO_2 are both

   A gaseous at room temperature.

   B linear molecules.

   C soluble in dilute HCl(aq).

   D soluble in concentrated NaOH(aq).

   E amphoteric oxides.

7 In which *one* of the following equations is silicon(IV) oxide acting as a base?

   A $SiO_2 + 4HF \rightarrow SiF_4 + 2H_2O$

   B $SiO_2 + 2KOH \rightarrow K_2SiO_3 + H_2O$

   C $SiO_2 + CaO \rightarrow CaSiO_3$

   D $SiO_2 + 4Mg \rightarrow Mg_2Si + 2MgO$

   E $SiO_2 + 4F_2 \rightarrow SiF_4 + 2F_2O$

8 As the atomic number of the Group IV elements increases, their dioxides become

   A more covalent.

   B stronger oxidising agents.

   C more acidic.

   D more stable to heat.

   E more soluble in water.

9 Which *one* of the following chlorides decomposes most readily on heating?

   A $SiCl_4$

   B $SnCl_2$

   C $SnCl_4$

   D $PbCl_2$

   E $PbCl_4$

10 Tin(IV) chloride

   A is formed when hydrogen chloride reacts with molten tin.

   B is a strong reducing agent at room temperature.

   C conducts electricity in the liquid state.

   D has a lower boiling point than tin(II) chloride.

   E has more ionic character than tin(II) chloride.

11 Which *one* of the following equations correctly shows the reaction of a Group IV tetrachloride with water?

    A $CCl_4 + 2H_2O \rightarrow CO_2 + 4HCl$

    B $SiCl_4 + H_2O \rightarrow SiOCl_2 + 2HCl$

    C $GeCl_4 + H_2O \rightarrow GeO + Cl_2 + 2HCl$

    D $SnCl_4 + 4H_2O \rightarrow Sn(OH)_4 + 4HCl$

    E $3PbCl_4 + 4H_2O \rightarrow Pb_3O_4 + 8HCl + 2Cl_2$

12 Which *one* of the following reagents will give a precipitate when added in excess to aqueous lead(II) nitrate?

    A concentrated HNO_3

    B concentrated HCl

    C dilute HCl

    D concentrated NaOH

    E dilute NaOH

13 What is the shape of the methyl carbocation, CH_3^+, with respect to atoms?

    A pyramidal

    B square planar

    C tetrahedral

    D trigonal planar

    E V-shaped

14 As the atomic number of elements in Group IV increases

    A the hydroxide XH_4 becomes more stable.

    B the oxidation state $+4$ becomes more stable.

    C the element becomes more electronegative.

    D the oxide XO becomes more acidic.

    E the chloride XCl_2 has increasing ionic character.

15 Which of the following has a non-zero dipole moment?

    A CO_2

    B CH_4

    C C_2H_4

    D CCl_4

    E H_2CO

TEST 19
The transition metals

This test is composed of twenty-three questions. For each question, five possible answers are suggested. These answers are labelled **A**, **B**, **C**, **D** and **E**. Select the most appropriate *one* of the answers and write its corresponding letter on a separate answer sheet.

1   Which *one* of the following represents the correct electronic structure of an isolated Cr^{3+} ion?
    ((Ar) $\equiv$ electron structure of an argon atom)

    A $(Ar)3d^34s^1$

    B $(Ar)3d^24s^1$

    C $(Ar)3d^14s^2$

    D $(Ar)3d^4$

    E $(Ar)3d^3$

2   Which *one* of the following provides the most satisfactory definition of a transition metal?
    A transition metal is an element which

    A occurs in the '*d*-block' of the periodic table.

    B has variable oxidation state in its compounds.

    C forms an ion with a partially filled '*d* sub-shell'.

    D has similar properties to its neighbours in the periodic table.

    E lies between scandium and zinc in the periodic table.

3   Transition metals are the only elements which

    A form complex ions with hydroxide ions.

    B form coloured ions in aqueous solution.

    C form amphoteric oxides and hydroxides.

    D form covalently bonded anhydrous chlorides.

    E show an oxidation number higher than 4.

4   Compared to the '*s*-block' metals, transition metals generally form

    A oxides which are more basic.

    B oxides which are more soluble.

    C salts which are more stable.

    D salts which are more ionic.

    E ions which are reduced more easily.

5   Which *one* of the following ions has the smallest radius?

    A Cr^{3+}

    B Ni^{2+}

    C Ni^{3+}

    D Ti^{2+}

    E Ti^{3+}

6   Which *one* of the following ions will catalyse the reaction of $I^-(aq)$ with $S_2O_8^{2-}(aq)$ least effectively?

    A Cr^{3+}

    B Fe^{3+}

    C Sc^{3+}

    D Ti^{3+}

    E V^{3+}

7   Which *one* of the following metals forms the complex ions $[M(NH_3)_4]^{2+}$ and $[M(NH_3)_2]^+$?

    A Cu

    B Ag

    C Sc

    D Pb

    E Zn

8   Which *one* of the following pairs of ions can form isomorphous salts?

    A Fe^{2+}, Fe^{3+}

    B $Cr_2O_7^{2-}$, CrO_4^{2-}

    C MnO_4^{2-}, MnO_4^-

    D CrO_4^{2-}, MnO_4^{2-}

    E Fe^{3+}, Mn^{2+}

9   The three commonest oxidation states of manganese are

    A $+2, +3, +4$

    B $+2, +3, +6$

    C $+2, +4, +7$

    D $+3, +4, +7$

    E $+3, +6, +7$

10 One of the isomers of $CrCl_3.6H_2O$ dissolves in water forming a solution from which only one-third of the total chloride present is precipitated by $AgNO_3(aq)$. Which *one* of the following represents the correct structure for the complexed chromium ion in the aqueous solution? .

A $[Cr(H_2O)_6]^{3+}$

B $[CrCl_2]^+$

C $[CrCl]^{2+}$

D $[Cr(H_2O)_5Cl]^{2+}$

E $[Cr(H_2O)_4Cl_2]^+$

Questions **11–18** refer to the five transition elements labelled **A** to **E** below.

A Cr

B Co

C Ni

D Ag

E V

Which *one* of these transition elements

11 has the greatest number of oxidation states?

12 most resembles the element with electronic structure 2, 8, 18, 15, 2?

13 is used as a catalyst in the hardening of vegetable oils?

14 might be left in the sludge at the bottom of a cell after the electrolytic refining of copper?

15 forms a complex anion of formula XO_3^-?

16 forms complex ions in which the cation normally has a co-ordination number of two?

17 has the smallest density?

18 forms compounds with similar properties to analogous sulphur compounds?

19 Which *one* of the following species *cannot* act as a ligand in the formation of complexes of transition metal ions?

A CH_3NH_2

B $H_2NCH_2CH_2NH_2$

C $(CH_3NH_3)^+$

D $C_6H_5NH_2$

E CN^-

20 Vanadium has the electron structure $1s^22s^22p^6 3s^23p^63d^34s^2$. Which one of the following suggested compounds of vanadium is *unlikely* to exist?

A $VOCl_2$

B Na_2VO_3

C $(NH_4)_3VO_4$

D Na_4VO_4

E K_2VO_4

21 In which of the following compounds does cobalt have an oxidation number of $+3$?

A $K_4Co(CN)_6$

B K_3CoF_6

C Na_3CoCl_5

D $Na_2Co(NO_2)_6$

E $Co(NH_3)_6SO_4$

22 Which element has the atomic configuration $1s^22s^22p^63s^23p^63d^54s^1$?

A V

B Cr

C Mn

D Fe

E Cu

23 How many orbitals are there with the principal quantum number, $n = 3$?

A 1

B 3

C 4

D 5

E 9

TEST 20
Metals and the activity series

This test is composed of twenty-one questions. For each question, five possible answers are suggested. These answers are labelled **A**, **B**, **C**, **D** and **E**. Select the most appropriate *one* of the answers and write its corresponding letter on a separate answer sheet.

1   Which *one* of the following *never* occurs as an uncombined element in the earth's crust?

   A carbon

   B copper

   C lead

   D silver

   E sulphur

2   Which *one* of the following statements helps to explain why limestone ($CaCO_3$) is added to the blast furnace during the manufacture of iron?

   A $CaCO_3$ forms an acidic gas on decomposition.

   B $CaCO_3$ forms a basic oxide on decomposition.

   C $CaCO_3$ provides a refractory lining for the furnace.

   D $CaCO_3$ floats on the hot molten iron.

   E $CaCO_3$ increases the furnace temperatures.

3   Which *one* of the following metals is used as a protective layer and as a sacrificial metal for iron and steel objects?

   A copper

   B magnesium

   C zinc

   D tin

   E nickel

4   Copper is extracted from copper pyrites ($CuFeS_2$) by roasting the concentrated ore in air to form copper(I) sulphide. The impure copper(I) sulphide is then heated in air forming copper(I) oxide. The copper(I) oxide is finally reduced to copper by

   A heating strongly in the absence of air.

   B heating with unchanged Cu_2S in the absence of air.

   C heating with silica in a closed furnace.

   D heating with coke in the absence of air.

   E heating with coke in a blast furnace.

5   In which *one* of the following formulae does copper show the highest oxidation state?

   A $CuFeS_2$

   B $CuClCO.2H_2O$

   C H_2CuCl_3

   D $Cu(NH_3)Cl.H_2O$

   E $K_3Cu(CN)_4$

6   Unlike the compounds and complex ions of most transition metals, those of the copper(I) ion are often white or colourless. The lack of colour in these compounds may be explained by the fact that the Cu^+ ion has

   A no unpaired electrons.

   B no electrons in the fourth quantum shell.

   C no unfilled *d*-orbitals.

   D no delocalised electrons.

   E *d*-orbitals of equal energy.

7   Which *one* of the following substances would *not* give a visible reaction with dilute sulphuric acid?

   A $Li_2CO_3(aq)$

   B $Ba(NO_3)_2(aq)$

   C $FeS(s)$

   D $NaOH(aq)$

   E $Na_2SO_3(s)$

Questions **8–14** refer to the five methods (**A**, **B**, **C**, **D** and **E**) listed below which are used to extract metals from their ores.

   A electrolysis of the molten chloride

   B electrolysis of a molten mixture containing the oxide

   C reduction of the oxide with coke

   D displacement from aqueous solution

   E reduction of the oxide or chloride with a more reactive metal

Which of these methods is used industrially to obtain

8 aluminium

9 barium

10 magnesium

11 silver

12 tin

13 titanium

14 zinc

Questions **15–21** refer to the five ions labelled **A**, **B**, **C**, **D** and **E** below.

A $Ca^{2+}(aq)$

B $Cu^{2+}(aq)$

C $Fe^{2+}(aq)$

D $Fe^{3+}(aq)$

E $Pb^{2+}(aq)$

Which *one* of these aqueous ions

15 gives a precipitate with $NaOH(aq)$ which dissolves in excess?

16 gives a precipitate with $NH_3(aq)$ which dissolves in excess?

17 gives a precipitate with both dilute $H_2SO_4(aq)$ and dilute $HCl(aq)$?

18 is the weakest oxidising agent?

19 gives a blood red solution with $NCS^-(aq)$?

20 gives a dark blue precipitate with $[Fe(CN)_6]^{3-}(aq)$?

21 gives a cream precipitate and a brown solution with $I^-(aq)$?

TEST 21
Equilibria

This test is composed of seventeen questions. For each question, five possible answers are suggested. These answers are labelled **A**, **B**, **C**, **D** and **E**. Select the most appropriate *one* of the answers and write its corresponding letter on a separate answer sheet.

1   The value of K, the partition coefficient for the distribution of a solute between two immiscible solvents changes when

   A the volumes of the solvents change.

   B the concentration of solute in one solvent approaches zero.

   C the volumes of the solvents differ greatly.

   D the mass of solute changes.

   E the temperature of the system changes.

2   The partition coefficient of a solute W between solvents X and Y is *a*. This statement can be written as

   A $\dfrac{[\text{W in X}]}{[\text{W in Y}]} = a$ **D** $\dfrac{[\text{X in W}]}{[\text{Y in W}]} = a$

   B $\dfrac{[\text{W in X}]}{[\text{W in Y}]} = \dfrac{1}{a}$ **E** $\dfrac{[\text{X in W}]}{[\text{Y in W}]} = \dfrac{1}{a}$

   C $\dfrac{[\text{W in Y}]}{[\text{W in X}]} = a$

3   The partition coefficient of solute X between tetrachloromethane and water is 4. If a solution of 20 g of X in $100\,cm^3$ of water is extracted with two $100\,cm^3$ portions of tetrachloromethane in succession, what mass of X is removed by the tetrachloro-methane?

   A 4.8 g   **D** 18.75 g

   B 8.75 g   **E** 19.2 g

   C 16.0 g

4   Which *one* of the following systems is *not* in dynamic equilibrium at room temperature?

   A iodine in a closed container

   B a strip of copper in $CuSO_4(aq)$

   C solid NaCl in saturated NaCl(aq)

   D a cell through which a constant current passes

   E gaseous NO_2 in a closed container

5   Which *one* of the following will change the value of K_c?

   A change in concentration

   B change in pressure

   C change in temperature

   D employing a catalyst

   E adding more reactant

6   At a particular temperature, the equilibrium constant for the reaction $P + Q \rightleftharpoons R + S$ is 10^{10}. From this information we can deduce that P and Q react

   A rapidly to form a high proportion of R and S at equilibrium.

   B slowly to form a high proportion of R and S at equilibrium.

   C at an unknown rate to form a high proportion of R and S at equilibrium.

   D rapidly to form a low proportion of R and S at equilibrium.

   E slowly to form a low proportion of R and S at equilibrium.

7   What are the units of K_p for the reaction represented by the equation $NO(g) + \frac{1}{2}O_2(g) \rightleftharpoons NO_2(g)$?

   A $(Pa)^{-\frac{1}{2}}$ **D** $(Pa)^{-1}$

   B $(Pa)^{\frac{1}{2}}$ **E** $(Pa)^{1\frac{1}{2}}$

   C Pa

8   The equilibrium constant, K_c, for the reaction

$$N_2(g) + 3H_2(g) \rightleftharpoons 2NH_3(g)$$

is $2\,mol^{-2}\,dm^6$ at 620 K. What is the concentration of NH_3 at equilibrium at 620 K, when the equilibrium concentrations of both N_2 and H_2 are 2 $mol\,dm^{-3}$?

   A $2\,mol\,dm^{-3}$

   B $\sqrt{8}\,mol\,dm^{-3}$

   C $4\,mol\,dm^{-3}$

   D $\sqrt{32}\,mol\,dm^{-3}$

   E $32\,mol\,dm^{-3}$

9 The equilibrium constant for the reaction represented by the following equation is 4.

$$W(g) + X(g) \rightleftharpoons Y(g) + Z(g)$$

How many moles of X are present in the equilibrium mixture formed when one mole of W is mixed with one mole of X?

A 2

D $\frac{2}{3}$

B $1\frac{1}{2}$

E $\frac{1}{3}$

C $\frac{3}{4}$

10 The numerical value of K_p for the reaction

$$X_2(g) + 3Y_2(g) \rightleftharpoons 2XY_3(g)$$

is 10^2 at a particular temperature.
What is the numerical value of K_p for the reaction

$$XY_3(g) \rightleftharpoons \tfrac{1}{2}X_2(g) + \tfrac{3}{2}Y_2(g)$$

at the same temperature?

A $\dfrac{1}{10^2} \times \dfrac{1}{2}$

D $\dfrac{-10^2}{2}$

B $\dfrac{1}{10}$

E 10^2

C $\dfrac{1}{10^2}$

11 The equilibrium constants for the following reactions were measured at a certain temperature.

$$CO(g) + H_2O(g) \rightleftharpoons CO_2(g) + H_2(g) \quad K_p = \tfrac{4}{10}$$

$$CO(g) + \tfrac{1}{2}O_2(g) \rightleftharpoons CO_2(g) \quad K_p = 10^4 (Pa)^{-\frac{1}{2}}$$

What is the numerical value of K_p for the reaction below at the same temperature?

$$H_2O(g) \rightleftharpoons H_2(g) + \tfrac{1}{2}O_2(g)$$

A 4×10^3

D $\dfrac{10^5}{4}$

B $\dfrac{1}{4 \times 10^3}$

E It is not calculable from the data given.

C $\dfrac{4}{10^7}$

12 The partial pressures of SO_2, O_2 and SO_3 in equilibrium at a particular temperature are

$$P_{SO_2} = 4 \times 10^5 \, Pa, \quad P_{O_2} = P_{SO_3} = 2 \times 10^5 \, Pa$$

What is K_p for the reaction,

$$2SO_2(g) + O_2(g) \rightleftharpoons 2SO_3(g),$$

at this temperature?

A $\dfrac{1}{8 \times 10^5} \, (Pa)^{-1}$

D $8 \times 10^5 \, (Pa)^{-1}$

B $\dfrac{1}{8 \times 10^5} \, Pa$

E $8 \times 10^5 \, Pa$

C $\dfrac{1}{4 \times 10^5} \, (Pa)^{-1}$

13 When nickel is heated with carbon monoxide at 70°C, the following equilibrium is established.

$$Ni(s) + 4CO(g) \rightleftharpoons Ni(CO)_4(g)$$

What is the equilibrium constant, K_c, for this reaction?

A $\dfrac{[Ni(s)][CO(g)]^4}{[Ni(CO)_4(g)]}$

D $\dfrac{[Ni(CO)_4(g)]}{[CO(g)]^4}$

B $\dfrac{[Ni(CO)_4(g)]}{[Ni(s)][CO(g)]^4}$

E $\dfrac{[Ni(CO)_4(g)]}{[CO(g)]}$

C $\dfrac{[CO(g)]^4}{[Ni(CO)_4(g)]}$

Questions **14** and **15** refer to the following equilibrium.

$$[Ag(NH_3)_2]^+(aq) + I^-(aq) \rightleftharpoons AgI(s) + 2NH_3(aq)$$

$mol\,dm^{-3}$	a	b	c	d
at equilibrium				

14 The numerical value of K_c for this reaction is

A $\dfrac{ab}{cd^2}$

D $\dfrac{cd^2}{ab}$

B $\dfrac{d}{ab}$

E $\dfrac{d^2}{ab}$

C $\dfrac{ab}{d^2}$

15 When concentrated $NH_3(aq)$ is added to the equilibrium mixture, which *one* of the following will be unchanged once equilibrium is restored?

A the concentration of $[Ag(NH_3)_2]^+(aq)$

B the concentration of $I^-(aq)$

C the concentration of $NH_3(aq)$

D the mass of AgI

E the value of K_c

Questions **16** and **17**. A mixture, initially containing 2 mol of $CO(g)$ and 1 mol of $Cl_2(g)$, reached equilibrium with $COCl_2(g)$ when 75% of the Cl_2 had reacted.

16 If the total final pressure was P Pa, what is the partial pressure of $COCl_2(g)$ in the equilibrium mixture?

A $\tfrac{1}{4}P$ Pa

D $\tfrac{3}{2}P$ Pa

B $\tfrac{1}{3}P$ Pa

E $\tfrac{9}{4}P$ Pa

C $\tfrac{3}{4}P$ Pa

17 What is the equilibrium constant, K_p, for this reaction?

A $\dfrac{3P}{4} \, (Pa)^{-1}$

D $\dfrac{3}{5P} \, (Pa)^{-1}$

B $\dfrac{12}{5P} \, (Pa)^{-1}$

E $\dfrac{12}{5} \, (Pa)^{-1}$

C $\dfrac{27}{5P} \, (Pa)^{-1}$

TEST 22
Factors affecting equilibria

This test is composed of twenty questions. For each question, five possible answers are suggested. These answers are labelled **A**, **B**, **C**, **D** and **E**. Select the most appropriate *one* of the answers and write its corresponding letter on a separate answer sheet.

1   The concentration of $PCl_5(g)$ in the equilibrium,

$$PCl_3(g) + Cl_2(g) \rightleftharpoons PCl_5(g)$$

is increased by

A adding phosphorus to the equilibrium mixture.

B decreasing the total pressure.

C adding a noble gas to the equilibrium mixture.

D decreasing the volume of the container.

E using an appropriate catalyst.

2   In which of the following equilibria will an increase in pressure at constant temperature increase the yield of products on the right-hand side of the equation?

A $NO_2(g) \rightleftharpoons NO(g) + \frac{1}{2}O_2(g)$

B $BaCO_3(s) \rightleftharpoons BaO(s) + CO_2(g)$

C $H_2(g) + Br_2(g) \rightleftharpoons 2HBr(g)$

D $3Fe(s) + 4H_2O(g) \rightleftharpoons Fe_3O_4(s) + 4H_2(g)$

E $4NO(g) + 6H_2O(g) \rightleftharpoons 4NH_3(g) + 5O_2(g)$

3   In the endothermic homogeneous gas-phase reaction

$$P + Q \rightleftharpoons R + S,$$

the yield of R at equilibrium is increased by

A raising the total pressure.

B using a suitable catalyst.

C reducing the volume of the container.

D removing S as it is produced.

E lowering the temperature.

4   For a certain reaction, K_p at 300 K is 1.0 and K_p at 600 K is 2.0. From this, we can deduce that

A K_p at 450 K is 1.5.

B increase in pressure favours the formation of products.

C the reaction is endothermic.

D K_p increases with increase in pressure.

E there is a decrease in volume on reaction.

5   In an equilibrium reaction, a positive catalyst increases

A the rate of the reverse reaction.

B the kinetic energy of the reacting particles.

C the equilibrium constant of the reaction.

D the activation energy of the reaction.

E the exothermicity of the reaction.

6   Positive catalysts

A are unchanged physically at the end of a reaction.

B are unchanged chemically throughout a reaction.

C affect the position of equilibrium of a reaction.

D are involved in the mechanism of a reaction.

E require the presence of a promoter.

7   Exothermic reactions always have

A fast reaction rates.

B small activation energies.

C small equilibrium constants.

D negative enthalpy changes.

E unstable reactants.

8   For the reaction, $N_2(g) + 3H_2(g) \rightleftharpoons 2NH_3(g)$; $\Delta H = -92\,kJ$. Increasing the temperature at constant pressure will increase

A the yield of ammonia at equilibrium.

B the time to reach equilibrium.

C the rates of forward and backward reactions.

D the value of the equilibrium constant.

E the partial pressure of ammonia at equilibrium.

9   Which *one* of the following sets of conditions would give the highest yield of $CO_2(g)$ from $CaCO_3(s)$ in the equilibrium below?

$$CaCO_3(s) \rightleftharpoons CaO(s) + CO_2(g); \Delta H = +178\,kJ$$

A 1000°C and 1×10^6 Pa

B 1000°C and 1×10^5 Pa

C 500°C and 1×10^6 Pa

D 500°C and 1×10^5 Pa

E 100°C and 1×10^5 Pa

10 The synthesis of ammonia from nitrogen and hydrogen is exothermic. During the manufacture of ammonia, this reaction is carried out at only moderate temperatures because high temperatures

    A reduce the efficiency of the catalyst.

    B reduce the yield of ammonia at equilibrium.

    C are very difficult to maintain.

    D result in a reaction rate which is too fast.

    E are attained once the reaction is underway.

11 $2SO_2(g) + O_2(g) \rightleftharpoons 2SO_3(g); \Delta H = -197\,kJ$

Which *one* of the following can be deduced from the information above?

    A the qualitative effect of temperature on the equilibrium mixture

    B the composition of the equilibrium mixture

    C the ideal reaction conditions

    D the fact that a catalyst is necessary

    E the activation energy of the reaction

12 The value of the equilibrium constant for the reaction

$$H_2(g) + I_2(g) \rightleftharpoons 2HI(g)$$

can be altered by

    A adding iodine to the system.

    B adding oxygen to the system.

    C increasing the total pressure.

    D increasing the temperature.

    E adding a suitable catalyst.

13 Assuming that K_1 and K_2 are the respective equilibrium constants for the reactions

$$H_2(g) + Cl_2(g) \rightleftharpoons 2HCl(g)$$

and

$$2H_2(g) + O_2(g) \rightleftharpoons 2H_2O(g)$$

under given conditions, what is the equilibrium constant for the reaction

$$4HCl(g) + O_2(g) \rightleftharpoons 2H_2O(g) + 2Cl_2(g)$$

under the same conditions?

    A $\dfrac{2K_1}{K_2}$ **D** $\dfrac{K_1^2}{K_2}$

    B $\dfrac{K_2}{K_1}$ **E** $\dfrac{K_2}{K_1}$

    C $\dfrac{K_2}{2K_1}$

14 Sulphuric acid is used in cleaning steel because it

    A dissolves grease.   **D** renders iron passive.

    B reacts with iron.   **E** prevents rusting

    C removes rust.

15 Which *one* of the following substances can be used to dry moist ammonia?

    A concentrated sulphuric acid

    B anhydrous copper(II) sulphate

    C calcium oxide

    D phosphorus pentoxide

    E glacial acetic acid

16 All explosives

    A contain oxygen.

    B decompose spontaneously.

    C liberate gases on explosion.

    D contain carbon compounds.

    E are made from concentrated HNO_3.

Questions **17–20**

17 Ethene may be obtained by the catalytic cracking of ethane.

$$C_2H_6(g) \rightleftharpoons C_2H_4(g) + H_2(g); \Delta H = +137\,kJ$$
$$K_c = 10^{-5}\,mol\,dm^{-3}$$

The proportion of ethane converted to ethene at equilibrium could be increased by

    A raising the initial pressure of ethane.

    B using a more efficient catalyst.

    C raising the temperature.

    D reducing the volume of the container.

    E mixing hydrogen with ethane before reaction.

18 What is the approximate equilibrium concentration of ethene in $mol\,dm^{-3}$, if the initial concentration of ethane is $10^{-1}\,mol\,dm^{-3}$ and the initial concentrations of hydrogen and ethene are both zero?

    A 10^{-6} **B** $\frac{1}{2} \times 10^{-6}$ **C** 10^{-4}

    D 10^{-3} **E** 10^{-2}

19 In order to obtain a correct result in the last question, it is necessary to assume that

    A only a small proportion of ethane has reacted.

    B almost all the ethane has formed ethene.

    C the equilibrium constant is effectively zero.

    D one mole of gas occupies $22.4\,dm^3$ at s.t.p.

    E the catalyst exerts zero pressure.

20 If the initial concentration of ethane were increased from $0.1\,mol\,dm^{-3}$ to $0.2\,mol\,dm^{-3}$, the concentration of ethene at equilibrium would change by a factor of about

    A $\dfrac{1}{2}$ **B** $\dfrac{1}{\sqrt{2}}$ **C** $\sqrt{2}$

    D 2 **E** 4

TEST 23
Ionic equilibria in aqueous solution

This test is composed of twenty questions. For each question, five possible answers are suggested. These answers are labelled **A**, **B**, **C**, **D** and **E**. Select the most appropriate *one* of the answers and write its corresponding letter on a separate answer sheet.

1 What is the expression for the solubility product of silver chromate(VI)?

  A $2[Ag^+][CrO_4^{2-}]$

  B $4[Ag^+]^2[CrO_4^{2-}]$

  C $[Ag^+]^2[CrO_4^{2-}]$

  D $\dfrac{2[Ag^+][CrO_4^{2-}]}{[Ag_2CrO_4]}$

  E $\dfrac{[Ag^+]^2[CrO_4^{2-}]}{[Ag_2CrO_4]}$

2 If the solubility of calcium carbonate, $CaCO_3$, is s $mol\,dm^{-3}$, what is the numerical value of its solubility product at the same temperature?

  A $\sqrt{s}$

  B s

  C $\dfrac{s^2}{4}$

  D s^2

  E $4s^2$

3 What is the solubility of lead chloride ($PbCl_2$) in water at 298 K, if $K_{sp} = 2 \times 10^{-5}\,mol^3\,dm^{-9}$?

  A $\dfrac{2 \times 10^{-5}}{3}\,mol\,dm^{-3}$

  B $\sqrt{2 \times 10^{-5}}\,mol\,dm^{-3}$

  C $\sqrt[3]{2 \times 10^{-5}}\,mol\,dm^{-3}$

  D $\sqrt[3]{\dfrac{2 \times 10^{-5}}{2}}\,mol\,dm^{-3}$

  E $\sqrt[3]{\dfrac{2 \times 10^{-5}}{4}}\,mol\,dm^{-3}$

4 If the solubility of bismuth sulphide (Bi_2S_3) in water at a given temperature is x $mol\,dm^{-3}$, what is the solubility product of bismuth sulphide at the same temperature?

  A x^5

  B $5x^5$

  C $(2x)^5$

  D $(2x)^2(3x)^3$

  E $(5x)^5$

5 The solubility product of aluminium hydroxide is $1 \times 10^{-33}\,mol^4\,dm^{-12}$ What is the maximum $[OH^-]$ in $mol\,dm^{-3}$, in a solution in which $[Al^{3+}]$ is $10^{-9}\,mol\,dm^{-3}$?

  A $\dfrac{10^{-24}}{3}$

  B 10^{-24}

  C 10^{-12}

  D $\dfrac{10^{-8}}{3}$

  E 10^{-8}

6 The solubility of lead sulphate in pure water at 298 K is $1.20 \times 10^{-4}\,mol\,dm^{-3}$. What is the numerical value of the solubility of lead sulphate in $1.00\,mol\,dm^{-3}$ H_2SO_4 at this temperature?

  A 1.44×10^{-8}

  B 1.20×10^{-4}

  C $\sqrt{1.2 \times 10^{-4}}$

  D $1.00 - 1.2 \times 10^{-4}$

  E 1.00

7 The solubility products of four metal sulphates in $mol^2\,dm^{-6}$ are $K_{sp}(BaSO_4) = 1 \times 10^{-10}$, $K_{sp}(PbSO_4) = 2 \times 10^{-8}$, $K_{sp}(SrSO_4) = 3 \times 10^{-7}$ and $K_{sp}(CaSO_4) = 9 \times 10^{-6}$. Which of these metal sulphates will be precipitated if a $0.0001\,mol\,dm^{-3}$ solution of sulphate ions, SO_4^{2-}, is mixed with an equal volume of a $0.0001\,mol\,dm^{-3}$ solution of the appropriate metal ions?

  A $BaSO_4$ only

  B $BaSO_4$ and $PbSO_4$ only

  C $BaSO_4$, $PbSO_4$ and $SrSO_4$ only

  D $CaSO_4$ and $SrSO_4$ only

  E $CaSO_4$, $SrSO_4$ and $PbSO_4$ only

8 The solubility of AgI will be greater in

  A $KNO_3(aq)$ than in water.

  B $KI(aq)$ than in water.

  C $AgNO_3(aq)$ than in water.

  D water than in $KNO_3(aq)$.

  E water than in $AgNO_3(aq)$.

9 If the pH of a strong monobasic acid is 2.17, what is the concentration of the acid in $mol\,dm^{-3}$?

  A between 0.0001 and 0.001

  B between 0.001 and 0.01

  C between 0.01 and 0.10

  D between 0.10 and 1.00

  E greater than 1.00

10 What is the pH of a solution of sulphuric acid containing $0.2 \, \text{mol dm}^{-3}$? (Assume the acid is completely dissociated and take $\lg 2 = 0.3$)

A 0.03   D 0.60

B 0.33   E 1.60

C 0.40

11 The pH of a $0.10 \, \text{mol dm}^{-3}$ solution of a weak alkali could be

A 4   D 12

B 6   E 14

C 9

12 The pH of an alkaline solution is 8. Which *one* of the following expressions is correct?

A $[OH^-] = 10^{-8}$ D $-\lg[H^+] = 6$

B $\lg[OH^-] = 8$ E $\lg[H^+] = -8$

C $-\lg[OH^-] = 8$

13 At 298 K, the numerical value of the ionic product of water, K_w, is 10^{-14}. The corresponding value of the equilibrium constant for

$$H_2O + H_2O \rightleftharpoons H_3O^+ + OH^-$$

is

A $10^{-14} \times \dfrac{18}{1000} \times \dfrac{18}{1000}$

B $10^{-14} \times \dfrac{18}{1000}$

C $10^{-14} \times \dfrac{18}{1000} \times 2$

D $10^{-14} \times \dfrac{1000}{18}$

E $10^{-14} \times \dfrac{1000}{18} \times \dfrac{1000}{18}$

14 The dissociation constant of butanoic acid ($CH_3CH_2CH_2COOH$) at 298 K is $1.5 \times 10^{-5} \, \text{mol dm}^{-3}$. What is the approximate hydrogen ion concentration, in mol dm^{-3}, of a $0.1 \, \text{mol dm}^{-3}$ solution of butanoic acid at 298 K?

A $\sqrt{1.5 \times 10^{-4}}$ D 1.5×10^{-5}

B $\sqrt{1.5 \times 10^{-6}}$ E 1.5×10^{-6}

C 1.5×10^{-4}

15 $1.0 \, \text{mol dm}^{-3}$ NaOH is added to $100 \, \text{cm}^3$ of $1.0 \, \text{mol dm}^{-3}$ CH_3COOH. How many cm^3 of $1.0 \, \text{mol dm}^{-3}$ NaOH must be added before the maximum buffering effect occurs?

A $33\frac{1}{3}$ D 75

B 50   E 150

C $66\frac{2}{3}$

16 The pH ranges and colour changes for two acid–base indicators are given below.

Indicator	pH range
Congo red	violet 3.0–5.0 red
Bromothymol blue	yellow 6.0–7.6 blue

A solution in which congo red is violet and bromothymol blue is yellow is

A strongly acidic   D weakly alkaline

B weakly acidic   E strongly alkaline

C neutral

17 The indicator, HX, is a weak acid.

$$HX(aq) \rightleftharpoons H^+(aq) + X^-(aq)$$

$$K_a(HX) = 10^{-10} \, \text{mol dm}^{-3}$$

When HX is used in the titration of a strong acid with a strong base, the indicator will change colour when

A $[H^+] = 10^{-10} \, \text{mol dm}^{-3}$ D $[H^+] = [X^-]$

B $[H^+] = 10^{-7} \, \text{mol dm}^{-3}$ E $[H^+] = [HX]$

C $[H^+] = 10^{-5} \, \text{mol dm}^{-3}$

Questions **18–20** refer to the graph below which shows how the pH of a solution changes during a certain titration.

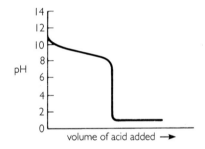

18 At which pH does the maximum buffering effect occur?

A 2   D 9

B 5   E 11

C 8

19 To which *one* of the following titrations does the curve relate?

A strong base with strong acid

B strong base with weak acid

C weak base with strong acid

D weak base with weak acid

E weak base with concentrated acid

20 If the initial concentration of the base is $0.1 \, \text{mol dm}^{-3}$, what is the approximate numerical value of its dissociation constant? (Assume the base is monoacidic.)

A 10^{-2} D 10^{-6}

B 10^{-4} E 10^{-7}

C 10^{-5}

TEST 24
Entropy and free energy

This test is composed of nineteen questions. For each question, five possible answers are suggested. These answers are labelled **A**, **B**, **C**, **D** and **E**. Select the most appropriate *one* of the answers and write its corresponding letter on a separate answer sheet.

1 For all spontaneous changes

    A S must increase.

    B ΔH must be positive.

    C K must be negative.

    D ΔS must increase.

    E W must decrease.

2 How many different ways are there of sharing 3 quanta of energy between two molecules?

    A 1

    B 2

    C 3

    D 4

    E 5

3 Substances with low standard entropies usually have

    A low densities.

    B low boiling points.

    C strong bonds.

    D low formula masses.

    E high volatilities.

Questions **4** and **5** refer to the five reactions labelled **A**, **B**, **C**, **D** and **E** below.

    A $2Zn(s) + O_2(g) \rightarrow 2MgO(s)$

    B $H^+(aq) + OH^-(aq) \rightarrow H_2O(l)$

    C ethene $\rightarrow$ polythene

    D $2NaNO_3(s) \rightarrow 2NaNO_2(s) + O_2(g)$

    E $CH_4(g) + 2O_2(g) \rightarrow CO_2(g) + 2H_2O(g)$

4 For which one of the above reactions does ΔS have a large positive value?

5 For which one of the above reactions is the value of ΔS approximately zero?

6 When ammonium chloride dissolves in water,

$$NH_4Cl(s) \rightarrow NH_4^+(aq) + Cl^-(aq)$$

$\Delta G^\ominus = -6.7\,kJ\,mol^{-1}$ and $\Delta H^\ominus = +16\,kJ\,mol^{-1}$.

The value of $\Delta S^\ominus_{surroundings}$ for this process in $J\,K^{-1}\,mol^{-1}$ is therefore

    A $\dfrac{-6700}{298}$ **D** $\dfrac{16\,000}{298}$

    B $\dfrac{6700}{298}$ **E** $\dfrac{16\,000}{273}$

    C $\dfrac{-16\,000}{298}$

Questions **7–9** refer to the processes labelled **A** to **E** below.

    A Exhaust gases mix with air.

    B Charcoal burns on a barbecue.

    C Water vapour evaporates from a puddle.

    D Photosynthesis occurs.

    E Petrol explodes in a car's cylinders.

7 For which of the above processes is ΔH positive and ΔS_{system} positive?

8 For which of the above processes is ΔH positive and ΔS_{system} negative?

9 For which of the above processes is ΔH zero and ΔH_{system} positive?

10 For the reaction,

$$N_2(g) + 3H_2(g) \rightarrow 2NH_3(g)$$

$\Delta G^\ominus = -67\,kJ\,mol^{-1}$ and $\Delta H^\ominus = -184\,kJ\,mol^{-1}$.

What is the value of $\Delta S^\ominus_{system}$ for the reaction in $J\,K^{-1}\,mol^{-1}$?

    A $\dfrac{(67 + 184)}{298} \times 10^3$ **D** $\dfrac{(67 - 184)}{10^3} \times 298$

    B $\dfrac{(67 - 184)}{298} \times 10^3$ **E** $\dfrac{(-67 + 184)}{10^3} \times 298$

    C $\dfrac{(-67 + 184)}{298} \times 10^3$

11 For the reaction:

$$3H_2(g) + N_2(g) \rightarrow 2NH_3(g)$$

$K_p = 6.8 \times 10^{-5}\,Pa^2$ at 298 K and $\Delta H^{\ominus} = -92\,kJ\,mol^{-1}$.

From this information, we can deduce that

A K_p will decrease as pressure increases.

B ΔS is positive.

C K_p will increase as temperature increases.

D $K_p = K_c$.

E K_c has units of $mol^{-2}\,dm^6$.

12 There is always an entropy increase in the system when

A an exothermic reaction occurs.

B the volume of a gas is increased.

C a solid reacts with a liquid.

D two gases react.

E a metal reacts with a non-metal.

13 For a reaction in equilibrium

A $K = 0$

B $\Delta H = 0$

C $\Delta S = 0$

D $\Delta G = 0$

E $T\Delta S = 0$

Questions **14–19** concern the Ellingham diagram below.

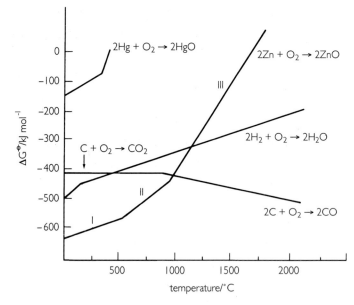

14 The diagram shows that the reaction,

$$2Zn + O_2 \rightarrow 2ZnO,$$

is in equilibrium at about

A 0°C.   **D** 1125°C.

B 475°C.   **E** 1750°C.

C 950°C.

15 From the diagram, we can deduce that mercury(II) oxide, HgO, decomposes

A at all temperatures.

B at temperatures below 0°C.

C between 0°C. and 400°C.

D between 400°C and 450°C.

E at temperatures above 450°C.

16 From the diagram we can deduce that the melting point of zinc is

A about 450°C.

B between 450°C and 900°C.

C about 900°C.

D between 900°C and 1750°C.

E above 1750°C.

17 From the graph we can deduce that

A mercury can reduce water at certain temperatures.

B mercury cannot reduce water at any temperature.

C carbon can reduce zinc oxide at 750°C.

D mercury is a better reducing agent than hydrogen.

E zinc can reduce water at 1500°C.

18 The slopes of the lines in the diagram have a gradient equal to

A ΔS.

B $-\Delta S$.

C $-RT$.

D R.

E $-zF$.

19 In the section of the graph labelled III, the correct equation for the reaction is

A $2Zn(s) + O_2(g) \rightarrow 2ZnO(s)$.

B $2Zn(l) + O_2(g) \rightarrow 2ZnO(s)$.

C $2Zn(g) + O_2(g) \rightarrow 2ZnO(s)$.

D $2Zn(g) + O_2(g) \rightarrow 2ZnO(l)$.

E $2Zn(g) + O_2(g) \rightarrow 2ZnO(g)$.

TEST 25
Reaction rates

This test is composed of fifteen questions. For each question, five possible answers are suggested. These answers are labelled **A**, **B**, **C**, **D** and **E**. Select the most appropriate *one* of the answers and write its corresponding letter on a separate answer sheet.

1   The velocity constant of a reaction is

   A independent of reactant concentrations.

   B independent of the activation energy.

   C proportional to the absolute temperature.

   D proportional to the reaction rate.

   E unaffected by the presence of a catalyst.

2   The rate of a reaction between aqueous solutions of M and N is given by Rate $=k[M][N]$. What are the units of k?

   A $mol\,dm^{-3}\,s^{-1}$

   B $mol^{-1}\,dm^{3}\,s$

   C $mol^{-1}\,dm^{3}\,s^{-1}$

   D $mol^{2}\,dm^{-6}\,s$

   E $mol^{2}\,dm^{-6}\,s^{-1}$

3   The graph below shows the initial rate of decomposition of X, catalysed by Y, at different concentrations of X. The concentration of Y was constant in all experiments. Which *one* of the following sets of conclusions is correct?

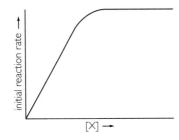

	Order with respect to X at low concentration of X	Order with respect to X at high concentration of X
A	0	1
B	1	0
C	1	2
D	2	1
E	2	0

4   On which *one* of the following values will the initial rate of a reaction depend?

   A ΔH

   B ΔS

   C E_A

   D $E^{\ominus}$

   E K_c

5   The half-life of bismuth-212 is 1 hour. If 12 g are allowed to decay, what mass of bismuth-212 is left after 3 hours?

   A 9 g

   B 4 g

   C 3 g

   D $1\frac{1}{2}$ g

   E 0 g

6   The activation energy of a reaction is

   A the minimum energy change for the forward reaction.

   B the minimum potential energy of the activated complex.

   C the minimum kinetic energy of colliding particles.

   D the minimum energy required to start a reaction.

   E the minimum energy needed by colliding molecules for a reaction.

7   In a reaction between substances V and W, some collisions between molecules of V and W do not result in reaction. Which *one* of the following suggestions may explain this?

   A The system has already reached equilibrium.

   B The activation energy of the back reaction is very low.

   C The molecules of *V* and *W* may collide inappropriately.

   D The activated complex is very unstable.

   E The molecules of *V* and *W* react endothermically.

8 The reaction between L and M,

$$L(g) + M(g) \rightarrow LM(g),$$

is zero order with respect to L. It may be inferred from this that

A the reaction rate is constant.

B the reaction is first order with respect to M.

C the reaction takes place in one step.

D the rate determining step does not involve L.

E L is present in large excess.

9 P and Q react according to the equation

$$P + 2Q \rightarrow PQ_2$$

The reaction is zero order with respect to P and second order with respect to Q. Which *one* of the following suggestions would be a possible mechanism for the reaction?

A $P + Q \xrightarrow{fast} PQ \quad PQ + Q \xrightarrow{slow} PQ_2$

B $P + Q \xrightarrow{slow} PQ \quad PQ + Q \xrightarrow{fast} PQ_2$

C $Q + Q \xrightarrow{fast} Q_2 \quad Q_2 + P \xrightarrow{slow} PQ_2$

D $Q + Q \xrightarrow{slow} Q_2 \quad Q_2 + P \xrightarrow{fast} PQ_2$

E $P + Q + Q \xrightarrow{slow} PQ_2$

Questions 10–12

Two gases, X and Y, react according to the stoichiometric equation

$$X(g) + 3Y(g) \rightarrow XY_3(g)$$

The following table gives the results of five experiments carried out at 350 K in order to determine the order of the reaction.

Experiment number	Initial concentration of X /mol dm^{-3}	Initial concentration of Y /mol dm^{-3}	Initial rate of formation of XY$_3$ /mol dm^{-3} s^{-1}
I	0.10	0.10	0.01
2	0.10	0.20	0.04
3	0.10	0.30	0.09
4	0.20	0.10	0.02
5	0.30	0.10	0.03

10 What is the order of the reaction between X and Y with respect to Y?

A 0

B 1

C 2

D 3

E 4

11 What is the initial rate of formation of XY$_3$, in mol dm^{-3} s^{-1}, when the initial concentration of X is 0.05 mol dm^{-3} and that of Y is 0.2 mol dm^{-3}

A 0.005   **D** 0.04

B 0.01   **E** 0.08

C 0.02

12 By what factor does the reaction rate increase if the concentrations of both X and Y are trebled?

A 6   **D** 18

B 9   **E** 27

C 12

Questions 13–15

A substance R undergoes a first order reaction forming the product S. The equation for the reaction is

$$R \underset{k_{-1}}{\overset{k_1}{\rightleftharpoons}} S$$

(k_1 and k_{-1} are the velocity constants for the forward and backward reactions respectively.)

13 Which *one* of the following expressions represents the rate of the *forward* reaction at any instant?

A $k_1([R] - [S])$

B $k_1 - k_{-1}$

C $k_1[R]$

D $(k_1 - k_{-1})[R]$

E $k_1[R] - k_{-1}[S]$

14 Which *one* of the following expressions represents the *overall* rate of the reaction at any instant?

A $k_1([R] - [S])$

B $k_1 - k_{-1}$

C $k_1[R]$

D $(k_1 - k_{-1})[R]$

E $k_1[R] - k_{-1}[S]$

15 Which *one* of the following conditions will apply when the reaction is at equilibrium?

A $k_1 = k_{-1}$

B $[R] = [S]$

C $\dfrac{[R]}{[S]} = 1$

D $k_1[R] = 0$

E $k_1[R] = k_{-1}[S]$

TEST 26
Introduction to carbon chemistry

This test is composed of nineteen questions. For each question, five possible answers are suggested. These answers are labelled **A**, **B**, **C**, **D** and **E**. Select the most appropriate *one* of the answers and write its corresponding letter on a separate answer sheet.

1 Silicon cannot form a stable series of hydrides (SiH_4, Si_2H_6, etc.) similar to carbon, because compounds containing silicon and hydrogen, unlike those of carbon and hydrogen

 A are energetically unstable in the presence of oxygen.

 B are kinetically unstable in the presence of oxygen.

 C react exothermically with oxygen.

 D form a solid product on reaction with oxygen.

 E decompose easily at room temperature and pressure.

2 To which of the following homologous series does the compound of molecular formula CH_2O belong?

 A alcohols

 B ethers

 C ketones

 D aldehydes

 E carboxylic acids

3 Which *one* of the following compounds contains the typical functional groups of both alkenes and ethers?

 A $HC{\equiv}C-CH_2-O-CH_3$

 B $H_2C{=}CH-C{\overset{H}{\underset{O}{\diagdown}}}$

 C $HC{\equiv}C-\overset{\displaystyle}{\underset{\parallel}{C}}-CH_3$
     $\phantom{HC{\equiv}C-}O$

 D $H_2C{=}CH-\underset{\parallel}{C}-CH_2-CH_3$
     $\phantom{H_2C{=}CH-}O$

 E $CH_3-CH{=}CH-CH_2-O-CH_3$

4 Which *one* of the following groups of compounds contains three members of the same homologous series?

 A $CH_3CH_2CH_2OH$, $CH_3CH_2OCH_3$, $CH_3OCH_2CH_3$

 B C_3H_8, C_4H_{11}, C_5H_{14}

 C C_2H_2, C_4H_4, C_6H_6

 D CH_3OH, CH_3OCH_3, $CH_3CH_2OCH_3$

 E $HCHO$, CH_3CHO, CH_3CH_2CHO

5 Organic compounds are sometimes identified by first preparing their derivatives. If this technique is used it is important that the derivative should

 A be a solid at room temperature.

 B have a melting point below $100°C$.

 C have a low boiling point.

 D be prepared and purified easily.

 E reform the original compound easily.

6 Which *one* of the following methods would be most appropriate in identifying the position of hydrogen atoms in an organic compound?

 A mass spectrometry

 B nuclear magnetic resonance

 C combustion analysis

 D X-ray diffraction

 E polarimetry

7 The hydrocarbon Q, was subjected to combustion analysis. On complete combustion, $0.2\,g$ of Q gave $0.66\,g$ of carbon dioxide and $0.18\,g$ of water. The empirical formula of Q is

 A CH_3

 B C_2H_3

 C C_3H_2

 D C_3H_4

 E C_3H_8

8 The structural formula of 3,4,4,5-tetramethylheptane can be written as

 Which *one* of the following represents a correct abbreviation for this structural formula?

 A $CH_3CH(CH_3)C(CH_3)_2CH(CH_3)CH_2CH_3$

 B $CH_3CH_2CH(CH_3)CH(CH_3)CH(CH_3)CH_2CH_3$

 C $CH_3CH_2CH(CH_3)C(CH_3)_2CHCH_3CH_2CH_3$

 D $CH_3CH_2CH(CH_3)C(CH_3)_2CH(CH_3)CH_3$

 E $CH_3CH_2CH(CH_3)C(CH_3)_2CH(CH_3)CH_2CH_3$

9 Isomers do *not* necessarily have the same

  A empirical formula

  B relative molecular mass

  C number and type of bonds

  D number of atoms per molecule

  E kind of atoms per molecule

10 Isomers have the same

  A structural formula

  B functional groups

  C crystal structure

  D optical activity

  E percentage composition

11 The number of isomers of formula $C_2H_3Cl_3$ is

  A 1

  B 2

  C 3

  D 4

  E 6

12 How many isomers, including enantiomers (optical isomers), are there of formula $C_3H_6Cl_2$?

  A 3

  B 4

  C 5

  D 6

  E 7

13 The number of asymmetric carbon atoms in one molecule of the compound $CHOCH(OH)CH(OH)CH(OH)CH_2OH$ is

  A 1

  B 2

  C 3

  D 4

  E 5

14 An organic compound contains 45.86% carbon, 8.92% hydrogen and 45.22% chlorine by mass. ($H = 1$, $C = 12$, $Cl = 35.5$.) Its empirical formula is

  A CH_2Cl

  B CH_6Cl

  C C_3H_7Cl

  D $C_6H_7Cl_2$

  E $C_6H_{14}Cl$

15 A compound contains 24% carbon and 76% fluorine by mass ($C = 12$, $F = 19$). Its molecular formula could be

  A CF

  B CF_2

  C C_2F_2

  D C_3F_6

  E $2CF_2$

16 Which *one* of the following compounds exists in optically active forms?

  A $CH_3CH_2OCH_3$

  B $CH_3CH{=}CH_2$

  C $CH_3CH(OH)CH_2CH_3$

  D CH_3CH_2CHO

  E $CH_3CH(OH)CH_3$

17 Which of the following characteristics can be deduced from the infra-red spectrum of a compound?

  A an asymmetric carbon atom

  B the existence of geometrical isomers

  C the existence of a dipole

  D hydrogen bonding to an −OH group

  E the structural formula

18 Which *one* of the following techniques will show the presence of a carbonyl bond in ethanal?

  A infra-red spectroscopy

  B electron diffraction

  C atomic emission spectroscopy

  D mass spectrometry

  E X-ray crystallography

19 The figure below shows a low resolution n.m.r. spectrum of compound X. Compound X could be

  A CH_4

  B CH_3OH

  C CH_2O

  D C_2H_6

  E CH_3OCH_3

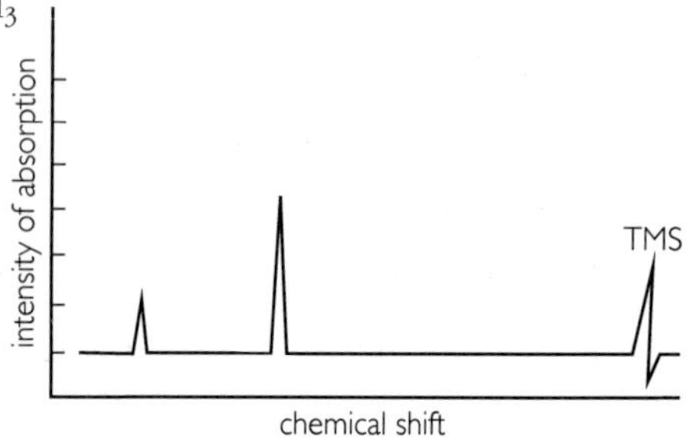

TEST 27
Petroleum and alkanes

This test is composed of twenty-one questions. For each question, five possible answers are suggested. These answers are labelled **A**, **B**, **C**, **D** and **E**. Select the most appropriate *one* of the answers and write its corresponding letter on a separate answer sheet.

1   Which *one* of the following fractions from crude oil contains the highest percentage of carbon?

   A diesel oil

   B gasoline

   C kerosine

   D naphtha

   E paraffin

2   If the cylinder of a motor-car engine was filled with nothing but petrol vapour and then sparked in the usual way, the petrol would

   A explode violently.

   B burn quietly.

   C remain unreacted.

   D decompose to soot.

   E ignite prematurely.

3   The simplest alkane to possess at least one structural isomer is

   A ethane

   B propane

   C butane

   D pentane

   E hexane

4   How many isomers are there of formula C_5H_{12}?

   A 2

   B 3

   C 4

   D 5

   E 6

5   Alkanes

   A are all straight-chain hydrocarbons.

   B have the general formula C_nH_{n+2}.

   C are unsaturated hydrocarbons.

   D include aliphatic and aromatic compounds.

   E undergo substitution reactions.

6   Alkanes will react with

   A molten Na.

   B concentrated H_2SO_4.

   C concentrated KOH.

   D gaseous Cl_2.

   E concentrated $KMnO_4$.

7   Three hydrocarbons were completely burnt in oxygen. In each case, the volume of carbon dioxide produced was found to be equal to the volume of water vapour produced, all measurements being made at the same temperature and pressure. What is the general formula of the hydrocarbons?

   A C_nH_n

   B C_nH_{n+2}

   C C_nH_{2n+1}

   D C_nH_{2n}

   E C_nH_{2n+2}

8   Which *one* of the following molecules is most likely to undergo homolytic fission?

   A I_2

   B HCl

   C BrF

   D CH_4

   E CH_3Cl

9   Cracking

   A is the opposite of reforming.

   B cannot occur without a catalyst.

   C must involve decomposition.

   D does not occur with branched-chain alkanes.

   E never produces branched-chain alkanes.

Questions **10–13**

The chlorination of an alkane involves several stages, some of which are shown below.

I	$Cl_2 \rightarrow Cl\cdot + Cl\cdot$
II	$RCH_3 + Cl\cdot \rightarrow RCH_2\cdot + HCl$
III	$RCH_2\cdot + Cl_2 \rightarrow RCH_2Cl + Cl\cdot$
IV	$RCH_2\cdot + Cl\cdot \rightarrow RCH_2Cl$
V	$RCH_2\cdot + RCH_2\cdot \rightarrow RCH_2CH_2R$

10 The stages which involve propagation are

    A I and II

    B II and III

    C III and IV

    D I, II and III

    E II, III and IV

11 Stage V of the process is an example of

    A an initiation reaction.

    B homolytic fission.

    C heterolytic fission.

    D catalytic reforming.

    E free radical addition.

12 Termination of the reaction takes place when

    A two free radicals collide and combine.

    B all the chlorine radicals have reacted.

    C all the chloride is converted to $Cl\cdot$.

    D the initiation process has finished.

    E the reaction has just finished.

13 Given the following bond energies in $kJ\,mol^{-1}$,
$E(Cl–Cl) = 242;$ $E(C–H) = 413;$ $E(C–Cl) = 339;$
$E(H–Cl) = 431;$
what is the enthalpy change for the reaction below?

$$RCH_3 + Cl_2 \rightarrow RCH_2\cdot + HCl + Cl\cdot$$

    A $+1086\,kJ\,mol^{-1}$

    B $+655\,kJ\,mol^{-1}$

    C $+563\,kJ\,mol^{-1}$

    D $+339\,kJ\,mol^{-1}$

    E $+224\,kJ\,mol^{-1}$

14 What is the shape of the methyl carbocation ($^+CH_3$)?

    A linear

    B trigonal planar

    C tetrahedral

    D pyramidal

    E spherical

Questions **15–21** refer to the five structures below.

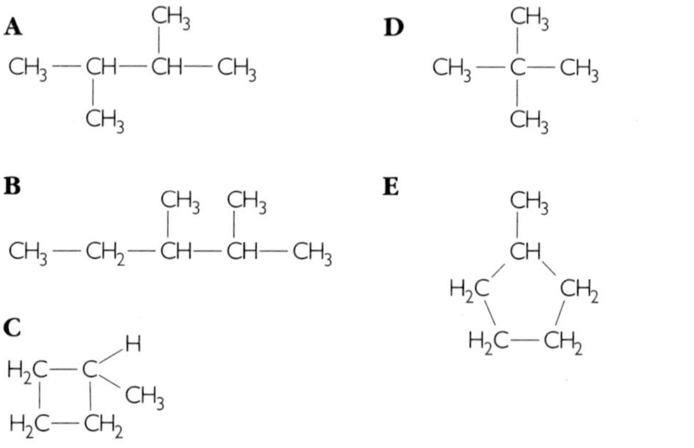

15 Which structure is under the greatest strain?

16 Which structure will exist as optical isomers?

17 Which is isomeric with pentane?

18 Which has a systematic name ending in -propane?

19 Which structure could form *two* and only two different monochloro-compounds when hydrogen atoms are replaced by chlorine?

20 Which structure has the most carbon atoms in *one* plane?

21 Which structure requires the least amount of oxygen per mole for complete combustion?

TEST 28
Unsaturated hydrocarbons

This test is composed of twenty-four questions. For each question, five possible answers are suggested. These answers are labelled **A**, **B**, **C**, **D** and **E**. Select the most appropriate *one* of the answers and write its corresponding letter on a separate answer sheet.

1 What is the systematic name for $CH_3CH=CHCH=CH_2$?

   A penta-1,2-diene

   B penta-1,3-diene

   C penta-1,4-diene

   D penta-2,3-diene

   E penta-2,4-diene

2 Which *one* of the following compounds is formed as the major product when but-1-ene reacts with iodine monochloride, ICl?

   A $CH_3CH_2CHClCH_2I$

   B $CH_3CH_2CHICH_2Cl$

   C $CH_3CHICHClCH_3$

   D $CH_3CHICH_2CH_2Cl$

   E $CH_2ClCHICH_2CH_3$

3 Using the bond energies given below, what is the enthalpy change in kJ for the following reaction?

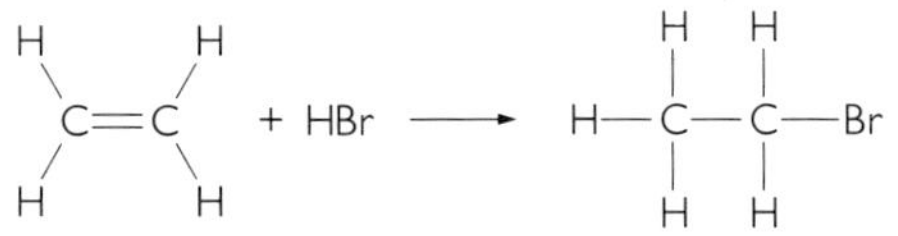

   $E(C–C) = 346\,kJ\,mol^{-1}$

   $E(C=C) = 610\,kJ\,mol^{-1}$

   $E(C–H) = 413\,kJ\,mol^{-1}$

   $E(C–Br) = 280\,kJ\,mol^{-1}$

   $E(H–Br) = 365\,kJ\,mol^{-1}$

   A −2014

   B −282

   C −64

   D +64

   E +282

4 Which *one* of the following compounds is formed as the major organic product when propan-1-ol is heated with excess concentrated H_2SO_4 at 150°C?

   A $CH_3CH=CH_2$

   B $\begin{array}{c}CH_3\\ \\ CH_3\end{array}\!\!>\!C=CH_2$

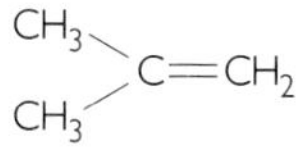

   C $CH_2=C=CH_2$

   D $CH_3CH_2CH_2OCH_2CH_2CH_3$

   E $CH_3CH_2CH=CHCH_2CH_3$

5 A simple reaction scheme is shown below.

   $$CH_3CH=CH_2 \xrightarrow{HBr(g)} X \xrightarrow[\text{NaOH(aq)}]{\text{Reflux with}} Y$$

   What is the formula of Y?

   A $CH_3CH_2CH_2OH$

   B $CH_3CHOHCH_3$

   C $CH_3CHBrCH_2OH$

   D $CH_3CHOHCH_2Br$

   E $CH_3CHBrCH_3$

6 Which *one* of the following reagents can be used in a simple chemical test to distinguish between propene and propyne?

   A HBr(g)

   B $Br_2(aq)$

   C $[Ag(NH_3)_2]^+(aq)$

   D $AgNO_3(aq)$

   E $KMnO_4(aq)$

7 A plastic with highly branched polymer chains is likely to have a

   A low tensile strength.

   B high melting point.

   C rigid structure.

   D high density.

   E high crystallinity.

8 How many structural and stereoisomers are there for chloroalkenes with the molecular formula C_3H_5Cl?

   A 2   **D** 5

   B 3   **E** 6

   C 4

9 When bromine reacts with cyclohexene at room temperature, the mechanism by which bromine attacks the cyclohexene can be described as

   A electrophilic addition.

   B electrophilic substitution.

   C free radical addition.

   D free radical substitution.

   E nucleophilic addition.

10 What are the $\overset{\frown}{C\text{–}C\text{–}C}$ bond angles in

   $(CH_3)_2C{=}C(CH_3)_2$ and $CH_3C{\equiv}CCH_3$?

   A 109° only   **D** 109°, 120° and 180°

   B 109° and 120°   **E** 120° and 180°

   C 109° and 180°

11 Hydrobromic acid reacts with ethene to form bromo-ethane. Which *one* of the following is a correct statement about the organic intermediate?

   A It is a free radical.

   B It contains carbon, hydrogen and bromine.

   C It has a planar structure.

   D It is an electrophile.

   E It is negatively charged.

Questions **12–18** refer to the five compounds labelled **A**, **B**, **C**, **D** and **E** below.

   A cyclohexane   **D** hex-1-yne

   B cyclohexene   **E** hex-2-yne

   C hexane

Which *one* of the compounds

12 decolorises bromine water most rapidly?

13 gives a pale yellow precipitate with ammoniacal silver nitrate solution?

14 has the empirical formula CH_2?

15 has only *one* monochloro-derivative?

16 has four carbon atoms arranged linearly?

17 undergoes the largest volume change when the vapour burns in excess oxygen to form gaseous products?

18 has one σ-bond and one π-bond between adjacent carbon atoms?

For each of questions **19–24**, one or more of the numbered alternatives (**1**, **2** and **3**) listed below may be correct. Decide whether each of the alternatives is or is not correct and then choose

   A if **1**, **2** and **3** are all correct.

   B if **1** and **2** only are correct.

   C if **2** and **3** only are correct.

   D if **1** only is correct.

   E if **3** only is correct.

(No other combination is used as a correct answer.)

19 Which of these compounds will have a geometrical isomer?

20 Which of these compounds will not produce butane on catalytic hydrogenation?

21 Which of these compounds could produce optical isomers on treatment with hydrogen bromide?

22 Which of these compounds will have zero dipole moment?

23 Which of these compounds will decolorise a very dilute acidified solution of manganate(VII) ions?

24 Which of these compounds could be obtained by partial hydrogenation of an alkyne?

TEST 29
Aromatic hydrocarbons

This test is composed of twenty questions. For each question, five possible answers are suggested. These answers are labelled **A**, **B**, **C**, **D** and **E**. Select the most appropriate *one* of the answers and write its corresponding letter on a separate answer sheet.

Questions **1–6** refer to the compounds labelled **A**, **B**, **C**, **D** and **E** below. Each compound may be chosen once, more than once or not at all.

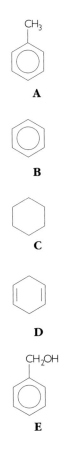

A

B

C

D

E

1 Which compound has no reaction with bromine plus iron filings in the dark?

2 Which compound absorbs two moles of hydrogen per mole of the compound at 150°C in the presence of a powdered nickel catalyst?

3 Which compound reacts with sodium at room temperature?

4 Which compound will decolorise dilute acidified potassium manganate(VII) at room temperature?

5 Which compound has the highest degree of unsaturation?

6 Which compound has a puckered ring of carbon atoms?

Questions 7–11

Choose from the list **A–E** the reaction conditions most suitable for carrying out the conversions in questions **7–11**. Each letter may be chosen once, more than once, or not at all.

A Boil the reactant with dilute hydrochloric acid.

B Warm the reactant with chloromethane in the presence of aluminium chloride.

C Treat the reactant with phosphorus(III) chloride at room temperature.

D Pass chlorine into the boiling reactant in sunlight.

E Pass chlorine through the reactant in the presence of aluminium chloride in the dark.

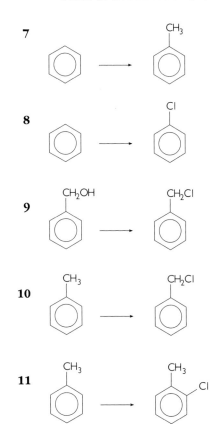

12 What is the total number of trichlorobenzenes of formula $C_6H_3Cl_3$?

 A 2

 B 3

 C 4

 D 5

 E 6

13 X-ray diffraction studies show that the molecule of benzene has

 A a distorted hexagonal shape.

 B alternate double and single bonds.

 C twelve atoms in the same plane.

 D longer C–C bonds than in ethane.

 E shorter C–C bonds than in ethene.

14 Which *one* of the following conditions and reagents is most suitable for preparing nitrobenzene from benzene?

 A Mix benzene with concentrated HNO_3 at room temperature.

 B Mix benzene with concentrated HNO_3 plus dilute H_2SO_4 at 15°C.

 C Warm benzene with concentrated HNO_3 at 50°C.

 D Warm benzene with concentrated HNO_3 plus concentrated H_2SO_4 at 50°C.

 E Reflux benzene with concentrated HNO_3.

15 Which *one* of the following could *not* be obtained as a main product when methylbenzene is heated with a mixture of concentrated HNO_3 and concentrated H_2SO_4?

 A 2-nitromethylbenzene

 B 3-nitromethylbenzene

 C 4-nitromethylbenzene

 D 2,4-dinitromethylbenzene

 E 2,4,6-trinitromethylbenzene

16 When benzene, methylbenzene and nitrobenzene are nitrated, the order of *increasing* rate of nitration is

 A benzene, methylbenzene, nitrobenzene.

 B benzene, nitrobenzene, methylbenzene.

 C nitrobenzene, benzene, methylbenzene.

 D nitrobenzene, methylbenzene, benzene.

 E methylbenzene, benzene, nitrobenzene.

17 Iodobenzene can be obtained by reacting benzene with iodine(I) chloride. What is the electrophile attacking the benzene in this reaction?

 A Cl^+

 B I

 C I_2

 D I^-

 E I^+

Questions **18** and **19**

Study the experimentally determined enthalpy changes in the figure below.

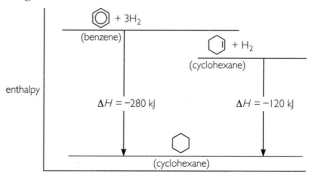

18 If benzene had the hypothetical cyclohexa-1,3,5-triene structure, ⬡ , as suggested by Kekulé, what would be the likely value of its enthalpy change of hydrogenation per mole?

 A −120 kJ   D −360 kJ

 B −208 kJ   E −448 kJ

 C −328 kJ

19 By how much is benzene more stable than the hypothetical cyclohexa-1,3,5-triene structure suggested by Kekulé, judging from the information in the figure above?

 A $0\,kJ\,mol^{-1}$ D $152\,kJ\,mol^{-1}$

 B $88\,kJ\,mol^{-1}$ E $240\,kJ\,mol^{-1}$

 C $120\,kJ\,mol^{-1}$

20 Which *one* of the following is an optically active (chiral) compound capable of hydrogen bonding with water?

 A Cl—⬡—CHClCH₃

 B HO—⬡—Br with Cl

 C ⬡—CH(OH)CO₂H

 D ⬡—CH=CHCO₂H

 E HO—⬡—CH₂CO₂H

TEST 30
Organic halogen compounds

This test is composed of nineteen questions. For each question, five possible answers are suggested. These answers are labelled **A**, **B**, **C**, **D** and **E**. Select the most appropriate *one* of the answers and write its corresponding letter on a separate answer sheet.

1 An organic halogen compound was hydrolysed by boiling under reflux for one hour. The reason for refluxing, rather than boiling in an open flask, is

   A to boil the mixture at a higher temperature.

   B to prevent escape of volatile reagents.

   C to increase the area of contact between reagents.

   D to avoid drops of liquid spitting out of the flask.

   E to alternately heat and cool the reacting substances.

2 Which *one* of the following reagents is most suitable for converting

   A $Br_2(l)$

   B $NaBr(aq)$

   C $NaBrO_3(aq)$

   D $CH_3Br(l)$

   E $PBr_3(l)$

3 For a given alkyl group, R, the iodo-compound reacts most readily, the bromo-compound less so and the chloro-compound reacts least readily. This is because

   A chlorine is more reactive than iodine.

   B chloro-compounds are more polar than iodo-compounds.

   C the C–Cl bond is shorter than the C–I bond.

   D the C–Cl bond is stronger than the C–I bond.

   E the chlorine atom is smaller than the iodine atom.

4 Which *one* of the following reagents is most suitable for converting $CH_3CH_2CH_2Br$ into

   $CH_3CH_2CH_2OCH_2CH_3$?

   A $NaOH(s)$ in ethanol

   B CH_3CH_2COCl

   C dry $CH_3CH_2COO^-Ag^+$

   D $CH_3CH_2O^-Na^+$ in ethanol

   E CH_3CH_2OH

5 Which *one* of the following reagents is most suitable for converting

   A PCl_5 at 50°C

   B concentrated HCl at 80°C

   C $SOCl_2$ at room temperature

   D NaCl in hot concentrated sulphuric acid

   E Cl_2 in bright sunlight at 100°C

6 Which *one* of the following is the main organic product when $BrCH_2COBr$ is treated with cold water?

   A $HOCH_2COBr$

   B $BrCH_2COOH$

   C $HOCH_2COOH$

   D CH_3COOH

   E $HOCH_2CHO$

7 Which *one* of the following is the major organic product when $ClCH_2CH_2COCl$ is refluxed with excess aqueous sodium hydroxide?

   A $HOCH_2CH_2COCl$

   B $ClCH_2CH_2COOH$

   C $HOCH_2CH_2COOH$

   D $HOCH_2CH_2COO^-Na^+$

   E $Na^+{}^-OCH_2CH_2COO^-Na^+$

8 Which *one* of the following sets of bromo-compounds is arranged in order of increasing reactivity of the bromine atom?

   A CH_3CH_2Br, C_6H_5Br, CH_3COBr

   B CH_3CH_2Br, CH_3COBr, C_6H_5Br

   C C_6H_5Br, CH_3CH_2Br, CH_3COBr

   D C_6H_5Br, CH_3COBr, CH_3CH_2Br

   E CH_3COBr, C_6H_5Br, CH_3CH_2Br

9 When propanoyl chloride reacts with methanol, the major organic product is

A $CH_3CH_2CO_2CH_3$

B $CH_3CH_2CH_2CO_2CH_3$

C $CH_3CH_2COCH_3$

D $CH_3CO_2CH_2CH_3$

E $CH_3CH_2CO_2CH_2CH_3$

10 1-Bromopropane can be converted to 2-bromopropane in a two-stage reaction. Which *one* of the following pairs of reagents can be used in succession for this conversion?

A aqueous NaOH $P(s)|Br_2(l)$

B concentrated NH_3 $Br_2(l)|NaOH(aq)$

C alcoholic NaOH $Br_2(l)$

D aqueous NaOH   concentrated HBr

E alcoholic NaOH   concentrated HBr

11 Investigations have shown that $CBrF_3$ is ten times more damaging to the ozone layer than $CClF_3$. This is mainly due to

A the longer C–Br bond compared with the C–Cl bond.

B the lower polarity of the C–Br bond compared with the C–Cl bond.

C the weaker C–Br bond compared with the C–Cl bond.

D the larger size of the Br atom compared with the Cl atom.

E the larger mass of $CBrF_3$ compared with $CClF_3$.

Questions **12–19** refer to the five organic halogen compounds labelled **A** to **E** below.

CH_3Cl

A

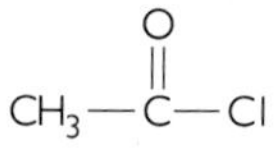

$CH_3{-}\overset{\overset{O}{||}}{C}{-}Cl$

B

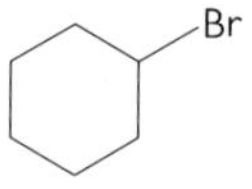

C

CCl_3F

D

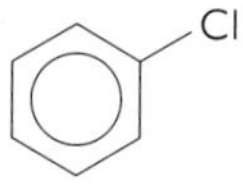

E

Which *one* of the above compounds

12 is the most volatile?

13 is the most suitable for use as an aerosol propellant?

14 is an acyl halide?

15 reacts least readily with aqueous sodium hydroxide?

16 reacts most readily with cold water?

17 reacts with alcoholic sodium hydroxide to form an alkene?

18 has a planar molecule?

19 reacts with alcohols to form esters?

TEST 31
Alcohols, phenols and ethers

This test is composed of twenty-two questions. For each question, five possible answers are suggested. These answers are labelled **A**, **B**, **C**, **D** and **E**. Select the most appropriate *one* of the answers and write its corresponding letter on a separate answer sheet.

1   Equal volumes of ethanol and water are completely miscible whereas equal volumes of ethoxyethane (ether) and water form separate layers on mixing. The main reason for this is that

   A molecules of ether are larger than those of ethanol.

   B the densities of water and ethanol are closer than those of water and ethoxyethane.

   C molecules of ethanol are polar, but those of ethoxyethane are non-polar.

   D the boiling points of water and ethanol are closer than those of water and ethoxyethane.

   E ethanol can form hydrogen bonds with water, but ethoxyethane cannot do so.

2   With which *one* of the following reagents do ethanol and phenol react in a similar fashion?

   A $FeCl_3(aq)$

   B $NaOH(aq)$

   C $HNO_3(aq)$

   D $Na(s)$

   E $CH_3COOH(l)$

3   The best conditions for preparing ethoxyethane (ether) by the dehydration of ethanol using concentrated sulphuric acid are

   A excess concentrated H_2SO_4 at 140°C.

   B excess ethanol at 140°C.

   C excess concentrated H_2SO_4 at 170°C.

   D excess ethanol at 170°C.

   E excess concentrated H_2SO_4 at 250°C.

4   Phenol could be separated from a mixture of phenol and benzene by

   A extracting the phenol with trichloromethane.

   B dissolving the benzene in concentrated sulphuric acid.

   C dissolving the phenol in sodium hydroxide solution

   D extracting the benzene with methylbenzene (toluene).

   E fractional crystallisation of the phenol.

5   Ethoxyethane, $(C_2H_5)_2O$, is useful as a solvent for many organic reactions because it is

   A unreactive.

   B volatile.

   C immiscible with water.

   D less dense than water.

   E non-polar.

Questions **6–13** refer to the five compounds labelled **A**, **B**, **C**, **D** and **E** below.

   A methanol

   B ethanol

   C propan-2-ol

   D phenylmethanol (benzyl alcohol)

   E phenol

6   Which is most frequently used as a solvent in the laboratory and in industry?

7   Which has the highest vapour pressure at 20°C?

8   Which, in aqueous solution, reacts most vigorously with sodium?

9   Which is oxidised to a ketone?

10   Which, when oxidised strongly, forms a solid mono-carboxylic acid?

11   Which reacts with ethanoyl chloride to form an ester, but does not react with ethanoic acid?

12   Which reacts with methanoic acid to form an ester which is isomeric with propanoic acid?

13   Which reacts readily with bromine water to form a brominated derivative?

14   With which *one* of the following reagents do phenyl-methanol ($C_6H_5CH_2OH$) and phenol (C_6H_5OH) react in a similar way?

   A bromine water

   B neutral iron(III) chloride solution

   C dilute acidified potassium manganate(VII)

   D phosphorus pentachloride

   E ethanoyl chloride

15 Phenol was added to X and a colourless homogeneous solution formed. Which *one* of the following could be X?

A $FeCl_3(aq)$

B $Br_2(aq)$

C $NaCl(aq)$

D $HCl(aq)$

E OH(

For each of questions **16–22** one or more of the numbered alternatives (**1**, **2** and **3**) listed below may be correct. Decide whether each of the alternatives is or is not correct and then choose

A if **1**, **2** and **3** are all correct.

B if **1** and **2** only are correct.

C if **2** and **3** only are correct.

D if **1** only is correct.

E if **3** only is correct.

(No other combination is used as a correct answer.)

$$CH_3CH_2CH(OH)CH_3$$
1

$$CH_3CH_2CH_2CH_2OH$$
2

$$(CH_3)_3COH$$
3

16 Which will decolorise dilute acidified potassium manganate(VII) (potassium permanganate) on warming?

17 Which will give gaseous hydrogen chloride on treatment with phosphorus pentachloride?

18 Which will give yellow crystals of CHI_3 on warming with iodine in alkaline solution?

19 Which could *not* be oxidised to a ketone?

20 Which could form an ester with ethanoyl chloride (acetyl chloride)?

21 Which could form methylpropene on dehydration?

22 Which will have optically active forms?

TEST 32
Carbonyl compounds

This test is composed of twenty-two questions. For each question, five possible answers are suggested. These answers are labelled **A**, **B**, **C**, **D** and **E**. Select the most appropriate *one* of the answers and write its corresponding letter on a separate answer sheet.

1 The order of *increasing* rate of reaction of ethanal, methanal and propanone with cyanide ion, CN^-, is

    A ethanal, methanal, propanone.

    B ethanal, propanone, methanal.

    C methanal, ethanal, propanone.

    D methanal, propanone, ethanal.

    E propanone, ethanal, methanal.

2 The reaction of compounds of the type HX with carbonyl compounds is best described as

    A addition–elimination.

    B electrophilic addition.

    C electrophilic substitution.

    D nucleophilic addition.

    E nucleophilic substitution.

3 The reaction of ethanal with HCN(aq) is slow, but a rapid reaction results if ethanal is treated first with NaCN(aq) and then with dilute HCl(aq). The most likely explanation for this is that the first step of the reaction involves attack of the

    A carbonyl oxygen atom by H^+.

    B carbonyl oxygen atom by Na^+.

    C carbonyl carbon atom by HCN.

    D carbonyl carbon atom by Cl^-.

    E carbonyl carbon atom by CN^-.

4 Which *one* of the following compounds would undergo the iodoform reaction?

    A CH_3CH_2CHO

    B HCHO

    C ⬡—CHO

    D ⬡—$COCH_3$

    E $CH_3CH_2COCH_2CH_3$

5 Which *one* of the following sets contains three ions, all of which react with ethanal?

    A CN^-, Cl^-, H^+

    B CN^-, H^+, HSO_3^-

    C CN^-, HSO_3^-, HSO_4^-

    D Cl^-, H^+, HSO_3^-

    E H^+, HSO_3^-, HSO_4^-

6 Butanone could be distinguished from butanal by observing their separate reactions with

    A hydroxylamine.

    B iron(III) chloride.

    C sodium hydrogensulphate(IV).

    D iodine in alkaline solution.

    E hydrogen in the presence of nickel.

7 Which *one* of the following reagents can be used to distinguish between C_6H_5CHO and $C_6H_5COCH_3$?

    A 2,4-dinitrophenylhydrazine

    B aqueous bromine

    C ammoniacal silver nitrate

    D aqueous iron(III) chloride

    E phosphorus pentachloride

8 Which *one* of the following compounds will give an orange precipitate with 2,4-dinitrophenylhydrazine and a yellow precipitate on warming with iodine and aqueous sodium hydroxide?

    A $CH_3CH_2CH(OH)CH_3$

    B $CH_3CH_2CH_2CHO$

    C $CH_3CH_2COCH_3$

    D $CH_3CH(OH)CH_3$

    E $CH_3CO_2CH_2CH_3$

Questions **9–18**

For each of questions **9–18** one or more of the numbered alternatives (**1**, **2** and **3**) listed below may be correct. Decide whether each of the alternatives is or is not correct and then choose

A if **1**, **2** and **3** are all correct.

B if **1** and **2** only are correct.

C if **2** and **3** only are correct.

D if **1** only is correct.

E if **3** only is correct.

(No other combination is used as a correct answer.)

HCHO	CH_3CHO	CH_3COCH_3
1	**2**	**3**

9 Which could be prepared by oxidation of a secondary alcohol?

10 Which will polymerise on evaporation of an aqueous solution?

11 Which will reduce diamminosilver(I) ions, $[Ag(NH_3)_2]^+$, to silver?

12 Which will undergo a condensation reaction with 2,4-dinitrophenylhydrazine?

13 Which will be oxidised to carbon dioxide and water on warming with dilute acidified $KMnO_4$ solution?

14 Which will convert Fehling's solution to either a red precipitate of copper(I) oxide or a deposit of copper?

15 Which will give a yellow precipitate on warming with a mixture of iodine and alkali?

16 Which will be gaseous at 0°C?

17 Which will undergo an addition reaction on treatment with HCN?

18 Which will be reduced to a primary alcohol with hydrogen in the presence of a platinum catalyst?

Questions **19–22** refer to the structures of five compounds **A**, **B**, **C**, **D** and **E** shown below. (The open-chain forms of compounds **A**, **B**, **C**, **D** and **E** shown here normally exist in equilibrium with the ring-form.)

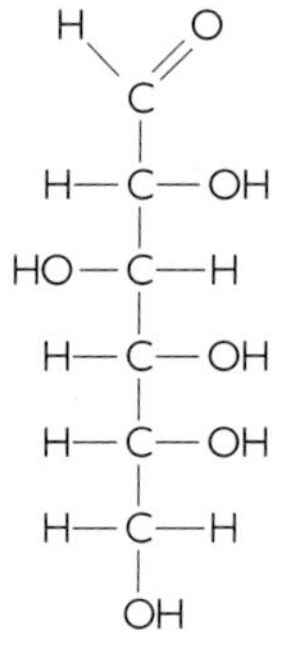

A

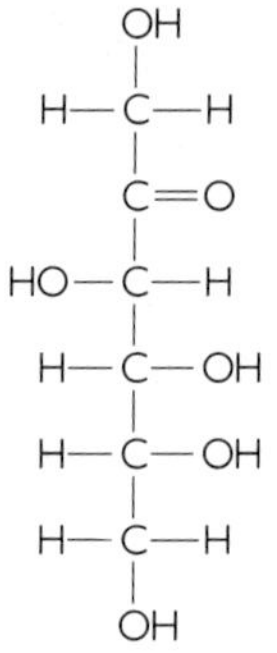

B

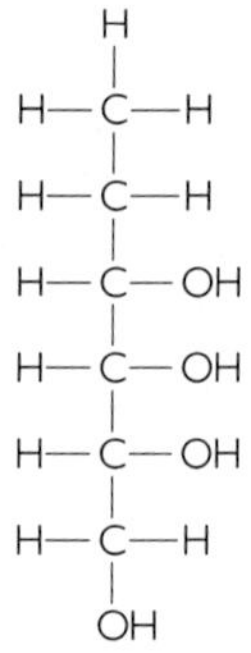

C

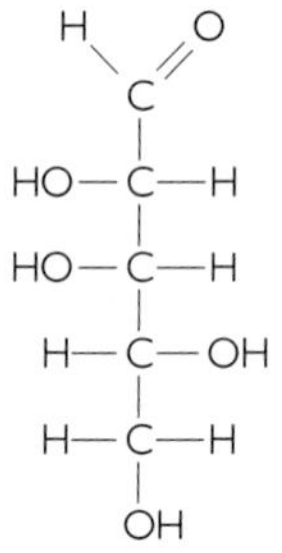

D

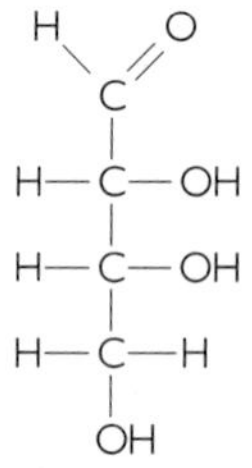

E

19 Which compound is a ketose?

20 Which compound is *not* a carbohydrate?

21 Which structure has four asymmetric carbon atoms?

22 Which compound is a component of RNA and vitamin B12?

TEST 33
Carboxylic acids and their derivatives

This test is composed of twenty-two questions. For each question, five possible answers are suggested. These answers are labelled **A**, **B**, **C**, **D** and **E**. Select the most appropriate *one* of the answers and write its corresponding letter on a separate answer sheet.

1 Which *one* of the following substances is the main organic product when $ClCH_2COOH$ is refluxed with aqueous NaOH?

  A $ClCH_2COO^-$

  B $HOCH_2COOH$

  C $HOCH_2COO^-$

  D $^-OCH_2COO^-$

  E $^-OCH_2COOH$

2 Which *one* of the following substances would be oxidised to 2-methylpropanoic acid?

  A $(CH_3)_2CHCH_2OH$

  B $CH_3CH_2CHOHCH_3$

  C $(CH_3)_3COH$

  D $(CH_3)_2CHCH_2CH_2CH_2OH$

  E $CH_3CH_2CH_2CH_2OH$

3 Which *one* of the following is the best description for the reaction between C_3H_7COOH and C_3H_7OH?

  A addition

  B condensation

  C dehydration

  D elimination

  E substitution

4 Which *one* of the following carboxylic acids is the strongest?

  A CHF_2CH_2COOH

  B CH_2FCH_2COOH

  C $CH_3CHFCOOH$

  D $CH_3CHClCOOH$

  E $CH_2FCHFCOOH$

5 When phenylmethanoate is hydrolysed by excess NaOH(aq), the products of the reaction are

  A phenol and methanoate ions

  B benzoate ions and methanol

  C phenate ions and methanol

  D phenoxide ions and methanoate ions

  E phenol and methanoic acid

6 To which *one* of the following classes of organic compounds does

  belong?

  A acid anhydrides

  B aldehydes

  C carboxylic acids

  D esters

  E ketones

7 Which *one* of the following compounds will be more acidic than ethanoic acid but less acidic than chloro-ethanoic acid?

  A CH_3CH_2COOH

  B $CHCl_2COOH$

  C $CH_2BrCOOH$

  D CCl_3COOH

  E $CH_3(CH_2)_4COOH$

8 An ester was refluxed with aqueous sodium hydroxide and then distilled. The distillate gave a yellow precipitate on warming with iodine in aqueous sodium hydroxide. The residue in the distillation flask gave a white precipitate when dilute hydrochloric acid was added. A possible formula for the original ester is

  A $HCO_2C_6H_5$

  B $CH_3CO_2C_6H_5$

  C $C_6H_5CO_2CH_3$

  D $CH_3CH_2CO_2C_6H_5$

  E $C_6H_5CO_2CH_2CH_3$

9 The organic compound Y gives a silver mirror on warming with a solution containing $[Ag(NH_3)_2]^+$ ions, but it gives *no* hydrogen chloride fumes with phosphorus pentachloride. Which *one* of the following compounds could be Y?

A CH_3CHO

B CH_3CO_2H

C CH_3COCH_3

D $CH_3CHOHCH_3$

E $CH_3CO_2CH_3$

10 Which *one* of the following compounds will react with the product of its own oxidation to form a sweet-smelling liquid?

A butanal

B butanone

C butan-1-ol

D butan-2-ol

E butanoic acid

Questions **11–17** refer to five carboxylic acids labelled **A**, **B**, **C**, **D** and **E** below.

A methanoic (formic) acid

B ethanoic (acetic) acid

C propanoic (propionic) acid

D ethanedioic (oxalic) acid

E benzoic acid

Which *one* of these acids

11 has the lowest boiling point?

12 is the least soluble in cold water?

13 is the strongest electrolyte?

14 is the strongest reducing agent?

15 forms two different sodium salts?

16 decolorises dilute acidified $KMnO_4(aq)$ only on warming?

17 readily dehydrates forming CO and CO_2?

For each of questions **18–22** one or more of the numbered alternatives (**1**, **2** and **3**) listed below may be correct. Decide whether each of the alternatives is or is not correct and then choose

A if **1**, **2** and **3** are all correct.

B if **1** and **2** only are correct.

C if **2** and **3** only are correct.

D if **1** only is correct.

E if **3** only is correct.

(No other combination is used as a correct answer.)

$$CH_3 - O - C - CH_3$$
$$\underset{\|}{} O$$
1

$$HOCH_2CH_2C \overset{O}{\underset{OH}{\diagdown}}$$
2

$$CH_3CH_2 - C - O - C - CH_3$$
$$\underset{\|}{} O \underset{\|}{} O$$
3

18 Which will form an acidic solution in water?

19 Which will form an immiscible layer with dilute NaOH?

20 Which can be obtained by reacting an acid with an alcohol?

21 Which will react with water at 20°C forming two different organic products?

22 Which will react with ethanol forming an ester?

TEST 34
Organic nitrogen compounds

This test is composed of twenty-one questions. For each question, five possible answers are suggested. These answers are labelled **A**, **B**, **C**, **D** and **E**. Select the most appropriate *one* of the answers and write its corresponding letter on a separate answer sheet.

1   Which *one* of the following reagents reacts in a similar fashion with both phenylamine ($C_6H_5NH_2$) and ethylamine ($CH_3CH_2NH_2$)?

   A $Br_2(aq)$

   B CH_3COCl

   C   concentrated H_2SO_4

   D   cold $HNO_2(aq)$

   E   concentrated HNO_3

2   Phenylamine(aniline) can be prepared by reducing nitrobenzene with tin and concentrated hydrochloric acid followed by addition of alkali and finally steam distillation. The alkali is added to

   A   prevent oxidation of phenylamine.

   B   react with excess tin.

   C   liberate free phenylamine from solution.

   D   dissolve excess nitrobenzene.

   E   dissolve the phenylamine.

3   Which *one* of the following statements best explains why trimethylamine $[(CH_3)_3N]$ has a lower boiling point than dimethylamine $[(CH_3)_2NH]$?

   A $(CH_3)_3N$ has a larger relative molecular mass.

   B $(CH_3)_3N$ molecules are symmetrical.

   C $(CH_3)_3N$ cannot hydrogen-bond with itself.

   D $(CH_3)_3N$ molecules are non-polar.

   E $(CH_3)_3N$ molecules have a larger volume.

4   The order of *increasing* strength as bases for dimethylamine, methylamine and phenylamine is

   A   dimethylamine < methylamine < phenylamine.

   B   methylamine < dimethylamine < phenylamine.

   C   dimethylamine < phenylamine < methylamine.

   D   phenylamine < dimethylamine < methylamine.

   E   phenylamine < methylamine < dimethylamine.

5   When CH_3CN is refluxed with aqueous KOH, the principal organic product is

   A CH_3OH

   B CH_3COO^-

   C CH_3CONH_2

   D CH_3CH_2OH

   E $CH_3CH_2NH_2$

6   Which *one* of the following is the principal organic product when ammonium propanoate is heated with P_4O_{10}?

   A   ethanenitrile

   B   isocyanoethane

   C   propanamide

   D   propanenitrile

   E   propanoic acid

7   An organic nitrogen compound, X, gives ammonia on warming with dilute aqueous sodium hydroxide. X could be

   A   ethanamide

   B   ethylamine

   C   aminoethanoic acid

   D   phenylamine

   E   dimethylamine

8   Which *one* of the following substances shows amphoteric character most prominently?

   A $CH_3.COONH_4$

   B H_2NCH_2COOH

   C $C_6H_5NH_2$

   D CH_3CONH_2

   E CH_3CN

9   Which *one* of the following terms best describes nylon?

   A   regenerated natural fibre

   B   synthetic protein

   C   condensation polymer

   D   semi-synthetic polypeptide

   E   natural polyamide

10 Amino acids can be identified by paper chromatography and the measurement of R_f values. Which *one* of the following factors would have the greatest influence on R_f values?

A the kind of paper used for the chromatogram

B the temperature in the chromatography tank

C the solvent employed for chromatography

D the size of the original spot on the chromatogram

E the time taken for chromatography

11 Which *one* of the following nitrogen compounds will be the most soluble in water?

A $CH_3.N(CH_3).CH_3$

B $CH_3.NH.CH_3$

C $CH_3.NCO$

D $CH_3.CN$

E $CH_3.NO_2$

12 Aminoethanoic acid, H_2NCH_2COOH, ($M_r = 75$) melts at 234°C, whereas propanoic acid, CH_3CH_2COOH, ($M_r = 74$) melts at −21°C. Which of the following statements helps to explain this difference? Aminoethanoic acid molecules

A are hydrogen bonded.

B are dimerised.

C have dipole–dipole interactions.

D have a dipolar-ion structure.

E have unshared electron pairs.

13 What is the correct name for the structure CH_3CHCH_3?
    |
    CN

A propane-2-nitrile

B 2-propanenitrile

C butane-2-nitrile

D 2-methylpropanenitrile

E 2-butanenitrile

Questions **14–21** relate to the five organic nitrogen compounds labelled **A**, **B**, **C**, **D** and **E** below.

A $CH_3CH_2NH_2$

B $C_6H_5NH_2$

C CH_3CONH_2

D $C_6H_5NO_2$

E $C_6H_5N_2Cl$

Which *one* of these compounds

14 is a strong electrolyte?

15 is the most volatile?

16 is the strongest base?

17 is insoluble in water, acid and alkali?

18 dissolves in dilute HCl, but not in water?

19 is explosive when pure?

20 gives nitrogen with HNO_2 at 5°C?

21 gives ammonia on warming with NaOH(aq)?

TEST 35
Synthetic routes for organic chemicals

This test is composed of twenty questions. For each question, five possible answers are suggested. These answers are labelled **A**, **B**, **C**, **D** and **E**. Select the most appropriate *one* of the answers and write its corresponding letter on a separate answer sheet.

Questions 1–4

The reaction scheme below shows five stages labelled A, B, C, D, and E.

$$RCOCH_3 \xrightarrow{A} RCHOHCH_3 \xrightarrow{B} RCH{=}CH_2 \xrightarrow{C}$$

$$RCH_2CH_2CHO$$

$$RCH_2CH_3 \xleftarrow{E} RCH_2CH_2COOH \xleftarrow{D}$$

Choose from A, B, C, D and E the stage which is carried out using

1 hot $CO + H_2$ at 2×10^7 Pa.

2 dilute acidified $K_2Cr_2O_7(aq)$.

3 $LiAlH_4$ in ether.

4 excess concentrated H_2SO_4 at 170°C.

Questions **5–8** concern the preparation of 2-bromo-butane (boiling point 91°C) from butan-2-ol (boiling point 107°C), concentrated sulphuric acid, potassium bromide and water.

5 Which of the following techniques is correct for the first stage of the preparation? The reagents are refluxed

 A using a water condenser.

 B using an air condenser.

 C over a water bath.

 D with a stopper in the top of the condenser.

 E at reduced pressure.

6 After refluxing is complete, impure 2-bromobutane is distilled from the reaction mixture. Which *one* of the following substances will *not* be present in the impure 2-bromobutane?

 A bromine

 B butan-2-ol

 C hydrogen bromide

 D potassium bromide

 E water

7 The impure 2-bromobutane is washed with a base to remove acidic impurities. Which of the following bases would be most suitable for this?

 A $Ca(OH)_2(aq)$

 B $NaOH(aq)$

 C $CaO(s)$

 D $CuO(s)$

 E $NaHCO_3(aq)$

8 After washing with base, the 2-bromobutane is washed with water and then dried. Which of the following substances would be the most suitable drying agent?

 A anhydrous calcium chloride

 B concentrated sulphuric acid

 C dry calcium oxide

 D metallic calcium

 E soda lime granules

Questions **9–14** concern the reaction scheme below.

$$CH_3COONH_4 \xrightarrow{I} CH_3CONH_2 \xrightarrow{III} CH_3CN$$

with CH_3NH_2 via stage II above CH_3CONH_2, CH_3COOH via stage IV above CH_3CN, then $CH_3CN \xrightarrow{V} CH_3CH_2NH_2 \xrightarrow{VI} CH_3CH_2OH$

9 The most suitable conditions for stage I would be to

 A bubble hydrogen gas through $CH_3COONH_4(aq)$.

 B distil $CH_3COONH_4(s)$ with dry phosphorus(V) oxide.

 C heat $CH_3COONH_4(s)$ strongly in a sealed tube.

 D heat $CH_3COONH_4(s)$ with calcium oxide.

 E reflux $CH_3COONH_4(s)$ with excess glacial acetic acid.

10 The most suitable conditions for stage II would be to

A add dilute HCl and $NaNO_2$(aq).

B heat strongly in a sealed tube.

C add Br_2(l), then warm with NaOH(aq).

D boil with NaOH(aq).

E reflux with concentrated NH_3(aq).

11 The most suitable conditions for stage III would be to

A pass dry H_2 gas over heated CH_3CONH_2.

B distil CH_3CONH_2 with concentrated H_2SO_4.

C heat CH_3CONH_2 with dry calcium oxide.

D dry CH_3CONH_2 with anhydrous $CaCl_2$.

E distil CH_3CONH_2 with dry phosphorus(V) oxide.

12 The most suitable conditions for stage IV would be to

A reflux with dilute HCl.

B add dilute HCl and $NaNO_2$(aq).

C boil with aqueous NaOH(aq).

D warm with dilute acidified $KMnO_4$(aq).

E reflux with NaOH in alcohol.

13 The most suitable conditions for stage V would be to

A react with H_2 in the presence of nickel.

B treat with $LiAlH_4$ in ether.

C pass H_2 slowly over heated CH_3CN.

D add dilute HCl and $NaNO_2$(aq).

E react with sodium in alcohol.

14 The most suitable conditions for stage VI would be to

A reflux with dilute HCl.

B heat strongly with water in a sealed tube.

C add dilute HCl and $NaNO_2$(aq).

D add Br_2, then warm with NaOH(aq).

E reflux with NaOH(aq).

15 Which *one* of the following reagents is most suitable for converting methylbenzene to bromomethylbenzene, $C_6H_5CH_2Br$?

A aqueous bromine

B liquid bromine in ultraviolet light

C liquid bromine with an $AlBr_3$ catalyst

D concentrated hydrobromic acid

E phosphorus tribromide

16 Which *one* of the following compounds is produced when methylbenzene is refluxed with an alkaline solution of potassium manganate(VII) for a prolonged period and then acidified?

A C_6H_5OH

B $C_6H_5CH_2OH$

C C_6H_5CHO

D $C_6H_5CO_2H$

E C_6H_6

17 In order to prepare phenylbenzoate, phenol was dissolved in aqueous sodium hydroxide and benzoyl chloride was added. The flask was then stoppered and shaken. Which *one* of the following is a good reason for carrying out the experiment in a fume cupboard?

A Phenol is flammable.

B Sodium hydroxide is caustic.

C Phenol causes blisters.

D Benzoyl chloride is an eye irritant.

E Phenylbenzoate gives off a choking vapour.

18 When $CH_3CH_2CH(CH_3)CH_2OH$ is refluxed with a mixture of solid potassium iodide and concentrated phosphoric acid, the principal organic product is

A $CH_3CH_2CI(CH_3)CH_2OH$.

B $CH_3CH_2CI(CH_3)CH_2I$.

C $CH_3CH_2CH(CH_3)CH_2I$.

D $CH_3CH_2CHICH_2OH$.

E $CH_3CH_2CHICH_2I$.

19 Which *one* of the following pairs of substances is produced when $CH_3CONHCH_3$ is refluxed with excess dilute hydrochloric acid?

A CH_3COOH and CH_3NH_2

B CH_3COO^- and $CH_3NH_3^+$

C CH_3COOH and $CH_3NH_3^+$

D CH_3COO^- and CH_3NH_2

E CH_3CONH_2 and CH_3OH

20 Which *one* of the following reagents and conditions is most suitable for converting CH_3CO_2H to CH_3COCl?

	Reagent	Conditions
A	conc. HCl	100°C
B	PCl_5(s)	room temp.
C	Cl_2(g)	$AlCl_3$ catalyst
D	Cl_2(g)	u.v. light at 100°C
E	conc. HCl	$AlCl_3$ catalyst

Appendix: Atomic numbers and relative atomic masses of the elements

Element	Symbol	Atomic number	Relative atomic mass	Element	Symbol	Atomic number	Relative atomic mass
aluminium	Al	13	27	neodymium	Nd	60	144.2
antimony	Sb	51	122	neon	Ne	10	20
argon	Ar	18	40	nickel	Ni	28	59
arsenic	As	33	75	niobium	Nb	41	93
barium	Ba	56	137	nitrogen	N	7	14
beryllium	Be	4	9	osmium	Os	76	190
bismuth	Bi	83	209	oxygen	O	8	16
boron	B	5	11	palladium	Pd	46	106
bromine	Br	35	80	phosphorus	P	15	31
cadmium	Cd	48	112	platinum	Pt	78	195
caesium	Cs	55	133	potassium	K	19	39
calcium	Ca	20	40	praseodymium	Pr	59	140.9
carbon	C	6	12	rhenium	Re	75	186
cerium	Ce	58	140.1	rhodium	Rh	45	103
chlorine	Cl	17	35.5	rubidium	Rb	37	85
chromium	Cr	24	52	ruthenium	Ru	44	101
cobalt	Co	27	59	samarium	Sm	62	150.4
copper	Cu	29	63.5	scandium	Sc	21	45
dysprosium	Dy	66	162.5	selenium	Se	34	79
erbium	Er	68	167.3	silicon	Si	14	28
europium	Eu	63	152.0	silver	Ag	47	109
fluorine	F	9	19	sodium	Na	11	23
gadolinium	Gd	64	157.3	strontium	Sr	38	88
gallium	Ga	31	70	sulphur	S	16	32
germanium	Ge	32	73	tantalum	Ta	73	181
gold	Au	79	197	tellurium	Te	52	128
hafnium	Hf	72	178	terbium	Tb	65	158.9
hahnium	Ha	105	–	thallium	Tl	81	204
helium	He	2	4	thorium	Th	90	232.0
holmium	Ho	67	164.9	thulium	Tm	69	169.9
hydrogen	H	1	1	tin	Sn	50	119
indium	In	49	115	titanium	Ti	22	48
iodine	I	53	127	tungsten	W	74	184
iridium	Ir	77	192	uranium	U	92	238
iron	Fe	26	56	vanadium	V	23	51
krypton	Kr	36	84	xenon	Xe	54	131
kurchatovium	Ku	104	–	ytterbium	Yb	70	173
lanthanum	La	57	139	yttrium	Y	39	89
lead	Pb	82	207	zinc	Zn	30	65
lithium	Li	3	7	zirconium	Zr	40	91
lutetium	Lu	71	175.0				
magnesium	Mg	12	24				
manganese	Mn	25	55				
mercury	Hg	80	201				
molybdenum	Mo	42	96				